THE PURPOSE & PRACTICE

OF

MOTION STUDY

ANNE G. SHAW

HARLEQUIN PRESS CO LTD

MANCHESTER AND LONDON

First published in 1952
Reprinted 1955
Harlequin Press Company, Limited
Old Colony House, Manchester, 2
and 20 Irving Street
Leicester Square, London, W.C.2
Printed in Great Britain
at the Buxton Press

To
LILLIAN M. GILBRETH

PREFACE

by Sir George E. Bailey, C.B.E.

Chairman, Associated Electrical Industries Ltd.

In 1930, when Miss Shaw returned from the United States, she joined the staff of Metropolitan-Vickers in the women's employment department. As I had been aware for some time of the possibilities of motion study the fact that we now had a trained person in the Company made me feel that this was the opportunity to try the idea. I therefore arranged for her to study a job which was considered especially as it had been recently re-planned. I knew that it might be difficult to make a further improvement but I felt that if motion study were successful here we should have less difficulty in convincing everyone of its value. The results obtained amazed most people and our faith was justified.

From the beginning I realised the importance of the workers' co-operation and the Works Committee and the Women's Works Committee were brought into the scheme as it started. This may seem common sense today but in 1930 it was revolutionary. This importance of the workers' attitude to motion study and the consideration of each operator as an individual was given the emphasis that it deserved, partly because later I combined Miss Shaw's motion study work with her position as Chief Supervisor of Women. She was in charge of the women's personnel department and canteens, which brought her into constant daily touch with the operators, both men and women. Over the fifteen years that she was with the Company this policy justified itself and today when one walks through any department one sees the influence of motion study in the methods of working.

Motion study does not consist only of making investigations. The training of all sections of the organisation in the best motion study practice must be undertaken if the best and most lasting results are to be achieved. Training schemes were organised at Metropolitan-Vickers from the beginning for operators and all grades of supervision. There were also courses for training motion study engineers from the other factories in the A.E.I. group. work and a full motion study course was included in the syllabus of all management trainees.

Sir Stafford Cripps was so much impressed by what he saw at Trafford Park that when he needed to increase output per man in the aircraft industries due to shortage of labour he borrowed Miss Shaw's services and asked the Company to open their motion study training facilities to other factories working for the Ministry of Aircraft Production, under which scheme many

vii

engineers were trained. This was so successful that an exhibition was organised in London in 1945 to demonstrate to other industries how they could apply motion study.

I recommend this book to all industrialists as a practical description of motion study applied to every kind of work as a means of increasing production per man hour. This is even more vitally important now than it was when we began to use motion study at Metropolitan-Vickers in the hard days of the 1930's.

The great value of this book lies in the fact that it is based on practical experience and a very high-class knowledge and understanding of the "human" factor.

Miss Shaw now ranks as one of the world's outstanding production experts and I consider it a great honour to have been asked by her to write this "Foreword" to what I know will be a great contribution to the fascinating science of " Motion Study."

CONTENTS

INTRODUCTION

The present need for increased efficiency in industry and commerce needs no emphasis from me. It has for many months been the theme of government White Papers, of the press and of the political platform, and many who are far better qualified for the task than I am have dealt at length with the economic problems which can be solved only by greater production at lower cost. It is not the purpose of this book to explain the need for increased productivity but to attempt to make more widely known and better understood the principles and practice of motion study. This study has already led to increases in productivity in a number of industries, and has, I believe, a considerable contribution to make in the next decade; a contribution the more important in that motion study is a means of increasing productivity which calls neither for heavy capital outlay nor for additional physical effort from operators.

If the potential value of motion study is to be properly grasped it is necessary to clear up certain misconceptions as to its nature and purpose which have arisen over recent years, partly as the result of a confusion in terminology. The name "Motion Study" was originally used by the Gilbreths in America, and it has been employed throughout this book, since the techniques described here are the Gilbreth techniques. It was indeed from Dr. Lillian Gilbreth that I received my earliest instruction on motion study. From time to time other terms, including "method study," "movement study" and "work simplification" are employed, but the differences that these various expressions represent are never of much significance.

On the other hand, an important misunderstanding has arisen from the frequent use of the phrase "time and motion study"—a phrase which tends to obscure the very real distinction between time study and motion study. The primary function of time study is to set standards of performance though, in the course of a time study analysis of work that has not previously been the subject of motion study, certain faults in the method will become obvious and improvements will be suggested. These improvements are not however motion study improvements. They arise out of a study of time and are based on an analysis of time, not of movement. They are therefore no real substitute for the sounder and more comprehensive improvements which would follow a full motion study analysis of the movements involved in the job. It is after methods have been developed by means of motion study that time study should be used in order to set standards, time study applied at this stage being a complement to motion study. Efficient management requires that standards should be laid down for every job, whether or not a system of payment by

xi

results is in operation, and the great measure of control and accurate planning that is made possible by correctly set standards is probably one of the most important contributions that time study can make to good management.

To avoid confusion, no description of time study methods is included in this book, which is deliberately restricted to the subject of motion study. But because the successful application of motion study demands so much more than a knowledge of techniques of analysis considerable space has been devoted to an attempt to set it against its proper background.

This book embodies the results of work by motion study specialists, both in this country and abroad, who have spent many years in developing these principles and methods. But after two World Wars the time is past when technicians are interested only in perfecting their techniques and not in the purposes for which these techniques are used. I am glad to believe that by assisting in the improvement of efficiency, motion study is helping to make more secure the material foundations on which social progress rests. Implicit also in the principles of motion study is the idea that the prosperity of the nation can never be satisfactorily built on the exploitation of the individual. It is essentially the task of the motion study specialist to secure at one and the same time the highest possible material and psychological satisfaction for the individual worker, for we know today that efficiency in any other terms is bought at too high a price, and is apt to prove short-lived. This reconciliation of industrial efficiency and individual needs is one of the major problems of our generation, and we believe that in its solution motion study has a small, but not insignificant part to play.

My thanks are due to those companies who have allowed the examples given in the book to be published; to Sir George Bailey, who gave me my first opportunity in this country to introduce motion study improvements; to Miss B. N. Seear, of the London School of Economics, for much help and advice. I am also particularly indebted to my partner A. B. Armstrong, and to members of the Beech House staff, especially J. C. Appleyard, G. R. Creyke, Miss H. D. James, F. Landmann, Miss G. E. Morrison and W. A. Walton, who have watched the book grow and supplied many of the illustrations and reports and who, during all the tedious process of collecting the material, had faith that the book would ultimately be finished; to Miss B. M. Fletcher, who from the beginning has most generously devoted her energy and much of her own time in collating material and editing the text and finally, to Mr. S. H. Hills, who saw the book through the press.

THE DEVELOPMENT OF MOTION STUDY

MOTION STUDY is the investigation and measurement of the movements involved in the performance of any piece of work; their subsequent improvement, and the application of easier and more productive methods. The study of the needs and problems of the operator is the starting point of any motion study investigation as its final purpose is to enable him to work with minimum effort and maximum efficiency. With this end in view, the investigator studies not only the worker himself, but also the conditions surrounding the job, including the movement of materials, tools and equipment and the organisation and layout of work, since these factors directly influence the efficiency and well-being of the worker. From this description it will be realised that motion study is a branch of the important and developing science of industrial psychology.

This is by no means, however, a new idea, nor is it the discovery of any one country. In Britain, in the early days of the nineteenth century, Robert Owen, in reaction against the unimaginative "laissez faire" doctrine of his day, saw more clearly than most of his contemporaries the problems and the possibilities of industry. Speaking in 1813 he said, "If then, the care as to the state of your inanimate machines can produce such beneficial results, what may not be expected if you devote equal attention to your vital machines, which are far more wonderfully constructed? When you shall acquire a right knowledge of these, of their curious mechanism, of their self-adjusting powers; when the proper mainspring shall be applied to their varied movements—you will become conscious of their real value, and you will readily be induced to turn your thoughts more frequently from your inanimate to your living machines."

A century later, in the very different environment of the United States, Frank B. Gilbreth, an engineer, and his wife Lillian, a psychologist, developed in great detail principles and methods of working which, for the first time, were called "Motion Study" and which took fully into account the physical and psychological characteristics of the human beings in industry.

Frank Gilbreth was born into a New England family of Scottish origin in 1868,[1] and was brought up by a widowed mother who had been a schoolmistress and who was an educational enthusiast. The Puritan ideals of his family and upbringing developed a sense of individual and social responsibility,

---

[1] For more detailed information about the life of Frank B. Gilbreth see *Partners for Life* by Edna Yost; Rutgers University Press.

which was reflected in his later work.   At the age of 17, feeling that he wanted
to be financially independent and preferring to work with his hands rather
than with books, he abandoned the idea of studying at Massachusetts Institute
of Technology, and went as a junior apprentice into the building contractor's
business (Whidden & Co.) run by his Sunday-school teacher.   From the very
beginning of his career he took great interest in the methods of work used by
the craftsmen who instructed him.   In "The Quest," a privately published
life of F. B. Gilbreth by his wife, she recalls how his first foreman complained
that he "was there to learn the bricklaying trade and not to criticise method."

During these early years Gilbreth gained wide and invaluable practical
experience as a manual worker in the various trades in the building industry.
It was no less important that he joined the trade union and learned to appreciate the point of view of the skilled workman.   Promotion came quickly, and
he soon began to distinguish himself in his trade.   In his early twenties he won
a prize at the Mechanics Institute for a scaffold based on the idea of making
the work of the skilled bricklayer as easy and as labour-saving as possible.

At the age of twenty-seven he was a superintendent of his firm, but he was
not satisfied.   When he first joined the firm of Whidden & Co. as a 17-year
old apprentice, he was given to understand that, if he made good, he would
be offered a partnership in ten years' time.   Unfortunately there was a change
in the management of the firm during that period and his Sunday-school
teacher was replaced by another member of the Whidden family.   As a result
of this he was not offered a partnership.   Since he had not planned to remain
in a subordinate position for longer than ten years, he broke away from the
firm to set up his own organisation as a building contractor.   The business
grew rapidly and he acquired contracts all over the United States.   To enable
him to control programmes effectively, he worked out a system of carefully
designed forms and records, supplemented by daily photographs, which made
it possible for him to study more closely all the details of the progress of each
job.   Since they were made daily and recorded the exact conditions at that
moment, they were useful, not only as records of progress, but also as records
of method.   In this way he used them as he later was to use motion pictures.

Some years after he had started his own business he met Lillian Moller,
a young graduate from California who had studied education and psychology,
and whom he married in 1904.   At his suggestion their marriage was to involve
partnership in his work as well as partnership in the home.   She became
intensely interested in his work in motion study and in the ideas on management that he had developed in his own organisation.   She was quick to grasp
his ideas of the application of his methods to a wider field, and encouraged
and helped him to put his thoughts on to paper.   Over the next fifteen years,
in addition to many articles, their published work included "Field System"
1908, "Concrete System" 1908, "Bricklaying System" 1909, "Motion Study"
1911, "The Primer of Scientific Management" 1912, "Fatigue Study" 1916,
"Applied Motion Study" 1917, and "Motion Study for the Handicapped" 1920.

During this period, the Gilbreths were in contact with other workers in the study of management, in particular F. W. Taylor, later recognised as the pioneer of scientific management, H. L. Gantt, and others. Taylor was very much interested in the work of Gilbreth, and later included a reference to Gilbreth's experiment on bricklaying in his famous book "The Principles of Scientific Management." Earlier, in 1898, Gilbreth had come into contact with the

FIG. 1. FRANK B. GILBRETH IN HIS LABORATORY WORKING ON A PROJECT
FOR THE HANDICAPPED

Taylor system, when a man who proved to be Sandford Thompson, Taylor's assistant, was found one morning with his stop-watch timing bricklayers on a Gilbreth site. He had asked neither the workers nor Gilbreth if he might make the study nor had he enquired if the methods were considered to be fully developed. This incident impressed Gilbreth unfavourably, since he considered that it was entirely wrong to take a secret time study and, furthermore, that working methods must be checked for accuracy before any records were made. He therefore felt that Thompson's time study under such conditions was inevitably unsound. Subsequent events in his contacts with Taylor and Thompson did nothing to make him feel that they had changed their approach and when Taylor suggested that he should collaborate with them to produce a book on bricklaying Gilbreth declined, feeling that there was still a fundamental difference between his outlook and theirs.

This difference probably arose out of a difference in experience. Taylor, whose eyesight early in life forced him to exchange an academic training for work in an engineering machine shop, began to develop his interest in management problems when he realised that the limitations of the worker restricted

FIG. 2. LILLIAN M. GILBRETH

the potential productivity of the machine. Perhaps because his starting point was the problems of the machine, Taylor never appeared to appreciate sufficiently the need to study and to respect the complicated human material with which he had to deal. Gilbreth, on the other hand, was from the first influenced by his early experiences in the essentially manual occupation of bricklaying, in which it was impossible to overestimate the importance of the human factor. This concern for the human element, which reflected his early ethical training, was reinforced by Mrs. Gilbreth's scientific interest in psychology and her increasing realisation of the importance of education and psychology in handling the human problems of industry. It was partly because there was no scope for these wider interests within Taylor's system that the Gilbreths, though keeping closely in touch with workers in the field of scientific management, continued independently, focussing their main attention on the problems of workers' movements.

Nevertheless, Gilbreth fully recognised the importance of Taylor's work, and realised that Taylor was making a real contribution by awakening industry to the need for the scientific study of industrial problems. Gilbreth, in fact, used Taylor's system in its entirety in 1912-13 at the New England Butt Company, where he was employed as a consultant. His disagreement with Taylor was over his use of the stop-watch as the basis for measuring movement and devising improvements. Although he recognised the importance of the time factor, he was completely out of sympathy with anything as scientifically inaccurate as the practice of using time study observations as a basis for improving methods. He felt that if time was needed in the measurement of movements it should be used much more accurately than was possible with a stop-watch. He considered that such measurements should be made only with the full consent and co-operation of the worker and that they should not be subject to the error of the observer. He felt that time study and motion study were complementary not opposing systems; that motion study should develop the method and time study should be used to check results and to set the standard of performance.

Taylor did, in fact, make a most important contribution to the improvement of time study and of management methods. He developed his techniques approximately twenty years before Charles Bedaux began his system of point rating in time study which has been so widely criticised. It is not possible to assess Bedaux's system properly, since there is no comprehensive published work on the method, and because the basis on which calculations are made is kept secret. As the practice is observed in industry, however, it appears to lay itself open to use in ways which are undeniably detrimental to the worker.

Gilbreth's attitude towards time study has been fully justified by more recent work in motion study. Modern time study, properly conducted, plays an extremely important part in assessing standards of output, but as its rating system grows more complex it becomes less and less suitable as a tool for devising improved methods. The function of motion study is to improve the way the job is carried out; the function of time study is to determine standards of work after the method of working has been decided.

Modern Motion Study in the U.S.A.

In the last twenty years there has been a growing interest in the United States in the development of motion study. Since Gilbreth's death in 1924, Mrs. Gilbreth has concentrated on teaching the principles of motion study in industry and at the universities and technical colleges, including Purdue University where she is a visiting professor.

Other developments in the academic field which are of particular interest include the work of Professor Barnes at the University of Iowa. He has written the most comprehensive textbook on the subject and has organised a motion and time study research laboratory within the University. For a number of years there has been a steady flow of publications recording the research done in this laboratory. This work is of considerable value, not only to industry, but also as a most important contribution to the general management training courses which are being successfully carried on at the university. Excellent work is also being done at New York University by Professor Porter, at Purdue University under Dr. Marvin Mundel and in many other educational centres throughout the United States.

Apart from the work of the universities and technical colleges, training schemes have been organised by consultants; notably by Allan Mogensen at Lake Placid, where the term "Work Simplification" is used instead of "Motion Study." By means of annual conferences at Lake Placid, Mogensen has extended the practice of simple motion study throughout industry by teaching the general principles and practices to men of management grade from different factories, who return to their own works to establish broad training programmes in "Work Simplification." In addition, some time before the second world war, Mogensen himself ran extremely successful courses for training foremen in "Work Simplification" in several large companies. During the war Mogensen, assisted by Don Capell, Harold Dunlap and others, extended this training to the armed forces while the Administration developed a simplified version for industry in its T.W.I. programmes. These developments made a considerable contribution to the great war production output of the United States.

Today, investigation and research is also being carried out by other consultants including the Methods Engineering Council. At the present time, all over the United States industrialists are well aware of the importance of motion study and in a large number of factories, with varying degrees of intensity, motion study principles are being applied.

Motion Study in Europe and Russia

Wherever the industrial system developed it might be supposed that some form of motion study would be devised. On the whole, remarkably little has in fact been achieved except in the U.S.A. and Great Britain. In nineteenth century France, however, there was a physiologist called Marey who was interested in measuring and recording human movement. He carried out his investigations in the early days of photography, at first by making a series of still photographs superimposed on a single plate. Later, after experimenting with a revolving circular plate, he developed a camera on the lines of a cine-camera which took a series of photographs on roll film. These he viewed as a sequence of still photographs, observing changes in movement between one picture and the next and converting his observations into diagrams. He was chiefly interested in studying the path of movement and could see the possible significance if his technique were applied to the study of industrial skill. Unfortunately he did not develop this idea and his investigations were so much in advance of the thought of his time that they were not followed up by his fellow countrymen. It was left to Gilbreth in another country and a later generation to develop the same idea quite independently in his work on chrono-cyclegraphs, but it is interesting to find an echo of Marey's point of view in the work of the Bureau de Temps Elementaires in modern France. This organisation is chiefly concerned with time study but is developing the physiological aspect of the study of work methods in a way that closely approaches Motion Study[1].

In Germany, before the first world war, Gilbreth had done some work as a consultant and motion study methods had been introduced into two important plants, one of which was the Zeiss lens factory at Jena. The work was carried on by those whom Gilbreth had trained but it does not appear to have had much general effect in the country and when in 1924 the Reichsausschuss Fur Arbeitsstudien (R.E.F.A.) (German National Committee on Time Study) was established, no reference seems to have been made to Gilbreth's work on motion study.

The function of R.E.F.A. was to assess times for certain jobs in order to determine a standard time for elements of jobs, so that standards for whole jobs could be worked out and applied throughout the German metal industry. Courses were organised in many districts to train time study men, but no attention was paid to the study of methods. During the Nazi regime, R.E.F.A. was at first in disfavour but later it was used extensively, particularly during the war period. R.E.F.A. handbooks were compiled, the last of which is still unpublished, but is reported to contain something of the elements of the study of method.

Kurt Pentzlin, author of "Rationelle Produktion" describes a form of work study, but although he appears to have made more progress than other Germans in the study of methods of working, he dismisses motion study as being of historical and academic interest only. When a B.I.O.S. mission, of which the author was a member, visited Germany, Kurt Pentzlin collected together all the available Germans connected with this sphere of work to give papers to the mission. These meetings produced no evidence of any German contribution to motion study and very little of the applications of the techniques. The Germans were surprised by the progress in Great Britain and in the United States since 1933 when they were last able to obtain international literature.

In Russia the Stakhanovite movement developed in the early days of the first Five Year Plan. Stakhanov was a miner in the Donetz basin, who found that he could produce more coal than any other miner. He began by trying to achieve a record output. With this aim he rationalised his methods of work, not as a result of scientific analysis, but by the application of common

---

[1] Paper to the International Management Conference, 1947.

sense. In a study of the development of motion study the importance of the
Stakhanovite movement lies less in the techniques employed than in the propaganda schemes adopted to alter traditional working methods. These schemes
included[1] the recognition of successful individual workers as Stakhanovites, a
term of honour carrying national prestige; the organisation of national conferences of Stakhanovites of sufficient importance to be addressed by Stalin
and Molotov; and the erection of a permanent exhibition in the Park of Rest
and Culture in Moscow. This exhibition consisted of demonstrations from a
wide variety of industries and included wall pictures in which the significant
changes from old to new methods were emphasised by a system of coloured
lights operated by the spectator pressing the appropriate switch. It is of particular interest to note that these schemes were planned to break down the
workers' inherent resistance to changing a traditional method, a resistance which
was found to constitute the major obstacle to the application of Stakhanovite
principles. As in other countries, the Russians found this psychological
problem of resistance to change one of the major difficulties in the path of
progress.

With the exception of France, it can be seen that none of the Continental
European countries has made any very significant contribution to the history
or development of modern motion study. Some have practised it within limits
but most, like Germany, have considered it to be of only academic interest.

Motion Study in Great Britain

In Great Britain, motion study developed later than in the United States
of America and until the 1914-18 war gave an impetus to new industrial ideas,
little progress was made. The first published accounts of motion study in this
country will be found among the reports of the Industrial Fatigue Research
Board which developed from the earlier "Committee on the Health of Munition
Workers." This series of reports on investigations into specific industrial problems is chiefly concerned with conditions of work but among the reports are a
few relating to motion study[2].

Eric Farmer's "Motion Study in Metal Polishing," which is an account
of a single investigation, does not give much information about the motion
study techniques used but it lays down in detail a prescribed method and
recommends that operators should be trained to follow it. His "Time and
Motion Study" published a little later is a critical survey of the results of a
number of contemporary motion study applications and an account of the
theory behind them. Farmer did not entirely understand the fundamental
ideas behind Gilbreth's techniques though he appreciated the main differences
between Taylor and Gilbreth. Unfortunately, these reports and many others

---

[1] At the time the author visited Russia in 1937.
[2] Ind. Health Research Board, No. 3, 1919, C. S. Myers: *A Study of Improved Methods in an Iron Foundry;* No. 15, 1921, E. Farmer: *Motion Study in Metal Polishing;* No. 14, 1921, E. Farmer: *Time and Motion Study.*

published by the Board did not have the wide circulation that they deserved, being read chiefly by those who were already converted to new ideas. As a result they made little impression upon industry in general.

In 1921 Dr. Myers founded the National Institute of Industrial Psychology which has done so much to emphasise the benefits of the application of the general principles of industrial psychology. In its early days it concentrated particularly on problems of vocational guidance and selection but its work on "Movement Study," as it was called, was restricted by Dr. Myers' original misconception of the meaning of Gilbreth's terminology and by Gilbreth's lack of appreciation of the different attitude in this country. This mutual misunderstanding led to the development of a study of movement which avoided using the full Gilbreth techniques. By the time the second world war broke out this attitude had altered and some of the more recent investigators had done very interesting work. During the war, Colonel Ungerson, who was seconded by the Institute to the Scientific Advisers' Department of the War Office, was very successful in applying motion study to military operations. He obtained some outstanding results which contributed greatly to the efficiency of the army. The section he began has survived the peace and still continues its work.

In 1930, after experience in the United States as research assistant to Gilbreth Inc., the author returned to this country and began a complete motion study programme at Metropolitan-Vickers Electrical Co., Ltd., Manchester. The work gradually developed until it covered the whole of the Associated Electrical Industries which employed upwards of 50,000 workers and of which Metropolitan-Vickers was a part. Training courses were organised for motion study engineers from each factory in the group and the type of motion study taught and developed was in the direct Gilbreth tradition since it had been derived at first hand from Mrs. Gilbreth herself.

The second world war gave a great impetus to the application of motion study. Before 1939, although the techniques had been used in a few advanced factories, chiefly in the engineering industry, there had been no general application of motion study to British industry. There were several reasons for this: In the first place, labour was comparatively cheap and therefore an increase in the output of each operator was less valuable. Labour was also plentiful which meant that employers had a wide choice in filling vacancies and could choose the best people for each job, dispensing with anyone who failed to become a good operator. Because there was considerable unemployment, workers were afraid to lose their jobs and they made the maximum effort for the sake of security. In addition, both employers and trade unionists were afraid that the application of motion study would cause further unemployment. A final difficulty was the lack of trained motion study investigators. Few firms were willing to pay for a training which was expensive and which, outside Associated Electrical Industries, could only be obtained in the U.S.A.

These difficulties did not apply to the same extent in the U.S.A. where labour, even in the depression of the 1930's, was much more expensive and where prices were so competitive that any improvement in output per operator was a matter of considerable importance. Motion study was applied there very widely and helped to contribute to a steadily increasing efficiency.

During the second world war, the situation in Great Britain changed entirely and maximum output was of primary importance as the labour shortage became acute.

In 1942 the Minister of Aircraft Production, Sir Stafford Cripps, formed a small board, the Production Efficiency Board[1], to advise him on the best utilisation of labour in the aircraft industry. This board, introduced training schemes for motion study engineers from the aircraft factories on the lines of those organised by Metropolitan-Vickers, using the same training facilities and a staff loaned by Metropolitan-Vickers. Some of the improved methods developed as a result of these courses were collected in a demonstration organised by the Ministry of Aircraft Production in 1945[2]. The object of this demonstration was to interest other industries in the possibilities of the application of motion study in post-war industry as a means of increasing output per operator. Although there was no general application of motion study in other industries, its adoption by the Ministry of Aircraft Production and the fighting services created a body of trained and experienced motion study investigators which was dispersed at the end of the war to many different industries and organisations.

These wartime measures aroused a general interest in motion study in other British industries and post-war conditions have increased that interest. A policy directed towards full employment necessarily means a limited choice of labour and a high level of wages. Unless this is combined with efficient production and a high output per operator, the country cannot maintain its place in world markets and this, in turn, will mean the failure of the full employment policy. If we are to enjoy the improved general standard of living that is our aim as a country, we must obtain the necessary increase in output per operator. Even if it were not socially undesirable, no permanent increase could be obtained by lengthening working hours, nor would an appeal for harder work be very effective. The desperate drive for increased production after the evacuation of the army from Dunkirk in 1940 gave amazing results over a short period because of the intense emotional stimulus of the national emergency, but the success was short-lived and there was a legacy of fatigue that hampered production in the period that followed. There can be no comparable emotional stimulus today and we are therefore obliged to obtain the necessary increase in output by improving methods of production without

[1] The Production Efficiency Board of the Ministry of Aircraft Production consisted of Sir Charles Bruce Gardner (chairman), Frank E. Chappell and Anne G. Shaw, with George (later Sir George) Buchanan and R. Pyser of the Ministry as executive officer and secretary respectively.
[2] *See* Production and Engineering Bulletin: Ministry of Labour, December, 1945, and January and February, 1946.

increasing hours of work or expecting very much extra physical effort from individual workers.

Improvements in production methods can be obtained in several ways: by better organisation and management, by the use of better machinery and tools and by the establishment of better working methods. All three are interdependent and must be tried and used to the fullest extent though motion study is primarily concerned with the third. Motion study can develop the better working methods that will give more output for the same or less effort on the part of the worker.

In any organisation motion study can be applied in three ways. Its most obvious use is to improve existing methods but it should also be used to develop correct methods on new work. In addition there is great advantage in training every member of the organisation to be "motion minded."

Motion Study Practice

A. IMPROVING EXISTING METHODS

There are four stages in any motion study investigation. The first is the measuring and recording of the present methods of work where these exist. This information is next analysed and a new method is devised, and in the third stage the suggested new method is tried out experimentally. At this stage it is adapted to suit the operator and he is trained to use it. The last stage covers the final installation of the new method and the arrangements made for its future maintenance.

1. *The Recording of Present Practice.* In this first stage it is important to obtain an accurate record of the present method. Some form of record is essential and some means of measuring must be adopted if the information is to be accurate; it will not be enough to ask questions of the operator or of his supervisor. Few people know what movements they make in doing even the most familiar work; they can perform the movements but they cannot describe them in words. The reader will find this understandable if he himself tries to describe the detailed movements that he makes in doing anything that he is accustomed to perform as a matter of routine, such as swinging a golf club or cleaning his teeth. The degree of detail required for the analysis of any particular job depends on its nature and there are a variety of techniques for use in different circumstances. The main techniques and their uses can be classified as follows: —

Simple process charts:

1. Small quantity jobs.
2. Jobs of long cycle time where the significant operations are of long duration.

More complex process charts:

Jobs which are simple to observe in detail.

Micromotion study:

    1. Jobs which are too quick for the eye to follow unaided.

    2. Large quantity jobs where small savings will have a wide application.

    3. Jobs which are very complex and require a close analysis and where production is large enough to warrant detailed study.

    4. Jobs which, though of small quantity production, have sections common to a large number of other jobs.

Study of the path of movement:

    (a) Chronocyclegraphs:

        (i) Jobs where the path of movement is the most significant feature.

        (ii) Small quantity jobs too fast to chart and not worth the expense of a micromotion study.

        (iii) Jobs where other techniques have failed to give accurate information.

    (b) String diagrams: Jobs with an operation sequence which is not repetetive but which is made up of the irregular repetition of a limited number of operations spread over a wide area (domestic work, the tending of a number of machines, etc).

Besides supplying a means of recording present practice in order to improve it, these techniques have two further uses. By recording the movements of the best operators, advantage can be taken of skill acquired over a long period. In exceptional cases where, after long years of work an operator has developed the ideal method unaided, it will be possible in this way to analyse it so that it can be taught to the less skilled.

Secondly, it is important to record present practice accurately so that it can be used as a standard to measure suggested improvements and as a means of convincing others of the need for improvement.

    2. *Analysis of Information Recorded*. The general principles of analysis are the same for all motion study techniques. In every investigation a process chart is made first and, if its analysis shows that further information and measurements are required, one or all of the other techniques are used to make a further analysis. From these analyses the new method is developed. Some investigators lay down a list of rules for developing new methods but this is a difficult and dangerous practice since it is not possible to draw up rules to cover every contingency. If the habit is formed of working to a set of rules, essential points may be overlooked and the best result may not be achieved.

    The recommended principles of analysis are very general and have been formed to act rather as a guide to the investigator in tackling each problem from first principles than with the intention of leading him towards any set solution. The first step is to question the necessity of every individual movement recorded on the process chart, simo-chart or chronocyclegraph. If this is not done at the beginning of an analysis, it is quite possible to develop an improved method for a section of a job that later proves to be quite inessential. Next, the sequence in which the movements are performed should be examined. An alteration in this sequence often results in considerable improvements. The third step is to see whether any of the movements can be combined with one another. Finally, when these first three possibilities have been thoroughly explored, it should be considered whether the remaining movements can be simplified. Simplification may be achieved by the introduction of some tool or fixture and it should only be attempted when the rest of the analysis has been completed. Investigators should resist the temptation to introduce any special tools and gadgets in the early stages of an investigation. Devices of this type exert a strong fascination, but the simplest solution to a problem is always the best and gadgets and special equipment should only be developed after all other possible improvements have been planned. Even then, they should be as simple as possible and should only be recommended if the improvements that can be expected to result from their adoption warrant their development and manufacture. When the sequence and nature of the movements have been settled, the workplace should be arranged so that the operator can carry them out effectively.

3. *Experimenting with a Suggested New Method.* Motion study is primarily the study of human movements. The development of a new method from recorded facts cannot therefore achieve ultimate success if it is confined to the laboratory. Time must be allowed in every investigation for a period of trial during which the new method can be tested by an operator in practice and modified in the light of experience. Without the operator's co-operation the job will never be successful and, although this stage in an investigation may occupy as much or more time and thought than is given to all the earlier stages, it is very important and should never be cut short.

4. *Installing a New Method in the Factory.* It is very important that the job should be carefully installed because an improvement that may be excellent theoretically can be of no practical use whatever until it is showing results in production. The installation of a new method must be made with the co-operation of the supervisors and again considerable time and thought must be given to preparing them to take the work over and to assisting them during its installation and afterwards. It must be made certain that there is no danger of the job failing because no one has learnt to maintain it in its correct form.

B. DEVELOPING A MOTION STUDY METHOD ON NEW WORK

When an organisation is establishing a motion study department, the first object should be the improvement of existing methods. During this period there should be a campaign of general explanation and training in all sections of the factory so that everyone understands the scheme thoroughly and can co-operate. Obviously, as soon as the department is fully established, motion study should be applied to all new jobs as they come into the factory so that they are manu-factured from the beginning in the most economical way. This is not only more efficient but it also prevents the complications that arise out of changing established methods.

In developing a method for a new job, the investigator must first study the prototype. He will then build up what seems to him to be the easiest way of making it. He will do this from his experience of similar work, but he will also be guided by certain general ideas of motion economy which have been formed as the result of practical experience in developing new methods on a large variety of jobs. When he has completed the building up of a method of work, he will chart it as if it were an existing method that has not been motion studied. In this way he will be certain that he has not made any mistakes. During this analysis, he should pay particular attention to sug-gestions for changes in design which might assist manufacture, as it will usually be possible to make modifications at this early stage. Finally, he will arrange the workplace so that it enables the worker to use the method most efficiently and easily.

C. TEACHING AN ORGANISATION TO BE MOTION MINDED

Besides investigating and improving specific existing methods and develop-ing correct methods of work on new jobs there is a third field for motion study in any organisation. Although in the setting up of a motion study pro-gramme thorough investigations are the main objective, they are by no means the only source of improvements. The thorough investigation has to be made by fully-trained motion study investigators but there are a number of common sense improvements in any organisation that become obvious as soon as anyone is conscious of the importance of looking at movement. To get the full benefit from a motion study programme it must therefore include some form of general training and propaganda to encourage every member of the organisation not only to co-operate with the motion study investigator but also, each in his own particular sphere, to introduce the minor day to day improvements that are needed.

The early sections of this book are devoted to the detailed explanation of the motion study techniques used in developing or improving methods of work. The later chapters deal with the application of these methods in practice and the training of the whole organisation to be motion minded. A thorough study of techniques is the most obviously necessary and interesting part of the equipment of the motion study specialist but, if he is to achieve success, the information contained in these later chapters is equally essential, although its importance is more often overlooked or forgotten.

PROCESS CHARTS

LTHOUGH in developing and formulating his motion study techniques Gilbreth turned his attention to process charting last, it has become the first technique to be applied in any modern motion study investigation. To find out which parts of a job will repay closer study by means of the micromotion and chronocyclegraph techniques a process chart is used to survey the whole field of the work.

A process chart records the movements of a job and the movements of the operator in performing it. By the adoption of standard symbols, a chart can be compiled from direct observation to show the details of the flow of a product through the factory, the movements of an operator, or any other phase of movement in the factory, office or home. The completed process chart recording each movement enables a detailed analysis to be made and reveals any wasteful movements which ought to be modified or eliminated.

Process Chart Symbols

Gilbreth used a fairly elaborate series of symbols (Fig. 3) which covers every possible contingency, but it will be found today that the symbols shown in Fig. 4 are usually sufficient for ordinary use.

A large circle is used to describe an " operation." The unit of work represented by one symbol will vary according to the scale of the chart. In some charts a single symbol may cover a whole process such as " assemble switch," in others where more detail is required, "pick up screw" might be the unit.

A smaller circle represents a " transport." This transport may be carried out by truck, by hand, by conveyor or by some other means. Where several methods of transport are recorded on the same chart, it is usual to note against the symbol the type of transport used.

A triangle standing on its base describes material received into stores. An inverted triangle indicates permanent storage. It usually describes material in a stores entered on a stock card and kept there for a period. In the case of a document it would indicate that it was in a permanent file.

A double inverted triangle is used to represent temporary storage. It may describe material brought from the stores and deposited in the department until an operator is ready to use it, or a job resting on a work-bench between consecutive operations performed by different operators or between batch operations performed by the same operator. A document in a filing or "in mail" basket would be described in this way.

A diamond represents inspection for quality.

A square represents inspection for quantity.

⬭ *Operation*

○ *Transport*

▽ *Material in Temporary Storage*

△ *Material received into Stores*

▽ *Material in permanent Storage*

◇ *Inspection for Quality*

□ *Inspection for Quantity*

Fig. 4. Process Chart Symbols
in Common Use

Combined Symbols. In some cases a symbol may be required to show that two things are happening at the same time. If an operation is performed, for example, during the course of which an incidental inspection is made for quality, the two symbols "inspection for quality" and "operation" to form a single symbol are put together (*see* Fig. 5*a*) the "operation" circle being outside the diamond representing "inspection" because the inspection is only a minor part of the work. If the inspection were the major part and the operation only incidental, the symbols would be combined with the diamond outside the circle as shown in Fig. 5*b*. This might happen, for instance,

(a) *Operation Including*
     Inspection for Quality

(b) *Inspection for Quality*
     including Operation

Fig. 5. Examples of
Combined Symbols

where an inspector manipulated a partly assembled instrument to test its efficiency before passing it on for final assembly. Further combinations of other symbols can be made as they are needed.

On a chart each symbol carries a number according to its position. This is used for identification.

American Experiments in the Standardisation of Symbols. The special committee of the American Society of Mechanical Engineers on the Standardisation of Therbligs, Process Charts and their Symbols have issued a list of standard symbols which differs considerably from the Gilbreth symbols listed above. These symbols have not yet been generally adopted in this country

STORES REQUISITIONED

STORES BOUGHT

STORES RECEIVED

SEVERAL KINDS OF COMPONENTS
NOT DESIRED TO LIST INDIVIDUALLY

WORKED MATERIALS REQUISITIONED

WORKED MATERIALS ORDERED

WORKED MATERIALS ON HAND

MERCHANDISE IN STORAGE READY TO SHIP

STORAGE AS PART OF PROCESS

PERMANENT FILE OF ANY DOCUMENTS
OR MATERIALS

TEMPORARY FILE OF ANY DOCUMENTS
OR MATERIALS

OPERATION SYMBOL (NUMBER SIGNIFIES OPERATION
38 OR BY OPERATOR NO. 38)

MOVEMENT SYMBOL (MOVED BY OPERATOR
PERFORMING OPER'N 38.

MOVED BY MAN

MOVED BY BOY

MOVED BY MESSENGER BOY

MOVED BY ELEVATOR

MOVED BY PNEUMATIC TUBE

MOVED BY CONVEYOR

gravity MOVED BY GRAVITY CONVEYOR

belt MOVED BY BELT CONVEYOR

MOVED BY TRUCK

electric MOVED BY ELECTRIC TRUCK (GASOLINE,
HAND LIFT, ETC. AS CASE MAY BE)

INFORMATION OR MESSAGE
CONVEYED BY PHONE

MOVED BY MAIL

INSPECTION FOR QUALITY

INSPECTION FOR QUALITY BY SEEING

INSPECTION FOR QUALITY BY SMELL

INSPECTION FOR QUALITY BY HEARING

INSPECTION FOR QUALITY BY TASTE

INSPECTION FOR QUALITY BY FEELING

INSPECTION FOR QUALITY BY KINAESTHESIA

INSPECTION FOR QUANTITY

INSPECTION FOR QUANTITY BY WEIGHING
OR WEIGHT COUNTING

INSPECTION FOR QUANTITY BY COUNTING

INSPECTION FOR QUANTITY BY DRY
OR LIQUID MEASURE

INSPECTION FOR QUANTITY BY SEEING

INSPECTION FOR QUANTITY BY AUTOMATIC COUNTING

INSPECTION FOR QUANTITY AND QUALITY
(QUANTITY MOST IMPORTANT)

INSPECTION FOR QUANTITY AND QUALITY
(QUALITY MOST IMPORTANT)

OVER INSPECTION FOR QUANTITY

OVER INSPECTION FOR QUALITY

INSPECTION FOR QUANTITY ON
EXCEPTION PRINCIPLE

INSPECTION FOR QUALITY ON
EXCEPTION PRINCIPLE

OVER INSPECTION FOR QUANTITY
ON EXCEPTION PRINCIPLE

OVER INSPECTION FOR QUALITY
ON EXCEPTION PRINCIPLE

INSPECTION FOR QUANTITY AND
OPERATION SIMULTANEOUSLY

INSPECTION FOR QUALITY AND
OPERATION SIMULTANEOUSLY

INSPECTION FOR QUANTITY & QUALITY & OPERATION
SIMULTANEOUSLY (QUANTITY MOST IMPORTANT)

INSPECTION FOR QUANTITY & QUALITY & OPERATION
SIMULTANEOUSLY (QUALITY MOST IMPORTANT)

BLANK FORM USED — INDICATES NO 2 COPY OF FORM
485; IF THERE IS BUT ONE COPY OF FORM MADE,
FORM NUMBER APPEARS IN CENTRE OF BLOCK

REPORTS NOT HAVING FORM NUMBERS WILL
HAVE BRIEF TITLE WRITTEN IN BLOCK

A SINGLE DEPARTMENT USED MORE THAN ONCE

BROKEN LINES INDICATE PROCESS OUTSIDE OF
THE DEPARTMENT CHARTED — USED ON DEPART-
MENTAL CHARTS.

PROCESS WITHIN THE DEPARTMENT IS CONN-
ECTED WITH CLOSED LINE

FIG. 3. GILBRETH'S STANDARD SYMBOLS FOR PROCESS CHARTS
(from a paper presented to the American Society of Mechanical Engineers,
New York, December, 1921)

and they appear to have no advantage over the Gilbreth symbols, although one extra symbol "delay" has been added. Except for this, they seem considerably less flexible as they are not at all easy to make into combined symbols. They have appropriated the symbol "material received into stores" to cover "an activity outside scope of investigation." This seems confusing and unnecessary.

Object of a Process Chart

A process chart should be more than a mere list of operations in sequence. Those who in recent times have been content to use only process charting in their motion study investigations, considering the other techniques as laboratory exercises or teaching media, often fail to appreciate this. They have too narrow a conception of the meaning of motion study.

If we examine Gilbreth's ideas about process charting we find that although the technique has developed since F. B. Gilbreth died, the first Gilbreth definition is wider and fuller than much that has been written on the subject more recently. In order that we may see the process chart in its proper perspective and in its true relationship to the other motion study techniques it is useful to examine this first definition: —

1. "The process chart is a device for visualising a process as a means of improving it. Every detail of a process is more or less affected by every other detail; therefore the entire process must be presented in such form that it can be visualised all at once before any changes are made in any of its subdivisions. In any subdivision of the process under examination, any changes made without due consideration of *all* the decisions and all the motions that precede and follow that subdivision will be found unsuited to the ultimate plan of operation.

2. The process chart is a record of present conditions. It presents, in simple, easily understood, compact form, data which must be collected and examined before any improvement in existing conditions and methods is undertaken. Even if existing conditions are apparently satisfactory, the chart is useful as presenting much information in condensed form.

3. The process chart serves as an indicator of profitable changes. It assists in preventing " inventing downwards," and stimulates invention that is cumulative and of permanent value. It is not only the first step in visualising the "one best way to do work" but is useful in every stage of deriving it." [1]

There has frequently been a tendency to misquote or paraphrase this definition and one particular aspect of it has been very much neglected. The words "visualising" and "visualised" appear three times and are in fact the clue to the successful use of the technique. This neglect has led to the development of formal charts and set forms. This was particularly evident

---

[1] *Process Charts. First steps in finding the one best way to do work.* F. B. & L. M. Gilbreth (Paper presented to the Annual Meeting of the American Society of Mechanical Engineers, New York, Dec. 5-9, 1921).

during the 1939-45 war in the large scale training in motion economy of foremen's groups. There, process charting became nothing more than the filling in
of a standard form. This systemisation of a fundamentally flexible technique
does not entirely destroy its value but it wastes much of its usefulness.

Form and Shape of a Process Chart

A process chart cannot be drawn up successfully on a standard form. Since
the value of the technique lies in its presentation of facts in such a way that
they can be visualised, it must be flexible. A chart may contain no information
that could not be written down in words but the facts are set out so that the
process can be seen as a whole more quickly and effectively. The significant
information can be made to stand out from the rest.

It can be easily appreciated that a chart of the type illustrated in Fig. 6*b*
is much more useful than the stereotyped straight line chart of Fig. 6*a* though
both contain the same information. The first is devised to show the transport
of material from department to department as the significant feature of the
job. The second gives all the information equal weight and the symbols showing this transport of material are lost in an unaccented list. If there had been
a second important feature in this instance, such as the division of the work
among several workers, a chart of the type shown in Fig. 7*b* might have been
drawn. Again, the more elaborate chart shows the same facts as the straight
line chart of Fig 7*a* but there is no doubt whatever which is the more useful.

To make a good chart which will present the necessary information in
the best way, the investigator must first be thoroughly familiar with the details
of the job and the plan behind it. He must discover which operations or other
features control the rest. He will find the best layout for his chart by building
it round these controlling factors and, although it may not always be easy at
the first attempt to discover the form that presents the facts most vividly, it is
worth while to persist until a satisfactory chart takes shape.

There is perhaps a tendency to consider process charts largely in connection with industrial processes but they are used to investigate many other
forms of work. The Gilbreths developed the technique originally for describing
standard procedure in any kind of management work. It is always the first
step in industrial motion study investigations but it can also be used in tracing
the movements of forms through an organisation, leading on to the use of both
micromotion and chronocylegraph techniques to study in detail the design
of individual forms. The author has used process charts on many occasions
to develop various procedures in the personnel function of management, to
analyse canteen problems and to modify production systems in workshops. The
technique has been used extensively by department stores to revise their many
procedures for dealing with merchandise[1].

---

[1] Paper presented to the American Society of Mechanical Engineers by B. E. Lies
and Marie P. Seeley and reprinted in *Motion and Time Study* by Mogensen
(McGraw-Hill).

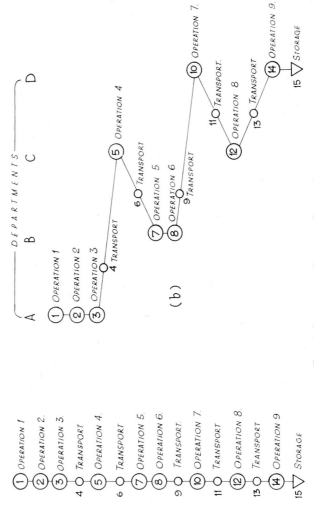

(a)

(b)

DEPARTMENTS
A   B   C   D

① OPERATION 1
② OPERATION 2.
③ OPERATION 3
4 TRANSPORT
⑤ OPERATION 4.
6 TRANSPORT
⑦ OPERATION 5
⑧ OPERATION 6.
9 TRANSPORT.
⑩ OPERATION 7.
11 TRANSPORT
⑫ OPERATION 8.
13 TRANSPORT
⑭ OPERATION 9
▽ STORAGE
15

FIG. 6. SHAPE OF A PROCESS CHART, 1

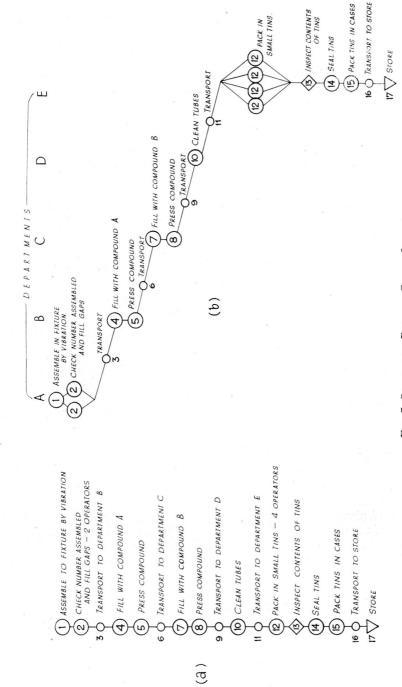

FIG. 7. SHAPE OF A PROCESS CHART, 2
Filling tubes with two compounds

Making a Process Chart

When a job has been selected for study, the first step in recording present practice and developing a new method is the gathering of material for a process chart. There are five stages in the making of a process chart.

1. *Determining the Scope of the Chart.* The exact limits of a selected job are already laid down but the process chart will go outside these limits and its field must be decided before any further work is done. It should be as wide as is practicable and in some industrial investigations it will cover the movements of the product from its entry into the factory as raw material to its despatch as a finished article. Observations of the manufacture of soap, for example, would begin with the oils and chemicals entering the factory and would end with the tablets wrapped and packed in boxes going out to the customer.

On the other hand, if the subject of the investigation is the assembly of a radio receiver it will not be useful to trace each part through to the raw material stage as the multiplicity of parts will make the chart too complex to help the investigator to visualise the process. It will probably be better to confine the original chart to the assembly department; this chart will then show which, if any, of the earlier processes have a special bearing upon the problem. These can then be charted separately.

2. *Making the Observations.* Once the field of the chart has been settled, the investigator should be ready to make his observations. He will aim at becoming thoroughly familiar with every detail of the work and he will not attempt to begin to draw up a chart until he can do so from memory. Even when he is making an investigation of a job with which he is already very familiar, he must not attempt to work without a process chart. Apparently well-known facts when they are set out in chart form often appear in an unfamiliar and revealing light and serve to clear the mind of prejudice.

3. *Choosing the Form of the Chart.* This next step will be taken in the motion study laboratory. After the investigator has become familiar with all necessary details of the work, he must consider this information from the point of view of planning the chart. He will look for those operations or other features of the work which control the rest. Examples of such operations can be found in many processes in the rubber trade where the drying of the adhesive often controls the sequence and arrangement of everything else. In engineering, a specialised machine process may have the same effect. The particular nature of the control will dictate the shape and layout of the chart which will be designed to give it prominence.

4. *Deciding upon the Scale.* Before the chart can be drawn its scale must be decided. The operation symbols must each represent a comparable unit of work and upon the size of that unit depends the size of the chart. For example: "assemble screw and tighten with driver" may be covered by a single

operation symbol or it may be described by five symbols "pick up screw," "assemble screw," "pick up driver," "tighten screw" and "put down driver." It is important that the same scale should be maintained throughout the chart.

Some investigators add a time scale to a process chart. This is a doubtful practice since it may detract from the value of the chart as a means of improving the job. The comparative times of the different sections of the work may bear no relation to their importance in making an improvement. For instance, in assembling the coin receiver of an electric meter[1], the key to the change in sequence that led to the main improvement was the greasing of the back plate disc. By greasing it before drilling instead of afterwards, a disassembling and a difficult reassembling operation were entirely eliminated. If there had been a time scale on the chart, the two or three seconds shown for this operation would have seemed very unimportant compared with the twenty seconds or more taken by other operations. For this reason its significance might have been overlooked. In addition, energy and concentration may be wasted on timing operations which would be better spent on watching movements.

5. *Drawing the Chart.* A process chart should usually be drawn backwards, starting with the final process at the bottom of the paper and working towards the beginning. In this way there will be less chance of forgetting any part of the process and the facts will appear in an unfamiliar order which will in itself help the investigator to see them more clearly. When the chart is finished it should be checked forwards against actual practice. It should present a true account of the processes as they are carried out at the moment of investigation. It may differ from the standard procedures originally laid down and any differences should be investigated at once before making any general analysis of the chart. They will probably owe their origin to something in the past. Tools or materials may have been faulty at one time, making it necessary to introduce extra processes or movements to keep up the quality of the finished product. The faults may have been remedied long ago but the extra movements remain and should be recorded on the process chart as they are part of the present practice. Again, improvements in the skill of the workers or in the quality of the material may have made some processes unnecessary. These, although they appear in the standard procedure will not be recorded on the process chart since they have been discarded and are no longer part of the present practice. It is necessary to know, before giving any thought to improvements, whether or not these additions or omissions are justified and full enquiries must therefore be made among those responsible for the technical side of production.

These five points cover the making of the first main chart in any investigation. In most cases more detailed information will be needed about the various processes recorded and further charts of different types will be made. However,

---

[1] See *An Introduction to the Theory and Application of Motion Study.* A. G. Shaw, published by H.M. Stationery Office.

a preliminary analysis must be made of the main chart at this stage to avoid the more detailed work being wasted or misdirected.

Analysing the Main Process Chart

In analysing the main chart or any of its subsidiary charts, it is essential to keep an open mind and not to accept anything in the existing method as inevitable until it has been thoroughly investigated. Every recorded movement of an operator or of material should be questioned.

The analysis is made by subjecting first the whole chart, then each section of it and finally each symbol to a critical examination under the following headings:

A. Necessity. Many movements and operations occur which are unnecessary. To take an example of the simplest form of this, the process chart of blanket cleaning at a dry cleaning works revealed that in one department blankets were carefully folded by one operator only to be unfolded by another before going through the next process. Many other less obvious examples of this kind could be quoted.

B. Sequence. A change in the order in which operations are performed may lead to a saving in movements. For example, in the assembly of the front plate of the coin receiver of the pre-payment meter referred to above, which consists of four parts, disc, shaft, plate and knob, all four were assembled and then a hole was drilled through the knob and shaft to hold a pin. Next the operator took the assembly apart to add a washer and a drop of oil before reassembling it and driving in the pin. If the washer and the oil had been added before the drilling, the disassembling and reassembling could have been eliminated and the pin could have been driven straight in after the drilling of the hole[1].

C. Combination. An operation or a sequence of operations may be combined with the other operations to give a reduction in the number of movements. To take an example from everyday work, silver and cutlery is frequently dried after washing-up and laid unsorted upon the kitchen table before being placed on a tray and carried to the dining room sideboard to be sorted into the various compartments in the silver drawer. Several operations can be combined if the tray is laid upon the kitchen table before washing-up begins. As each knife, fork or spoon is wiped, it is laid on the tray with others of the same size and category and, when all are dry, each group already sorted is transferred to the correct section of the silver drawer without further individual handling.

D. Simplification. In many instances work may be made easier by a change of layout or the provision of special tools or fixtures or a modification of the design of the product. To return to the washing-up example, it is often possible to simplify the work by rinsing the plates in clean water so that they

---

[1] For a full account of this see *An Introduction to the Theory and Application of Motion Study.* A. G. Shaw, published by H.M. Stationery Office.

can be left to dry in a rack instead of being wiped by hand. Again, special kitchen scissors may be used to simplify the removal of rind from bacon.

Subsidiary Charts arising out of the Main Chart

By making an analysis of the main chart under the headings above, it will be possible to see where more detail is required in the form of subsidiary charts. These charts will vary in type according to their purpose and the emphasis required of them. It may be that in one particular section of a chart the work of a gang of operators is involved and it becomes necessary to throw into relief the work of each member of the gang in its relation to the rest. On the other hand, the relationship between the work of one operator and that of a machine may be important. Again, considerably more detail may be needed to facilitate the analysis of a single operation. This may involve the charting of the movements of each of the operator's hands.

Some investigators differentiate between the various types of detailed chart, giving names to each—Flow Process Chart, Gang Chart, Operator Chart, Man-machine Chart, Two-handed Chart and so on, but they are all fundamentally process charts and the same theory and method of analysis applies to all. If each chart is made with the definite object of "visualising a process as a means of improving it," it will be built up so that the controlling factors of the work are brought into prominence by the form of the chart. The result may resemble other charts and fall roughly into one of these categories or it may be something quite new and original though appropriate to the presentation of the facts it records. It is unwise to set out to make a chart conforming to a particular type. A suitable shape and form should emerge in each case if a careful attempt is made to set out the material logically and vividly.

Numerous examples of the use of process charts will be found in the descriptions of actual motion studied jobs in Appendix *B,* but a more detailed examination of some typical examples may be helpful at this stage.

Examples of the Making and Analysis of
Three Representative Types of Process Chart

Three charts of widely different types and made to serve quite different purposes, have been chosen. The first, a main chart, was intended to give a general picture of the movements of material during the making of a fairly complicated tin box. It covers the work of a number of operators and several processes. The second shows a comparatively simple series of operations performed by one girl of a group of three pressing shirts. Here the controlling factor was not the movements of the operator or the material, though both were relevant to the investigation, but the work done by the presses. The third chart shows the detailed movements of an operator's hands on an inspection job.

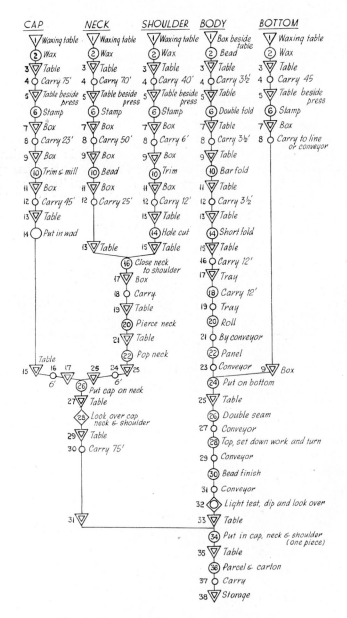

FIG. 8. MAKING AN EIGHT-SIDED TALCUM TIN
Process Chart of old method

1. THE MAKING OF TALCUM POWDER TINS

This chart, shown in Fig. 8, was constructed in the following way:

(*a*) *Scope.* It was decided that the investigation concerned the work of one department only and that it was not necessary to chart anything outside that department. The chart was therefore made to cover work on the tin from the stamping out of the parts to the parcelling of the finished tins at the end of the line.

(*b*) *Making the Observations.* As this was a line operation involving the use of a number of machines and considerable detail, the investigator spent some time in gathering information about the work and the existing routine before attempting to make the chart.

(*c*) *Form.* Most of the work was performed at a straight line conveyor by a team of eleven girls working four on one side and seven on the other, but observation showed that it was the movement of the material that was the controlling feature of the work rather than the movements of the individual operators. Further charts of their detailed movements would obviously be needed but in the first instance the chart should aim at showing the movement of the material through the department from the waxing table to the final storage. This would dictate the shape of the chart since each piece of material must be followed back to its first appearance in the department.

(*d*) *Scale.* Since the work covered a number of machine and hand operations which obviously needed detailed study at a later stage it seemed sufficient in this first chart to use one operation symbol to cover each whole operation (e.g. "close neck to shoulder").

(*e*) *Drawing the Chart.* Starting at the end of the process, where the parcels of cartons containing the tins were placed in a stillage before being removed from the department, the work was traced backwards through the various processes until it had divided into five branches showing the five original parts of the tin. The resulting chart gave satisfactory emphasis to the junctions of the different parts and the sequence of operations involved in bringing them together. All "transports" were labelled with the distances covered and the means of transport and the nature of each "temporary storage" was recorded. The final chart was a complete general record of the making of an eight-sided talcum powder tin.

(*f*) *Analysis.* In analysing this chart it was clear from the beginning that improvements in the individual operations recorded on the outline chart could be made only after further study by means of more detailed charts and the micromotion or chronocylegraph techniques. There were, however, some immediate possibilities for improvement and the following points emerged when the chart was examined under the headings "necessity," "sequence," "combination" and "simplification."

(i) *Necessity.* Since most of the operations were necessary stages in the manufacture of the tin there was little that could be entirely eliminated. Two operations were queried.   The first was the light test (body operation 32), where the method used was to pass ten or twelve tins held in the hands over a light in one continuous sweeping movement.   It seemed very doubtful whether as a test it was at all effective and it was felt that it might prove possible to

FIG. 9. MAKING AN EIGHT-SIDED TALCUM TIN
Process Chart of new method

eliminate it altogether.   The second was the dipping of the tins (body operation 32).   This was also a form of inspection which might perhaps be cut out if the beading operation that it was designed to test was made entirely efficient.

The "transport" symbols were also examined.   It was noticed that after the stamping of the cap, neck and shoulder, the parts were placed in boxes and carried 23, 50 and 6 feet respectively (cap, neck and shoulder operation 8). Also, after beading the body, the box of bodies was carried from one table to another (body operations 3, 4 and 5).   It seemed that a re-arrangement of the layout might cut out these movements or at least make a considerable reduction in them.

(ii) *Sequence.* The beading of the body was completed in two stages. The first beading operation (body operation 2) took place at the beginning of the line before the double folding operation (body operation 6) and the remainder of the work on the body. The second beading operation was the bead finishing before the light test (body operation 30). It seemed possible that all the beading might be done at one time, either at the time of the existing first operation or when the second beading took place.

(iii) *Combination.* Again, if the light and dip tests (body operation 32) could be eliminated, the remaining essential inspection might be combined with the assembly of the shoulder piece (body operation 34). Secondly, since the "bead finish" (body operation 30) and "top set down" (body operation 28) operations were both hand screw press operations which would gain by being done in the flat, they might perhaps be combined.

(iv) *Simplification.* The frequent "temporary storage" symbols on the chart suggested that a change of layout might simplify the handling of materials.

Fig. 9 shows the new method as it was finally developed. It can be seen that it incorporates most of these points, although it was not found possible to eliminate the light test. It was not, of course, until the details of the individual operations had been studied by means of more detailed charts and by micromotion study that the new method was installed.

A comparison of the two charts shows how much the organisation of the job was simplified by the reduction of temporary storages. In the new method it will be seen that the packing was divided so that the cap, neck and shoulder were packed separately instead of being tucked into each body separately. This alteration was made to simplify the customer's work in filling the tins and although it shows additional operations on the chart the actual work involved in separate packing was not very great.

2. PRESSING THE COLLARS, CUFFS AND SLEEVES OF SHIRTS

This example of a more detailed chart (Fig. 10a) was made during an investigation into the work of a complete shirt pressing unit. It shows the work of a single operator pressing three shirts at a time and using three different presses. It was made in the following way:

(a) *Scope.* The complete process of shirt pressing was carried out by three operators, each performing a specified operation group — collars, cuffs and sleeves—body pressing—touching up and folding. A main chart was made to cover all three in outline and the chart shown in Fig. 10b was drawn in addition to meet the need for a more detailed examination of each group of operations. It covers the work of the collar cuff and sleeve presser only.

(b) *Making the Observations.* The operator attended to three presses, three shirts being dealt with in one cycle of work, each being at a different

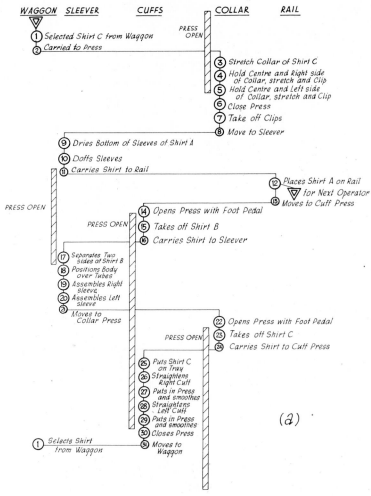

WAGGON SLEEVER   _CUFFS_   _COLLAR_   _RAIL_

PRESS OPEN

① Selected Shirt C from Waggon
② Carried to Press
③ Stretch Collar of Shirt C
④ Hold Centre and Right side of Collar, stretch and Clip
⑤ Hold Centre and Left side of Collar, stretch and Clip
⑥ Close Press
⑦ Take off Clips
⑧ Move to Sleever
⑨ Dries Bottom of Sleeves of Shirt A
⑩ Doffs Sleeves
⑪ Carries Shirt to Rail
⑫ Places Shirt A on Rail
▽ for Next Operator
⑬ Moves to Cuff Press
PRESS OPEN
⑭ Opens Press with Foot Pedal
PRESS OPEN
⑮ Takes off Shirt B
⑯ Carries Shirt to Sleever
⑰ Separates Two sides of Shirt B
⑱ Positions Body over Tubes
⑲ Assembles Right sleeve
⑳ Assembles Left sleeve
㉑ Moves to Collar Press
㉒ Opens Press with Foot Pedal
㉓ Takes off Shirt C
PRESS OPEN
㉔ Carries Shirt to Cuff Press
㉕ Puts Shirt C on Tray
㉖ Straightens Right Cuff
㉗ Puts in Press and smoothes
㉘ Straightens Left Cuff
㉙ Puts in Press and smoothes
㉚ Closes Press
① Selects Shirt from Waggon
㉛ Moves to Waggon

_(a)_

Path of Movement of Operator performing One Cycle of Operation.

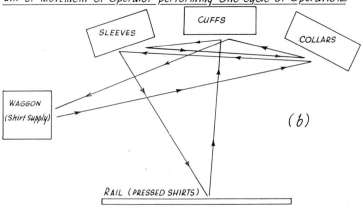

FIG. 10. SHIRT PRESSING (FIRST OPERATION GROUP)
Process Chart of old method

stage in the process. Detailed observations were made of the work over a period.

(c) *Form*. The investigation showed that the workcycle was formed by the relationship between the position of the presses, the operations performed on each press and the movements of the operator. A chart was required to illustrate this relationship and to cover a complete cycle of the work. The positions of the presses, rail and wagon and the journeys of the operator between them were shown by spacing them across the chart to enable the investigator to visualise a complete cycle of work.

(d) *Scale*. In deciding the unit of operations to be used in making the chart, it was necessary to consider the amount of detail that was likely to be useful. The observations showed that the handling of individual sections of the shirt at each press was significant and a unit was therefore chosen that would allow this handling to be analysed, e.g. "straighten right cuff" and "pick up shirt by collar."

(e) *Drawing the Chart*. The chart was drawn in the usual way, starting at the end of the sequence of operations and working backwards. Since the process was found to involve considerable periods when the presses were left open, it was thought advisable to add the details of the opening and shutting of presses.

A further diagram was prepared to show the layout of the presses and the operator's path of movement from one to another.

(f) *Analysing the Chart*. The chart was analysed under the following headings as usual:

(i) *Necessity*. Since all the pressings were obviously necessary it was accepted that none could be eliminated. An examination of the chart, however, showed that the presses themselves were not in full use all the time. There were periods when they were open and when no work was in progress on them. It seemed likely that some of this unproductive time might be eliminated. The chart also showed an excessive amount of movement between the presses.

(ii) *Sequence*. Further examination showed that some of the unproductive press time was caused by the fact that the operator had no shirt ready to go on to a press as she removed one from it. In operation 10 she doffed the sleeves of shirt A from the sleeve drier leaving it empty while she took the shirt to the rail ready for the next operator. On the way back from the rail she collected shirt B (operation 15) from the cuff press leaving this press empty while she carried the shirt to the sleeve drier for operations 17—20. Next she took shirt C off the collar press to fill the cuff press which had been empty since she removed shirt B (operation 15). This left the collar press empty until she had collected a further shirt from the wagon.

The chart and diagram show that the operator retraced her steps as she moved from collar press to sleeve drier and to the rail and back to the collar and cuff presses. She visited each press twice in dealing with each shirt in each cycle. These movements were caused by the layout of the presses and the fact that the operator was only working on three shirts in each cycle of operations. For this reason, she was handling one shirt only on each visit to a press. To use the presses most productively she should have put another shirt on a press as soon as she had taken one off. In this way she would have visited each press only once in each cycle of work. These considerations suggested the possibility of combining the operation of taking-off one shirt with the laying on operation of the next. This could only be arranged by changing the sequence of operations and would involve a change in layout and the introduction of a fourth shirt into the cycle.

(iii) *Combination.* As well as the question of combining the taking off of one shirt with the laying on of another, there was a further point to be considered. It seemed that it might be possible to pull off and lay down a shirt in such a way that the hands could pick it up at once in the correct position for laying it on the next press. If this was to be done, some further alteration might have to be made in the sequence and in the layout of the presses.

(iv) *Simplification.* The chief obstacle to the laying on of a fresh shirt immediately after removing the previous one was the lack of equipment for laying down work in progress. It was necessary to make some arrangement to allow shirts to be laid down between operations. At the same time, an examination of the wagon suggested that it made handling much less easy than it would have been from a rail. Since the previous process was tumbling, the shirts could just as easily be placed on a movable rail as into a wagon.

(g) *Developing the New Method.* It was decided as a result of this analysis to work with four shirts at a time and to press them in the order shown on the chart shown in Fig. 11a, arranging the presses so that the cuff press was first, followed by the collar press and the sleeve drier. The operator picked up shirt D by its sleeves from the rail which took the place of the wagon and moved with it to the cuff press where she dropped it into one side of a tray, tail first. She then peeled off the cuffs of shirt C, leaving it on the other side of the tray of the cuff press, shoulders upwards. Next, she picked up the cuffs of shirt D from where they lay in position on top of the shirt on the tray and laid them on the cuff press. After closing this press, she picked up shirt C by its collar with one hand, using the other hand to stretch it as she moved to the collar press. Here she opened the press with a foot lever, peeled off shirt B with one hand and laid it on a tray. She then used both hands to lay shirt C on the press. Moving on to the sleeve drier she doffed shirt A and carried it to the rail by its shoulders, leaving it ready for the next operator. As she returned, she picked up shirt B from the collar press tray and arranged it on the sleeve drier, thus completing a cycle of work.

In comparing the charts of these two methods it will be seen (Fig. 11b) that the operator's path of movement has been considerably shortened and that the presses remain open very much less under the new method. Both these changes mean a considerable saving in unproductive time.

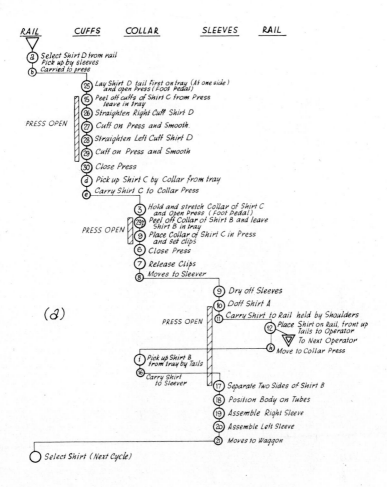

RAIL   CUFFS   COLLAR   SLEEVES   RAIL

(a) Select Shirt D from rail
Pick up by sleeves
(b) Carried to press

(25) Lay Shirt D tail first on tray (At one side) and open Press (Foot Pedal)
(15) Peel off cuffs of Shirt C from Press leave in tray
(26) Straighten Right Cuff Shirt D
(27) Cuff on Press and Smooth.
(28) Straighten Left Cuff Shirt D
(29) Cuff on Press and Smooth
(30) Close Press
(d) Pick up Shirt C by Collar from tray
(e) Carry Shirt C to Collar Press

PRESS OPEN

(3) Hold and stretch Collar of Shirt C and Open Press (Foot Pedal)
(23) Peel off Collar of Shirt B and leave Shirt B in tray
(9) Place Collar of Shirt C in Press and set clips
(6) Close Press
(7) Release Clips
(8) Moves to Sleever

(9) Dry off Sleeves
(10) Doff Shirt A
(11) Carry Shirt to Rail held by Shoulders
(12) Place Shirt on Rail, front up Tails to Operator
To Next Operator
(h) Move to Collar Press

PRESS OPEN

(a)

(i) Pick up Shirt B from tray by Tails
(16) Carry Shirt to Sleever
(17) Separate Two Sides of Shirt B
(18) Position Body on Tubes
(19) Assemble Right Sleeve
(20) Assemble Left Sleeve
(21) Moves to Waggon

Select Shirt (Next Cycle)

Path of Movement of Operator performing One Cycle of Operation

CUFFS   COLLAR

SLEEVER

RAIL FROM PREVIOUS OPERATOR

(b)

RAIL FOR NEXT OPERATOR

FIG. 11. SHIRT PRESSING (FIRST OPERATION GROUP)
Process Chart of new method

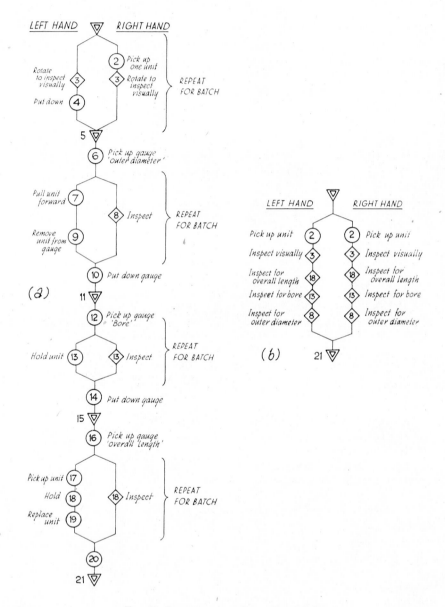

FIG. 12. INSPECTION OF BOMB EXPLODER
Process Chart: (a) old method, (b) new method

It should be understood that this example is an illustration of the improvements that can be made simply by studying movements and without altering the equipment except in minor ways such as by the provision of a tray beside the collar press and the substitution of a rail for the original wagon. If changes in the type of presses used had been possible the new method might have been quite different. This chart however, records only one part of a larger investigation and should not be regarded as complete in itself.

3. INSPECTION OF BOMB EXPLODERS[1]

This is an example of a detailed chart showing the work of two hands (*see* Fig. 12). It was constructed in the following way:

(*a*) *Scope.* The investigation was only concerned with the inspection of the finished article. It was not therefore necessary in the first instance to chart anything other than the inspection process. As this largely consisted of picking up and putting down exploders and gauges, it was necessary to study in considerable detail the work performed by each hand.

(*b*) *Making the Observations.* As the complete work cycle was performed by one operator, all the information required for the chart was obtained by intensive study of the performance of the work cycle.

(*c*) *Form.* A preliminary survey showed that the work cycle consisted of four inspection operations. These were performed in batches for each separate gauging. It was important that the chart should show this clearly in addition to showing the details of the work of each hand.

(*d*) *Scale.* Since the investigation was concerned with the detailed movements of the hands each symbol was required to cover only one small movement, e.g. "pick up part," "hold part," "put down part."

(*e*) *Construction.* The chart was made in two columns, one for each hand. Since it was a straightforward chart of a simple work cycle it was not necessary to begin it at the bottom of the paper and it was drawn forwards. As it was intended to emphasise that the work was done in batches, the temporary storages between batches were brought in to a centre line, as was the picking up and putting down of gauges when these were single operations and not repeated within a batch. The double lines of symbols were therefore left to describe the work of the two hands in the sections which were repetitive.

(*f*) *Analysing the Chart.* The chart was then analysed under the usual headings:

(i) *Necessity.* The need to inspect for the four points "exterior surface," "outer diameter," "bore," and "overall length" was accepted. The shape of the chart indicated clearly that by inspecting the exploders in batches each exploder was picked up and put down four times before it was completely inspected. It suggested that three of these handlings might be eliminated it

---

[1] This operation was exhibited by the Aeronautical Inspection Department at the Ministry of Aircraft Production Exhibition, October, 1945.

all the inspections could be completed at one time on each exploder so that it was picked up and put down once only.

(ii) *Combination and Simplification.* As the method existed it was not possible to inspect all four points at once without picking up and putting down each gauge. This would have been no improvement and a means was therefore sought of mounting the gauges so that they need not be handled. In considering this, the path of movement of the hands holding the exploders was studied so that it should be as easy as possible. It was arranged that, wherever it was practicable the movement out of one gauge should lead directly

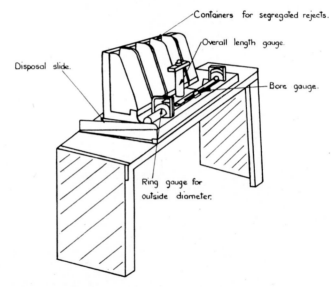

FIG. 13. INSPECTION OF BOMB EXPLODER
Work-place showing combined and duplicated gauges. Materials are placed in containers on both sides of the operator's chair

into the next. In addition, containers were provided to take the different types of rejects which had previously not been segregated (*see* Fig. 13).

(g) *Developing the New Method.* The new method as it was finally developed is shown in Fig. 12b. Because the mounting of the gauges freed one hand entirely they were duplicated. Both hands were then free to introduce exploders simultaneously. An exploder was picked up in either hand, visually inspected and placed in the overall length gauges which were fixed so that they gauged the exploders in a vertical position; the easiest movement after the visual inspection. From these gauges, they moved to the bore gauges which were arranged in line with the ring gauges for the outside diameter. The movement of removing them from the bore gauges passed them through the ring gauges and if they were correct they rolled down slides directly to the packer. If there was a reject the examiner was instructed to place it in the appropriate container and to complete the inspection of the other exploder with one hand.

In addition to this, where the examiners collected and removed their own material in the old method, in the new the material was brought to them by labourers and stored on stillages, and the inspected material rolled directly to the packer. The examiner's stamp on individual exploders was eliminated and instead an examiner's slip was put on each box of inspected exploders. The complete new method raised his hourly output from 120 to 900.

3

MICROMOTION STUDY

IN the last chapter the application of motion study on a broad scale has been discussed. Whole groups of processes can be visualised and studied by means of flow process charts and other charts have been devised for the examination of individual processes and operations. Although this technique is adequate for the improvement of many processes, it provides no accurate measurements and deals only with whole movements.

Modern motion study investigators usually make some sort of process chart at the beginning of every investigation, even when the main part of the study will have to be made by more intensive methods. In this way they avoid wasting time on detailed analysis of operations which may prove to be redundant when the processes are examined as a whole. Gilbreth, on the other hand, though he always made a list of operations in beginning an investigation, developed and used the much more accurate and more detailed system of micromotion analysis before he turned his attention to developing the process chart technique. In his earliest motion study work on bricklaying, his first observations were of the detailed movements of an experienced bricklayer. He noticed that he used three sets of movements; the first when working at normal speed, the second when making a conscious effort to work quickly, the third when demonstrating to a pupil. In trying to discover why these movements differed from one another, Gilbreth was led to divide all movements into common elements which he called "therbligs"—his own name backwards.

These elements were not based on a physiological analysis of movement, since it was recognised that the least observable movement might involve whole groups of muscles. His method of classification was based on an analysis of the purpose for which a movement or part of a movement was performed, not on the nature of the movement itself. For example, if the empty hand moves towards an object, its purpose is to reach that object. Having reached it, the purpose changes, first to picking it up and secondly to moving it from one place to another. Three different therbligs are needed to distinguish between these three distinct movements, "transport empty," "grasp" and "transport loaded." The operator's next intention may be to put it into a container—to "assemble" it. Before this "assemble," some rearrangement may be necessary which involves the therblig "position." If, on the other hand, the purpose of a movement is to separate two parts, "disassemble" will be the therblig used.

If a tool is needed, the therblig will be "use" and in putting it down "release load." If it is being arranged at the same time for easy use at a later stage in the work, it will be described by the therblig "pre-position."

All these therbligs are productive or service elements but there are other parts of a work cycle which are only ancillary to the productive part. Sometimes, after the preliminary "transport empty" and before the other therbligs can begin, it may be necessary to "search" for, or "find," or "select," the object to be "used" or "assembled." Again, there may be a point in the work cycle where the purpose of a movement or the reason for an absence of movement is the need to "inspect" or test an article. Other pauses in the activity may have other causes and they will be classified as "unavoidable delay" outside the operator's control, "avoidable delay" where the pause is deliberate, or even "rest for overcoming fatigue."

These original sixteen elements were used by Gilbreth to analyse movement. Thirteen were active elements and three accounted for absence of activity. A seventeenth, "plan," was added later to the second group. Those who have used the micromotion technique in recent years have added one more to the first group, "hold." This new therblig is sometimes useful though Gilbreth would have called it a prolonged "grasp." Others again have developed entirely different elements but these, in their ultimate analysis, are only therbligs or combinations of therbligs and they have not added any further knowledge or given any assistance to the techniques of motion study.

Therblig Definitions

1. Search (Black)

"Search" denotes the part of the work cycle taken up in locating an article among a number of other articles. The hand is ready to grasp the object but either the hand or the eye is still searching for it.

2. Find (Grey)

This terminates the search period and, since it is really a mental reaction, it will probably appear as a momentary pause or hesitation in the movement.

3. Select (Light Grey)

"Select" describes the movement involved in getting the hand in position to pick out the required article from among a number of other articles after it has been searched for and found.

These first three therbligs are often very difficult to differentiate. Unless they are very distinct in the work cycle and therefore of obvious significance in the investigation, it is usually convenient to group them under the therblig "select."

4. Grasp (Red)

This therblig describes the act of taking hold of an object. It begins when the hand or a holding device, after "transport empty," touches the article to be grasped, or when the movement of some other therblig such as "assemble" or "transport loaded" ceases and an object is held in a stationary position. It ends when the object begins to move or when the hand leaves go.

A finger or hand grasp may be of more than one type. The easiest is that used in sliding an object along a flat surface without lifting it, but, even when a full grasp[1] is necessary it may be either the hook grasp used in picking up something that is free on all four sides, such as a tool from a properly arranged tool rack, or it may be the pressure grasp needed to pick up a spanner from a bench. The second is much more difficult than the first (*see* Figs. 22 and 23, Chapter 4).

When the grasp is prolonged and does not immediately merge into "transport loaded" or "position," an extra therblig "hold" may be used if it is preferred.

5. Transport Loaded (Green)

Transport loaded is the act of moving an article from place to place by means of muscular effort directly or indirectly applied. In its simplest form of direct muscular effort, the hand grasping an object moves with it from one position to another. In more complex cases muscular effort is indirectly applied by means of a hand operated mechanical device for moving one or more articles. It begins when the hand holding an object moves. It can often be identified during the analysis of a film by finding a slight change of position between one frame and the next. This change may not necessarily appear in the position of the fingers immediately involved but, because so many muscles take part in even a simple grasping movement, it may be found, for example, in a movement of the wrist or the muscles of the forearm.

If, during transit, the fingers or other parts of the hand or arm are doing more than carrying the object, the purpose of the additional movement should be recorded. In such cases the upper and lower arm will be "transport loaded" while the fingers are "position" or "assemble." This combination of therbligs often shows a smoother movement than a mere sequence of therbligs and is one of the characteristics of the movements used by a skilled workman.

[1] Professor Ralph M. Barnes, of the University of Iowa, describes experiments with various types of "grasp" in his book, *Motion and Time Study*.

6. Position (Blue)

"Position" represents the movement involved in preparing something so that it can be placed directly into its intended location. Almost anything picked up in the hand requires positioning before it can be assembled or used. A screw, for example, must be turned in the fingers so that its point is towards the hole into which it is to go. A screwdriver must be handled until it is directed to fit into the slot in the screw. This therblig is sometimes performed by the whole hand and arm. A pencil may be "grasped," "transport loaded" to a point in mid-air and there turned round until it is in position to be used in writing before the "transport loaded" is allowed to continue towards the paper. On the other hand the pencil may move continuously, being turned into position by the fingers during transit. In this second case the movement of the upper and lower arm will be described by the therblig "transport loaded" and the fingers by the therblig "position" during the period in which the pencil has been changing its place in relation to the arm.

7. Assemble (Violet)

"Assemble" is the movement of putting together two or more objects to form a combination. This combination may be a complete unit in itself, such as a nut and its bolt, or a combination of articles, such as a screw and screwdriver, which can only function together. The therblig begins when one part is brought into contact with the other and ceases when that contact is complete and the two parts are correctly placed. Occasionally, "assemble" may be combined with a "transport loaded" as, for instance, when the right hand picks up the top of a toothpaste tube and the left hand the tube itself and "assembles" them during the move towards the bathroom shelf. In this case, as with "position" above, the upper and lower arm would be described as "transport loaded" and the fingers as "assemble" during that part of the transport in which tube and cap were being put together.

8. Use (Purple)

"Use" describes a movement which results in a tool or device performing its intended function. This therblig describes such movements as those used in writing with a pen, sawing wood, turning a tap or brushing the hair. It begins as soon as the hand moves a tool to begin its work and continues until that work is ended and the tool is ready to be withdrawn.

9. Disassemble (Light Violet)

"Disassemble" is the separating of two parts of a combination or the removal of a tool from the work it has been doing. It covers the movement of the object from its first withdrawal until it is completely clear of the remainder of the assembly. It is subject to the same type of combination as was seen above in the case of "assemble," though here, of course, the process is reversed.

10. Inspect (Burnt Ochre)

"Inspect" is the act of examining or testing a part for defects irrespective of how such testing is carried out. It may be performed by any of the senses or by a combination of them and may, therefore, in some cases, appear not as a movement but as a pause. It may be carried out by one of the senses during the operation of other therbligs. In this case it is not recorded unless it has some significance in the process.

11. Pre-position (Pale Blue)

This therblig is more fully described as "pre-position for the next operation." It covers the movement involved in placing a tool or an article ready for further use so that "position" will not be needed subsequently. For example, tools may be supported to allow their immediate return to a set position so that they can be grasped without fumbling when they are next needed. The therblig begins with a movement to place the article in the required position and ends when this movement is complete.

12. Release Load (Carmine Red)

"Release load" describes the act of releasing an object held in the hand or by some tool. It begins at the instant in which the controlling force of the hand is relaxed and ends when the hand is entirely clear of the object.

13. Transport Empty (Olive Green)

"Transport empty" is the movement of the empty hand from the point where one operation is completed to the place where the next begins. It describes the hand reaching for an object or returning after disposing of an article or a tool. It should be noted that the hand itself is idle in this therblig, only the upper and lower arm being active. In colouring a simo-chart, therefore, the columns referring to the hand are left blank.

The following therbligs describe, not the active purpose of an element of movement, but the passive reason for an absence of movement.

14. Unavoidable Delay (Yellow Ochre)

This covers a period of idleness forming part of the cycle of operations and outside the operator's own control. It is often found where one hand has more than its share of the work and the other waits for it, or when a machine causes the hands to remain idle until a mechanical operation is complete and they can continue with the work. A delay may be charted as unavoidable in an existing sequence although a simple change in routine will eliminate it.

15. Avoidable Delay (Lemon Yellow)

"Avoidable delay" is a delay that an operator can control without altering the existing sequence of movements. It often appears as the result of incomplete training which causes one hand to wait for the other unnecessarily instead of continuing its work. It may also be due to inattention on the part of the operator.

16. Rest for Overcoming Fatigue (Orange)

This is an approved pause in the activities under investigation to enable the operator to recover from the fatigue induced by the job.

17. Plan (Brown)

"Plan" covers delay caused by stopping work to think out subsequent action.

The last two therbligs do not often appear in a film analysis. They were used by Gilbreth before micromotion photography was developed and they are still useful where a therblig analysis is made of work that is not suitable for filming.

As an example of a sequence of therbligs, the locking of a door would be described as follows:—

> ⌣ To key ring.
> ⌖ Feeling for bunch of keys.
> ⌖ Locating bunch of keys.
> ⟶ Choosing key.
> ∩ Key.
> ⌒ Key to lock.
> ⟩ Turning key to fit in lock.
> ⧺ Fitting in lock.
> ∪ Unlocking door.
> ⧺ Withdrawing key from lock.
> ⌒ Carrying keys back.
> ⤳ Putting keys down.

Therblig Symbols and Colours

When Gilbreth devised the therbligs, he gave each the descriptive symbols shown in Fig. 14. These symbols are pictorial and devised for easy memorising. *Search* is the roving eye. *Find* is the eye which has become focussed when the object is reached. *Select* is an arrow directed to its object and *Grasp* shows

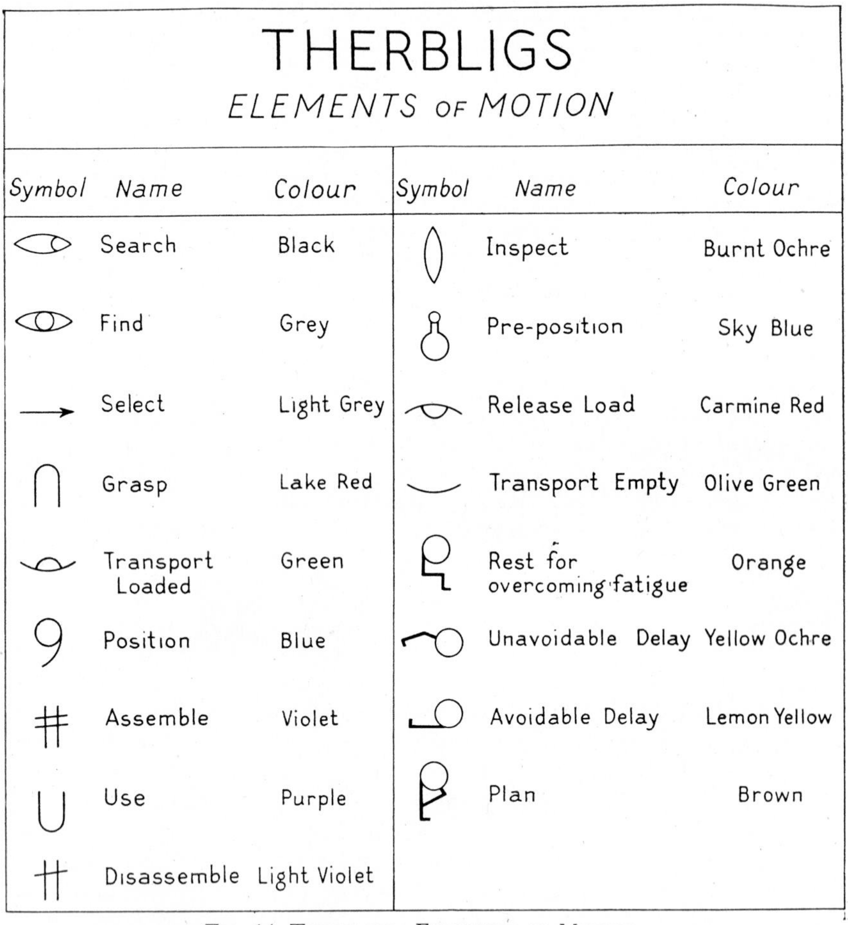

THERBLIGS
ELEMENTS OF MOTION

Symbol	Name	Colour	Symbol	Name	Colour
	Search	Black		Inspect	Burnt Ochre
	Find	Grey		Pre-position	Sky Blue
	Select	Light Grey		Release Load	Carmine Red
	Grasp	Lake Red		Transport Empty	Olive Green
	Transport Loaded	Green		Rest for overcoming fatigue	Orange
	Position	Blue		Unavoidable Delay	Yellow Ochre
	Assemble	Violet		Avoidable Delay	Lemon Yellow
	Use	Purple		Plan	Brown
	Disassemble	Light Violet			

FIG. 14. THERBLIGS: ELEMENTS OF MOTION

the fingers or tongs ready to pick something up. *Transport Loaded* is represented by an object lying in the curve of the hand, and *Position* by the same object now balanced at the tips of the fingers in a hand that has changed direction. *Assemble consists* of woven threads and *Disassemble* is the same symbol but with one thread removed. *Use* is the letter U. In the symbol for *Release Load* the hand again appears, reversed, and ready to drop its load.

Preposition is represented by a ninepin and *Inspect* by a lens. The three delays are all pictures of the operator. *Rest for overcoming fatigue* shows him sitting in a chair. In *Unavoidable delay* he is tripping up, and in *Avoidable delay* he is lying down. The final therblig *Plan* shows him scratching his head in contemplation.

Colours were added to the symbols later when film analysis became possible and the simultaneous motion cycle or simo-chart was developed. Again there was a reason for each colour. "Search," "find" and "select" show the light strengthening from black darkness at "search" to the first glimmer of light in the dark grey of "find" and the final pale grey dawn of "select." "Grasp," being stationary, is red. Any undue length of grasp thus shows a danger signal. "Transport loaded" on the other hand is green to describe movement. "Position," "assemble" and "use" are a sequence of blues and purples beginning with the blue of "position" followed by the violet of "assemble" and the rich purple of the central therblig "use." After that the opposites begin. "Disassemble" is the opposite to "assemble" and is therefore a paler shade of the same violet. "Pre-position" is a lighter shade of blue than "position," and "release load" and "transport empty" are carmine red and olive green respectively—softer shades of the "grasp" and "transport loaded" colours. "Inspect," having no direct connection with the other therbligs, has a colour of its own—burnt ochre. The delay symbols are all shades of yellow beginning with orange for the respectable "rest for overcoming fatigue" and a less cheerful yellow ochre for "unavoidable delay," ending with a most definite lemon yellow to express the disgrace of lying down on the job in "avoidable delay." "Plan" is, of course, the brown of a brown study.

Micromotion Photography

Gilbreth developed and used therbligs long before the cine-camera was available but he began to take films in the very early days of cine-photography. His original purpose in taking motion pictures was to record the movement of an expert for examination and demonstration but he soon discovered their use for analysis into therbligs. He was obliged to do his filming with a hand-cranked camera and to vary his camera speed still further because of deficiencies in lighting. He therefore introduced into his picture a chronometer so that he could check this speed when the film was projected. This chronometer or counter had a pointer making twenty revolutions per minute round a dial marked off into a hundred divisions. Each of these divisions therefore represented a two-thousandth of a minute. Gilbreth called this division of time a "wink." Modern counters are electrically driven and a second or even a third pointer can be introduced to record the revolutions of the first and the second pointers. The "wink," however, has not been changed. Having introduced the chronometer for this purpose of checking the camera speed, Gilbreth found that it gave him new opportunities in film analysis because it provided the accurate timing device which allowed an examination of the time relationship of the different therbligs, a feature of modern micromotion study. To this he tried to add the accurate measurement of the path of movement by using a background made up of 4-inch squares. (He chose 4 inches as a unit since it is easily converted into centimetres.) He also tried what he called a "penetrating screen" which appeared as a squared foreground to the picture. It was made by the double exposure of the film[1].

As his work progressed the technique of cine-photography became much easier and, although he maintained the chronometer or counter as essential for the measurement not of total time but of the time relationships between the movements of the different parts of the body, the squared background was discarded as too cumbersome when filming. The measurement of the path of movement for which it was designed was made more accurately by the chronocyclegraph (*see* Chapter 4). Except for this and the abandoning of the "penetrating screen" the technique remains essentially the same today. The phraseology, however, has been changed, and the modern motion study investigator, though he uses Gilbreth's technique to develop his new method, seldom calls it "the one best way." Gilbreth coined his famous phrase "the one best way to do work" to suit the American mentality of his time but he used it only as a standard against which to measure individual differences; just as the psychologists use standards in their methods of testing. The phrase was a little crude and aroused antagonism in the quite different and rather over-sensitive atmosphere of British contemporary thought.

So many of those who have followed Gilbreth have had an engineer's training and background without the knowledge of psychology which Mrs. Gilbreth contributed to the Gilbreth partnership. This has resulted in too mechanical an approach to a technique which has its foundations in the study of the human being who performs the job. Those investigators who have tried to improve upon Gilbreth's original "elements of movement" and those who have assigned standard times to these elements though adding to the equipment of the skilled investigator have tended to base their work on a much narrower conception of motion study than that of its originators. The Gilbreths found that there were no standard solutions which could be applied ready-made to new problems. Improvements should be made in each separate case from an unbiassed and complete analysis of the facts including not only the detailed movements of the operator but all the surrounding variables, both human and material.

Apparatus needed for Micromotion Work

Micromotion study, as it is practised now, is derived directly from Gilbreth's original work but today photographic technique, though it may still seem complex to the uninitiated, is simple and straightforward compared with that of Gilbreth's time. The modern motion study investigator can, for

---

[1] For an example of these devices in filming, see *The Original Films of Frank B. Gilbreth*, a film embodying shots from many of Gilbreth's early pictures, and edited by James S. Perkins.

example, pack all his filming equipment into a large suitcase and, with this portable outfit, obtain results that Gilbreth would have envied.   Before discussing further details of micromotion methods it would be as well to list the equipment considered useful if the micromotion technique is to be adopted as a part of the development of motion study in an organisation.   (A fuller description of this equipment and its use will be found in Appendix C).

1. Films—16 mm. substandard reversal.
2. Camera — a cine-camera with interchangeable lenses and variable speeds.
3. Exposure meter.
4. Lighting equipment.
5. Counter or chronometer.
6. Projector (which must have a device for hand framing).

Making the Micromotion Film

The important part of a micromotion study is the analysis of the film and the subsequent development of a new method.   To the investigator who is anxious to achieve results, the taking of the film is only a preliminary operation.   To the operator who is to be filmed and to the immediate supervisory staff in the workshop it appears as the most prominent part of the study.   The operator who is probably being filmed for the first time, looks upon it as a very important occasion.   It is essential that the investigator should be aware of this and that he should not appear to regard filming as mere routine necessity.

Before making preparations for filming the investigator should go over his ground thoroughly, choosing with care the subjects to be filmed and making the foreman or supervisor play his part in selecting the operators.   Where there is a choice he will usually film two or three operators, the best, the least efficient, and an average worker.   Operators should always be asked if they would like to be filmed.   The writer has never met with a refusal.   Ample warning of the date and time of filming should be given to the chosen operators.   When filming women, it is important to give them time to make what they consider adequate preparations since they will not co-operate happily if they do not feel that they look their best.   The reasons for making the film and an explanation of what is to be done with it and why the counter is necessary should be given at this stage to the operators concerned and to their representatives. During the actual filming the counter face should, if possible, be visible to the operator.   It usually interests him to be allowed to look through the camera viewfinder to see the set-up.   This can be done while camera, lights and other equipment are being arranged.   He will also like to have some memento of the occasion and a still camera should be used to take a photograph to be given to him afterwards.

A micromotion investigator will carry out all his preparations for filming, bearing in mind that the actual photography on the shop floor must be carried out as expeditiously as possible.   There should be the least amount of

disturbance consistent with gaining the interest and co-operation of the operators to be filmed.   One of the chief causes of delays during filming is electrical
trouble.   It is always wise to consult the electrician responsible for the section
before setting up filming apparatus.   His help and local knowledge are essential
to the success of the operation.   When lighting equipment and camera are in
their final positions, the lights should be switched on fully and the operator
should be allowed some time to get used to working in a dazzling light before
the filming begins.   The correct moment to start shooting is when he is doing
his job normally.   Several cycles of the work should be filmed.

If a hand-cranked or electrically driven camera is not available and if the
operation cycle is longer than the running time of the camera clockwork
(usually about one minute), the job obviously cannot be filmed in one shot.   A
continuous shot of the whole operation can, however, be obtained by later
editing of the film.   When this is necessary the camera man must note accurately
the point in the cycle at which he has to stop and should carry on very slightly
before that point when he has rewound the camera.

When the filming operation is complete the film will be sent away for
processing.   When it returns it should be shown as soon as possible to those
who were concerned with making it.   In particular it should be shown to the
operators.   This is important and it is easily forgotten in the anxiety to begin
the analysis.

Analysing Cycles from the Film

The investigator begins his analysis of the film by running it through
a number of times at normal speed to make himself familiar with the general
sequence of movements.   He next considers the form of the work cycle that
he is going to use for his analysis and decides at which point he will begin.
This point must be the same in each cycle and he will not necessarily choose
the moment when the operator begins work on an article unless that point is
consistent in each cycle and is easily identified.   It quite often happens that
another point in the cycle is more suitable, such as the pressing of the lever
of a machine.   It is best, wherever possible, to choose a place where both hands
finish their therbligs together, but, whatever point is selected, the therblig that
begins that part of the work cycle will be used to start the analysis and the
therblig preceding it will be the finishing point of the last cycle.

Having decided upon the dividing point between the cycles the investigator
then examines the whole film, taking counter readings at that point whenever
it appears.   This will give him a list of cycles with their lengths in terms of
'winks' and he will be able to select those which it is most important for him to
analyse first.   They will probably be either the longest and the shortest or
cycles that are particularly outstanding for some other reason.   He will then
begin his detailed analysis by operating the projector by hand to examine each
consecutive frame of the chosen cycles for changes in movement of any part
of the body.   On finding a change of therblig he records the counter reading

and the appropriate therblig on a film analysis sheet (*see* Fig. 15). He watches for all changes of movement wherever they appear, considering both right and left arm at once. Recording the movements of all parts of the body at the same time makes film analysis more difficult for beginners but has the

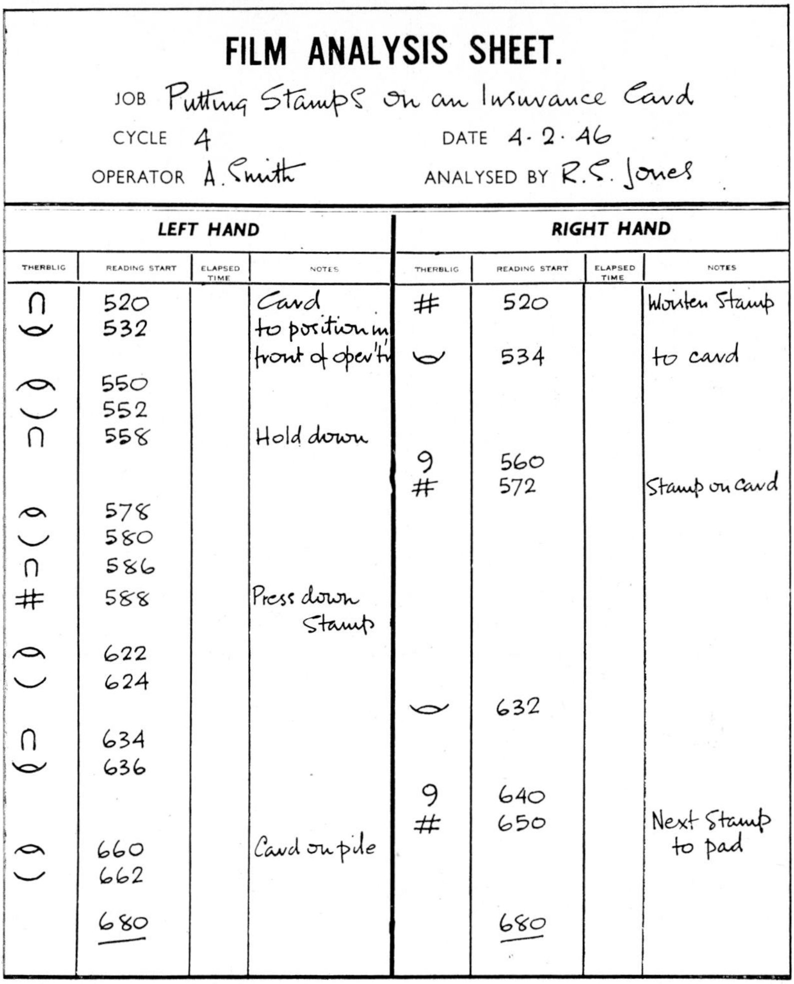

FILM ANALYSIS SHEET.

JOB Putting Stamps on an Insurance Card

CYCLE 4   DATE 4·2·46

OPERATOR A. Smith   ANALYSED BY R.S. Jones

LEFT HAND				RIGHT HAND			
THERBLIG	READING START	ELAPSED TIME	NOTES	THERBLIG	READING START	ELAPSED TIME	NOTES
∩ ◡	520 532		Card to position in front of open'ng	# ◡	520 534		Moisten Stamp to card
⌒ ◡	550 552						
∩	558		Hold down	9 #	560 572		Stamp on card
⌒ ◡	578 580						
∩ #	586 588		Press down Stamp				
⌒ ◡	622 624			◡	632		
∩ ◡	634 636			9 #	640 650		Next Stamp to pad
⌒ ◡	660 662		Card on pile				
	680				680		

Fig. 15. Recorded Analysis of a Film

great advantage of keeping a complete picture of the whole movement in front of the investigator as he works. If he divides his analysis and considers all the movements of the right hand before examining the left, he misses the inter-relationship of the two and does not re-discover it until he has completed his simo-chart at a later stage.

Making a Simo-chart

When the analysis into therbligs is complete, all relevant information has been extracted from the film but it is not in such a form that can easily be visualised as a whole. It is necessary, then, before attempting to develop a new method to put the facts into chart form. The Gilbreths developed a chart in which the various parts of the body were recorded along the top of the paper and the counter readings down the left hand side with the therblig symbols appearing against the correct counter reading and the vertical columns filled in with the appropriate therblig colour. These charts were called simultaneous motion cycle charts or, more shortly, simo-charts. The modern motion study investigator makes the same kind of chart. It is usually drawn up on 1/10th of an inch squared paper with the inch line heavily ruled.

Counter readings are plotted vertically on a scale of one or two winks to each square according to the size or intricacy of the cycle to be charted. The horizontal scale shows the parts of the body used in the cycle. It can be adapted to include any member of the body but most industrial processes do not require the analysis of anything but finger and arm movements and the typical chart (*see* Fig. 16) uses only the following headings: upper arm, lower arm, wrist, thumb, first, second, third, and fourth fingers, and palm. Further columns are added for other members where they are needed, but normally these columns are enough. Very few movements of wrist or palm, however, are observed and the spaces allotted to them are therefore frequently left blank.

Having compiled the headings and decided upon the scale of the chart, the investigator uses his analysis sheet to enter the therbligs recorded there on the chart at their appropriate counter readings. In some particularly complex analyses the work of each finger may have to be differentiated, but the investigator charts only such detail as he needs in each particular case. He fills in the space covered by each therblig in its appropriate colour and, as he analysed left and right together, so he will make his simo-chart, filling it in in such a way that both columns grow equally to give him a developing picture of the whole. The complete chart is an accurate graphic record of the details of the various parts of the movements and of their time relationship to one another. To an experienced investigator the distribution and extent of the different colours on the chart are of immediate significance. His attention is at once drawn to the form of the work cycle and to those parts which most need improvement.

Analysing a Simo-chart and Developing a New Method

The making of the simo-chart completes the first stage of a micromotion investigation. It is the final record of the information about present practice that has been obtained from a therblig analysis of the film. This information is now available in readable form and it remains for the investigator to develop his new method from it.

In the analysis of a motion study investigation whatever method of

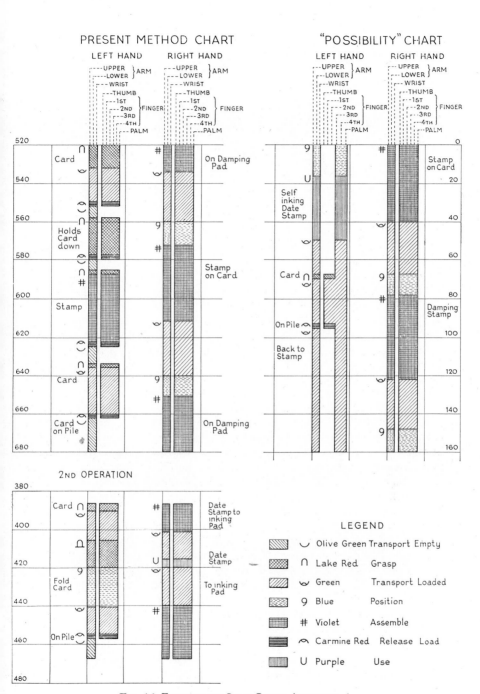

FIG. 16. EXAMPLE OF SIMO-CHART ANALYSIS, 1

measurement is used there are four basic ideas which should be explored by the investigator:

1. The necessity of performing each movement.
2. The sequence of movements.
3. The combination of different movements.
4. The simplification of all movements.

Because of the detail involved in micromotion study, the investigator makes his examination in three parts. He may begin by considering the simo-chart in its broad operation grouping, dividing it later into smaller groups of therbligs and finally examining each individual therblig. Some such division is always necessary but its form will depend on the nature of the job under investigation. Some jobs fall naturally into operation groups, which at once contribute ideas towards a solution of the problem. In these cases the investigator goes on immediately to examine the individual therbligs without at first subdividing the large operation groups into therblig groups, though he may return to do this later. Each investigation varies, though the ultimate and essential analysis of individual therbligs always follows the same pattern. The unproductive therbligs such as "search," "find" and "select" and the delay therbligs, can most usually be eliminated while the service therbligs "grasp," "transport loaded," "position," "release load," "transport empty" and "pre-position" are good subjects for combination. Again, the productive therbligs "assemble," "use" and "disassemble" may often be simplified.

In searching for ideas for a new method the investigator will usually begin by accepting the productive therbligs as the only essential part of the cycle, later considering which service therbligs are necessary to them. In this way he will build up short theoretical sequences of therbligs which may give him suggestions towards a new method. It may help him at this stage to act as the operator himself and to try out any ideas as they come to him during his analysis of the simo-chart. As these ideas for a new method begin to fall into place and are tried out in practice the investigator lists the suggested sequence of therbligs on an analysis sheet in the same way as the original therblig analysis but without a time scale. If the new idea seems likely to be successful, he may then check his results by counting the number of therbligs used by each hand. It is very frequently found that a comparison of these numbers can give an approximate idea of the balance of the work of the two hands. If it seems that a balance has not been obtained, the new sequence of therbligs should receive the same criticism as the old sequence to discover whether anything can be simplified.

When the therblig list is reasonably complete, the investigator uses it to form a "possibility" simo-chart, giving each therblig the same number of winks as the equivalent therblig on the old chart. Where simplification or combination of therbligs makes the old timing invalid, he makes reasonable allowance, shortening or lengthening according to probability. In balancing a list of therbligs and in making a "possibility" chart of any operation in which the work is not exactly the same in both hands it will usually be found that there are certain key sequences that have to be performed by one hand at a certain point in the cycle. The therbligs used by the other hand have to fit in with this and it will therefore usually be best to build the chart backwards and forwards from this point.

It is not possible to give exact rules for the analysis of a simo-chart and the development from it of a new method. Each job varies, but during the analysis the investigator must be careful to keep the path of movement in mind. He must make certain that the movements he is developing will be pleasant and easy for the operator to perform. He must not draw up his new chart as he would make a crossword puzzle or apply to it the principles of mathematical analysis. The symbols and colours before him are only a form of expression of a human problem and the analysis is a tool used in finding a solution to that problem. He must not allow it to become an end in itself. He is not trying to make a beautifully balanced "possibility" chart based on a series of intricate and fascinating fixtures, perfect from an engineer's point of view. Ultimate and lasting success will only be achieved if each job is worked out from first principles with the primary aim to make the work of the operator easier and more productive. The test of the success of any new method is that the operator likes using it and produces more with less effort. If in the later stages of an investigation, part of the suggested method is diffi-cult to teach or is disliked by the operator, the investigator should always be ready to examine his theories again and if necessary to seek some further means of measuring to find out where the method fails. A chronocyclegraph (*see* Chapter 4) can be used for this purpose to supplement the micromotion film as it records the path of a movement and shows where the lack of ease lies.

An Example of Simo-chart Analysis

Examples of simo-chart analysis will be found in Appendix *B* but it may be helpful at this stage to consider a simple job in detail and purely from the point of view of analysis. The following example may be useful:

PUTTING STAMPS ON AN INSURANCE CARD AND DATE-STAMPING THEM

The simo-chart shown in Fig. 16 describes the operation of putting stamps on to an insurance card and cancelling them by means of a rubber date-stamp. To do this, the operator uses her left hand to take a folded card from a pile on her left and to place it open in front of her. Her right hand meanwhile takes a strip of stamps, damps one of them and puts it on to the card as it is brought forward. Both hands assist one another in sticking down the stamp and detaching it from its strip. The left hand then moves the open card for-ward on to a pile in front and collects the second card from the left hand pile, while the right hand damps a second stamp. When a number of cards has been collected and stamped, the resulting pile is drawn back in front of the operator and the right hand takes up the date-stamp to cancel the insurance stamp on the top card. The left hand then moves the top card forward, folding it on to a pile in front of the others. At the same time the right hand holding the date-stamp returns to the pad for more ink and then cancels the stamp on the second card.

The simo-chart is made in two parts: (i) sticking insurance stamps on the card; and (ii) cancelling the stamps with a date-stamp. These two groups are the operation groups in this analysis and they can be further subdivided into therblig groups. The first operation group falls easily into the original Gilbreth categories of "get ready" (prepare the card for putting on the stamps), "do it" (put stamp on the card) and "clean up" (put the card away). It is obvious that in this main group the work of the left hand controls the pace of the work of the right hand since it has considerably more to do. In determining the limits of the three subdivisions, therefore, the therbligs of the left hand would be used as a basis. The second main group, the cancelling of the stamps, can be subdivided in the same way and again the "get ready" and the "clean up" will refer to the handling of the cards. The "do it" in this group is the actual date-stamping.

On examining the two main groups as a whole and then considering their subdivisions the investigator concentrates on the two "do it" therblig groups. It becomes apparent that both require a similar handling of the cards and that the cards are in the same position when the stamps are stuck on as when they are cancelled. This suggests that some handling of the cards could be eliminated by performing the two productive, "do it," groups of therbligs one after the other without moving the cards in between; i.e., cancelling a stamp immediately after it has been stuck to the card. This would cause a fundamental alteration in the sequence of work and it is therefore necessary to leave the analysis of the groups and to consider the analysis of individual therbligs. The two productive therbligs, the assembling of the insurance stamp to the card (572 right hand) in the first main group and the using of the date-stamp (415 right hand) in the second group will receive attention first and the investigator will begin to build up his new method round them. At present both are performed by the right hand because the left hand is exclusively occupied in handling the cards. This suggests that the service therbligs of the left hand should be examined for necessity and the investigator decides that some can be eliminated by a rearrangement of the workplace. If the operator starts work with a pile of open cards in front of her instead of with a pile of folded cards to the left, the first handling of the individual cards (520-552 left hand) is unnecessary. This will mean that it will be possible for the left hand to use the date stamp while the right sticks on the stamps. At this point the investigator tries out his ideas in practice and finds that with this simple alteration in layout the operator can in fact apply the insurance stamp with the right hand and cancel it with the left hand. He therefore draws up a new sequence of therbligs on an analysis sheet to see how they fit together and to estimate whether a reasonable balance can be expected between the two hands.

He begins by writing down the therbligs of the right hand from where it grasps a strip of stamps until it assembles them on the card. He then transfers his attention to the left hand column and fits in the "use" of the date-stamp on the line below the "assemble" of the right hand. He follows this on the next line in the right hand by a "disassemble" describing the detaching of the stamp from its strip. On the next line in the left hand, after a "transport loaded," are listed the therbligs necessary to describe the movements involved in putting the card on to a pile away from the operator, using the thumb and first finger while the rest of the hand holds the date stamp. From here the left hand sequence is continued with the therbligs involved in inking the stamp. This brings the cycle back to "use" where it began. Having completed the left hand cycle, the investigator returns to the right hand therbligs. After the "disassemble" of the stamp from its strip, there is a sequence of therbligs describing the damping of the next stamp and its final "assemble" on the card. Here the investigator begins to suspect that the work of the two hands does not balance very well and that there will be an "unavoidable delay" between "assemble" and "disassemble" while the left hand catches up. This is likely to be intensified because the right hand movements, dealing as they do with the rather fragile strip of stamps, will demand a large proportion of the operator's attention possibly causing her to neglect the left hand movements and to make them fall still further behind the right hand movements. On counting the therbligs of the two hands he finds that the left hand sequence involves ten therbligs while the right hand has only seven. He is therefore led to consider whether something in the left hand cannot be simplified and he arrives at the idea of a self-inking date-stamp which would eliminate the three therbligs involved in inking the ordinary date-stamp. The result of this would be an equal number of therbligs in each hand which, although it is only a very rough measure of balance, has some significance and makes it worth while to draw up a "possibility" simo-chart to check the suggestions. (*See* Fig. 17.)

To make this chart he takes the "assemble" of the stamp to the card in the right hand as his starting point and he builds his chart from it. The therbligs that have not been changed are given the same number of winks as the equivalent therbligs on the old method chart. In this way, as the right hand sequence is the same as the first group on the old method chart, its therbligs will be given the same values on the possibility chart although they may be unduly long as they have to fit in with the left hand which is rather overloaded. The "disassemble" was included in the "assemble" of the stamp on the old chart and the same will be done again to avoid confusion. The therbligs of the left hand are all different in some way from those on the old chart and can only be estimated roughly. The length of the "use" therblig will depend to some extent on the right hand and can be estimated to run beyond the end of the right hand "assemble." The "transport loaded" of putting the card on the pile at the end of the operation is difficult to estimate because it has been simplified by taking away the necessity for folding the card and complicated by the hand-carrying of the date stamp. The two changes would probably cancel one another out and it is reasonable to leave it the same length as in the old method. The return journey from the pile on the other hand must be much longer than the "transport empty" of the old method since the hand is carrying the date-stamp. It is reasonable, however, to suppose that it would not end until the right hand had positioned the next stamp on the card when it would itself merge into a combined "position and transport loaded" as is shown at the top of the left hand column.

The total number of winks involved seems to be 160 as against 241 in the old method. This leads to an estimate of a possible saving by the new method of about 33 per cent.

An analysis of an average cycle in a film made of the same operator using the new method shows that the possibility chart was distinctly conservative in its estimate of improvement. (*See* Fig. 17.) The result is not unexpected for a number of reasons. The lengths of the therbligs "transport loaded" were taken unchanged from the old method chart to the possibility chart, as were all the therbligs, although it was probable that they would be reduced in length when the new workplace was set out. In the new layout (*see* Fig. 18) the stamps and the damper were placed within the areas of easiest reach and arranged so that they were in the most convenient position for use. There was no accurate way of forecasting any reduction and it was felt that it was better not to make any alteration on the possibility chart. It was also likely that a reduction in the overall length of the chart would appear in the new method because of the development of a rhythm when the movements became balanced. This again could not be estimated in the possibility chart and there was no means of finding out how much the awkward left hand movements in the old method interfered with and lengthened the therbligs of the right hand. It was therefore likely that actual performance would show that the possibility chart was over-cautious in its assessments of the time value of the therbligs. In addition, psychological factors must be allowed for, as the operator, properly handled, will be stimulated by the interest of the investigation. It is not surprising that an actual analysis of the new method showed a saving not of 33 per cent but of 56 per cent.

This example has been chosen because its technique and material are easily comprehended by the general reader. The basis of assessment of the length of the therbligs transferred to the possibility chart has been restricted to the information available in the simo-chart of the existing method and no attempt has been made to alter the length of an individual therblig to allow for any improvement in the conditions of the new method. An experienced investigator would be able to re-assess with some accuracy the length of such new method therbligs as "transport load" which are shortened by changes in workplace layout but some other factors affecting the total length of the

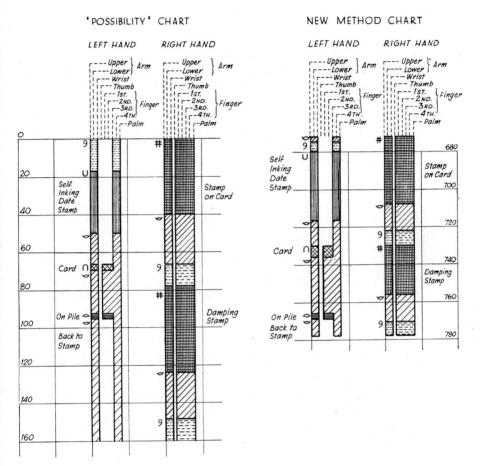

'POSSIBILITY' CHART   NEW METHOD CHART

LEGEND

⧄ (Lake Red pattern)	∩	Lake Red	Grasp
⧄ (Green pattern)	◡	Green	Transport Loaded
▤ (Blue pattern)	9	Blue	Position
▦ (Violet pattern)	#	Violet	Assemble
▬ (Carmine Red)	◠	Carmine Red	Release Load
▥ (Purple pattern)	U	Purple	Use

FIG. 17. EXAMPLE OF SIMO-CHART ANALYSIS, 2

FIG. 18. STAMPING INSURANCE CARDS
Upper: Old Method. *Lower*: New Method

cycle, such as the building up of a rhythm, could not be assessed with any degree of accuracy. The average investigator will therefore be well advised to keep to the facts of the original chart. The time factor in a micromotion analysis is used to discover the time relationship between the various elements of the job and not to assess a standard for its total length though it is useful to make a comparison between the total length of the existing simo-chart and any possibility chart that is built up. In this way a rough estimate of the percentage improvement can be made. The final extent of this improvement, however, can be discovered only when an operator has been trained and the new method completely installed. It will be influenced by a number of psychological factors and the percentage improvement shown by the possibility chart can be regarded only as a minimum estimate which may be useful as an argument to justify the cost of instalment. The final result will usually be better than this minimum.

Therbligs were originally developed before the days of cine-photography and they were used for many years before film analysis was possible. Since then, however, they have been associated almost exclusively with micromotion photography and most investigators have lost sight of their use as a means of detailed analysis without the time element given by a film. As the example above shows, the listing of therbligs was useful in developing the new method before the value of the individual therbligs was considered at all. It was only in forming a "possibility" simo-chart to obtain a comparison with the old method and an estimate of a possible saving that the time element became important.

Therblig Analysis without Micromotion Photography. An observer who has been properly trained to see movements and who has used film analysis extensively can make a therblig analysis of an old method without taking a film. Although he may not attempt to assess the time relationships of his therbligs he will have very much more detailed information about his problem than if he were content to study it solely by means of process charts. He will indeed approach the analysis by way of a two-handed process chart. He will never try to do this therblig analysis from memory although when he is really experienced he may dispense with the two-handed chart and make an analysis into therbligs from the beginning.

The use of therblig analysis without filming greatly increases the scope of micromotion study. Though the information obtained by this means may not be quite as detailed as the information that can be obtained from a film analysis it is still very considerably fuller than anything that a process chart can provide. It has the additional advantage that it keeps the observer's attention focussed upon the operator and not only upon his work as is the tendency in making process charts.

Further Developments of Micromotion Study

Standard Times for Therbligs. As we have seen above a thoroughly trained motion study investigator can list the therbligs required to do a job.

Gilbreth used therbligs in this way and he felt that the difference between the total number of therbligs found in two different methods gave a rough indication of the comparative time taken by the two methods. He maintained that the greater the number of therbligs involved the longer was the job and modern experience has not disproved this generalisation. Gilbreth, however, made no attempt to assess standard times for individual therbligs and most investigators who have concentrated on the movement rather than the time aspect of the work have felt that the dangers likely to arise out of assessing time values for therbligs are very great. It is, however, generally agreed that some estimate of time values would be useful if it were properly applied and if it were accepted as approximate rather than absolute. The author after many years of experience, has developed a series of values of a very approximate kind for certain therbligs under certain conditions. The length of such therbligs as " grasp," "release load," "transport loaded" and "transport empty" are comparatively easy to assess, while "position," "assemble," "disassemble, "pre-position" and "inspect" are extremely difficult and vary greatly, particularly in industries other than engineering. These approximate values have only been used in estimating new work and only then to obtain a general idea of the length of time that ought to be allowed for an operation as part of a larger plan. They have never been used for setting output standards. There is a real danger that approximate values of this kind may be given a validity that they cannot possess and that they may be used to develop mathematical formulæ based on inadequate data. Because of this no account of this extension of the micromotion technique has been published and it has never been thought advisable to teach it.

Other investigators, notably A. B. Segur, have claimed accurate results in assessing standard times for therbligs but though claims have been made that standards have been set by using these time values, such secrecy has been maintained as to cast doubt on the success of the results obtained.

Methods - Time Measurement. In their book " Methods - Time Measurement,"[1] Maynard, Stegmerten and Schwab define their subject as follows: "Methods-Time Measurement is a procedure which analyses any manual operation or method into the basic motions required to perform it and assigns to each motion a predetermined time standard which is determined by the nature of the motion and the conditions under which it is made." They claim that they have developed a useful tool for anyone interested in the study of methods but that it is not intended to replace other techniques but rather to supplement them.

The Methods-Time Measurement technique analyses a movement cycle into elements based on but differing slightly from the Gilbreth elements. Each element is assigned standard time values in a variety of circumstances.

It is important here to examine the possible uses of these time values

[1] Published by McGraw-Hill, 1948.

in motion study work. The originators, while putting forward their work in the first place as a supplementary aid to motion study and time study work in general, go on to claim that Methods-Time Measurement procedure can be used in almost every circumstance that is at present covered by ordinary motion study and time study techniques. They have, in fact, built up an application which draws a large part of its procedure from both motion study and time study, though the emphasis is more on time study than on motion study, eliminating the stopwatch and the micromotion film and substituting for them the tables of time values.

In assessing the possible contribution of Methods-Time Measurement to motion study it must always be remembered that absolute time values play a very small part in micromotion analysis, which can be profitably used, in the form of a therblig chart made from direct observation, with no reference to time at all. The motion study techniques, as Gilbreth developed them, are a series of tools used to record and analyse the different aspects of movement and to develop improved methods suited to the particular circumstances of each individual job. Methods-Time Measurement may have a limited application among the tools used for developing new methods but it can never be a universal substitute for the established motion study techniques, especially since it is confined to one aspect of movement only. There is also the danger of losing the flexibility of micromotion analysis in return for a rigid technique based on standard data.

STUDY OF THE PATH OF MOVEMENT

IN the last two chapters, on process charting and micromotion study, work cycles have been considered as a series of individual movements or therblig elements rather than as a single pattern of movement. Process charting provides the investigator with a means of analysing movements in their correct sequence; micromotion study gives more detailed information by dividing the movements into their elements and studying the time relationship of these elements. Neither technique, however, shows any picture of the path of a movement, its orbit or shape. In many operations the path of the movements involved has particular significance and it is often this aspect which presents the greatest opportunities for economy in fatigue. There are two main types of work where it is particularly important to study the movement path and each must be approached from a different angle and on a different scale.

In work consisting of short repetitive cycles of movement, the length of the path often matters less than its shape and its freedom from obstruction or changes in direction. In this type of work movements are usually confined to hand or arm operations and they must be studied in considerable detail.

The second main type of movement path that must be studied is that of the general movements made by an operator as he performs work which is spread over a wide area of floor space and which occupies a considerable period of time. Instead of detailed hand or arm movements, it is the path followed by his body that must be recorded and studied.

Because of the difference in the scale of the movement paths to be studied, two different techniques are used for these two types of work cycle. The first, the path of detailed hand and arm movements, is recorded by means of the chronocyclegraph, a photographic technique of the greatest accuracy. This technique is, however, limited to the study of comparatively short work cycles. The second main type of movement path, which involves widespread movements taking place over longer periods of time can only be recorded more generally by means of string diagrams made on scale drawings of the workshop or working area.

Chronocyclegraphs

The chronocyclegraph technique records the path of movement as a figure composed of pear-shaped spots. This figure is obtained by taking a photograph, preferably stereoscopically, of the path of movement followed by an operator in a single cycle of work.   Lights are attached to the operator's hands and the plate is exposed for the whole length of the cycle.   Because, in making it, the shutter of the camera is open for the whole length of a work cycle, a chronocyclegraph records instantaneously on a single plate the path of a movement that has occupied a definite period of time.   The investigator is able to see the movement as a whole, at his leisure, and also to compare and examine its different parts.   The shape and spacing of the spots gives him information about acceleration and deceleration which make it possible for him to pick out hesitations that suggest obstacles in the way of the movement and he can judge the effect of sudden changes in the direction of the movement.   By taking a series of chronocyclegraphs of different cycles, superimposed either on a single plate or during viewing, he can discover whether a rhythm is being built up by the variation, or lack of variation, in the paths of movement.

Before Gilbreth's day, various people tried to measure the path of movement.   They usually concentrated on the analysis of the movements involved in walking and other common natural actions and on those used in sports of all kinds.   The Frenchman, Marey, used his "chronophotography" in this way in the nineteenth century, making a series of exposures on a single plate which were later turned into diagrams.   He obtained some interesting results in studying the movements of athletes and, although he confined his experiments to non-industrial subjects, he realised the significance of the possible application of his methods to industry.   He said "The same method could equally well be applied to the teaching of movements necessary for the execution of various skilled industries.   It would show how the stroke of a skilful blacksmith differed from that of a novice. It would be the same in all manual performances . . ." Like Gilbreth, he had the idea that there was a "best way" of performing any movement.   In writing of his experiments in analysing the movements of a runner, he says[1], "The data afforded by these measurements may be put to practical use, for they indicate, according to the object in view, the best way of utilising muscular force in walking or running . . ."

Gilbreth was the first to apply the analysis of the path of movement to solving industrial problems.   He developed his technique without any knowledge of Marey's work and, when his attention was drawn to it as the result of correspondence with a friend in England, he felt that it would have helped him considerably if he had known of it earlier.   His technique differed from Marey's in that instead of taking a series of photographs on one plate he took a single photograph of lights placed on the operator's hands or on some other part of the body.   He used a stereoscopic camera opening the shutter at the beginning of the work cycle and closing it at the end.   This gave him a line graph in three dimensions when the result was viewed through a stereoscope. He was not satisfied with the information given by this "cyclegraph" and continued his experiments until he had developed an apparatus which interrupted the light of the lamps at regular intervals giving a graph made of

[1] See *Movement* by E. J. Marey, translated by E. Pritchard, Heinemann, 1895.

rectangular spots of a length varying according to the speed of the movement and showing the acceleration and deceleration along its path. Finally, by re-arranging the interruption of the lights so that they came on quickly and went off slowly, he developed the chronocyclegraph as we know it with its characteristic pear-shaped spot showing the direction of the movement.

Gilbreth was still working on the development of the chronocyclegraph technique when he died in 1924. He had taken many successful chronocycle-graphs himself but the method had not been sufficiently standardised for others to use it easily. He was planning to adapt his material so that it would be in a suitable form for teaching others but unfortunately, in the inevitable re-arrangements after his death, the apparatus was lost, though the photographs shown in Fig. 19 were found later. Since Gilbreth died chronocyclegraphs have been very little used by other motion study experts. Alford, in his "Production Handbook" published in 1945, lists the chronocyclegraph among present day research techniques but most other writers only refer to it as one of Gilbreth's experiments.

A commutator type of apparatus was developed at Metropolitan-Vickers in 1930 but its effective use was limited as it was not possible to give sufficient intensity to the light of the lamps. Recently a new type of apparatus has been designed and developed to overcome this difficulty. It is portable and easy to control and in addition the method of photography has been so standardised that the making of a good chronocyclegraph is much less a matter of chance. This apparatus and photographic method have been used to make the chrono-cyclegraphs reproduced in Figs. 22 and 23. As a result of this work the chrono-cyclegraph is taking its proper place beside the process chart and micromotion as the third essential motion study technique.

Chronocyclegraph Apparatus

Before discussing the uses of chronocyclegraphs some details of the apparatus and photographic method are necessary. The apparatus is required to furnish lights which go on quickly and off slowly at a definite speed that can be varied to suit the type of movement to be measured. These interrupted lights can be obtained in three ways: by interrupting the supply of electricity to the lamps; by using special filament lamps; by using a camera with a rotating screen in front of the lens[1].

The first of these is the most practicable at present. If lamps with special filaments are used there is a danger of their being broken during the experiments and the fact that they are very much more expensive than ordinary lamps will tend to make the operator nervous. A rotating screen in front of the lens will give the necessary interruption and experiments are being made, notably at the College of Aeronautics, with a special screen designed to give the characteristic spot. Meanwhile, available chronocyclegraphs

[1]Since this was written Professors Connolly and H. C. Wiltshire at the College of Aeronautics have developed such a shutter.

FIG. 19. GILBRETH'S ORIGINAL CHRONOCYCLEGRAPH APPARATUS

Upper: The interruption of electric current controlled by a tuning fork
Lower: The interruption of the current controlled by a commutator

apparatus is based on the principle of interrupting the supply of current to ordinary electric torch bulbs.

Several models have been designed, accomplishing this by different means. We have no specifications for Gilbreth's apparatus but from the photographs shown in Fig. 19, it is obvious that his early apparatus embodied a tuning fork as the interrupter of the electric supply. The bottom photograph shows an apparatus embodying a disc commutator. It was this type of apparatus, consisting of a disc commutator with four concentric contacts, that was developed later at Metropolitan-Vickers. As the disc revolved each contact engaged a stationary contact finger connected to a resistance so arranged that first four, then three, and then two contacts were linked, the circuit being broken completely on the last contact, making the light progressively dimmer until it went out altogether. The disc had two series of these contacts and revolved at five, ten, or fifteen revolutions per second by means of a pair of stepped pulleys, driven by a belt from an electric motor. It gave lights blinking 10, 20 or 30 times per second. Fig. 20 (top).

This apparatus was noisy and cumbersome but its chief disadvantage was that because it functioned by delaying the extinguishing of the lamps, it was only possible to increase the speed of the flashes at the expense of the intensity of the light. This caused difficulty in photographing anything but the very shortest cycle except in almost total darkness. Also, because of the interruption of the current, the intensity of the light must always fall below the maximum for the same lamp on uninterrupted current since the disc was liable to stop at a point where the maximum current could reach the lamps. It was therefore unsafe to use more than the nominal amount of current recommended for the particular type of lamp employed.

To obtain a spot not suffering from these limitations various ideas were explored. It was finally established that a relay-operated apparatus (Fig. 20, bottom) was the most successful in every respect and it is this apparatus that has been used to make the chronocyclegraphs shown in this book. The apparatus is based on the principle of stepping up the lighting of the lamps and using their natural extinguishing rate to produce the characteristic spot. This effect is achieved by the interaction of a condenser and a high speed relay. When the lights are off, the current from a battery charges the condenser and energises the relay. As the condenser becomes charged the current supply to the relay falls off, and the coil is de-energised, which establishes a circuit between the condenser and the lamps. The illumination of the lamps is governed by two resistances, one of which is variable, so that the maximum rate of discharge of the condenser and hence the brilliance of the lamps, can be controlled. Since this discharge is only momentary it is possible to provide a charge far in excess of that recommended for this type of lamp, giving an extremely brilliant flash. The characteristic tail of the spot is provided automatically by the cooling of the overheated filament. The number of flashes per second is governed by a calibrated variable resistance which

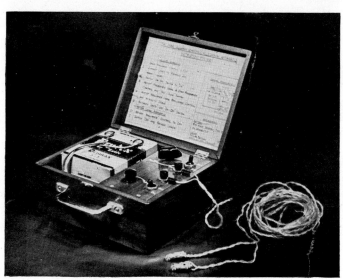

FIG. 20. MODERN CHRONOCYCLEGRAPH APPARATUS
Upper: Disc-commutator Type. *Lower*: Relay Type

controls the supply of current from the battery to the condenser. A wiring diagram of the apparatus is given in Fig. 21.

As an alternative to this relay apparatus, an electronic valve of the thyratron type has been used experimentally but at present it shows little advantage for the extra expense, unless extreme accuracy is required or an unusual range of speeds.

Taking a Chronocyclegraph

Before switching on the apparatus the lamps are attached by means of tapes or elastic bands to the operator's hands or to any other part of the body

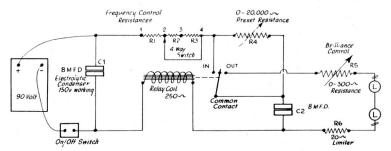

FIG. 21. WIRING DIAGRAM OF RELAY-OPERATED CHRONOCYCLEGRAPH
APPARATUS (Patent applied for)

making movements that are to be recorded. The cables serving the lamps should then be arranged so that they do not impede the operator's movements. If the lights are attached to the hands, it is as well to tie the cables to the forearm and upper arm before leading them over the shoulders to connect to a plug behind the operator. This plug should pull out easily if the operator moves beyond the limit of the main cable. This will prevent any anxiety about pulling down the apparatus and will encourage free and normal movements. When these arrangements are satisfactory the apparatus should be switched on and the operator allowed to work for a sufficient time to become used to the equipment and to feel at ease. The operator and his representative must thoroughly understand the object of the study and, as with the other two techniques, all possible explanations of the methods should be given to them. It must never be forgotten that what is routine to the investigator is exceptional to the operator who will regard the taking of the chronocyclegraph as an important occasion.

The opening and closing of the camera shutter is the part of the work requiring most experience and skill. A stereoscopic camera should be used wherever possible so that the result can be viewed in three dimensions. The investigator must examine the work cycle very carefully to choose the best point to use as the beginning of the chronocyclegraph. It must be definite and easily identified so that by opening the shutter when it first appears and closing it just before it happens again a complete work cycle is recorded on the negative. If a background photograph such as that in Fig. 24 is required, the negative must be exposed a second time with the chronocyclegraph apparatus switched off and the additional lighting directed on to the subject. If the chronocyclegraph spots are to show clearly on this background it must be comparatively dark. The exposure length is therefore usually only one-tenth to one-half of the normal exposure for such a subject, depending on its tone values.

To set both chronocyclegraph apparatus and camera so that a satisfactory result is obtained the following points must be considered:

1. *The Chronocyclegraph Apparatus.* The rate at which the lights flash on and off should be set so that the spots produced will not be too close in the slower parts of the cycle or too far apart where the movement is faster. If there is a very big variation in speed between different parts of one cycle, the speed should be set to accommodate the slowest section and the constant trace should be used to ensure that no part of the cycle is lost. This constant trace should not be used if it can be avoided by any reasonable compromise between the requirements of the fastest and the slowest sections as it complicates the reading of the resulting chronocyclegraph.

2. *The Camera.* A correct exposure of the spots depends on three factors (*a*) the intensity of the lamps, (*b*) the sensitivity of the film, and (*c*) the distance of the lamps from the camera. If lamps of a known characteristic operated at a known voltage are used, their intensity need not vary. The film used can also be standardised but the distance between the camera and the lamps cannot be fixed and as the lamps constitute single points of light, their intensity falls off in inverse proportion to the square of their distance from the camera.

The correct exposure of the background, which should as far as possible record no image, is controlled by the setting of the camera lens aperture, by the sensitivity of the film and by the general lighting, which should not be modified below a certain reasonable minimum. Since the shutter of the camera is opened when the operator begins the cycle and closed when he completes it, the exposure time is out of the control of the investigator.

To ensure that conditions are right for the correct exposure of the spots and the complete under-exposure of the background and at the same time to have reasonable general illumination to allow the operator to work normally, a very slow type of film must be used. Kodak microfile regular or panchromatic is the best for the purpose. It can be used in any 35 mm. camera.

The following is the procedure for finding the correct aperture setting: —

(1) Decide on the best rate of spots and set the chronocyclegraph apparatus.
(2) Measure the distance of the camera from the lights.
(3) Find the correct aperture setting on the table supplied with the apparatus by reading setting of apparatus against distance in feet from the lamps.
(4) Time the length of the cycle.

(5) Take the light meter reading for the general picture when the chrono-cyclegraph apparatus is switched off and find the length of time needed for a normal exposure at the aperture setting which has already been worked out as correct for the spots. If this length of exposure is the same or shorter than the cycle time it is obvious that an image will be recorded on the background. To avoid this, the aperture setting can be safely reduced to the setting shown three squares along on the table. If this modified setting still gives a length of exposure too near that of the cycle time, the decision has to be made whether it is better to have a blurred background photograph or to reduce the general lighting of the working area. If the length of exposure on the other hand is much longer than the cycle time, then the photograph can be taken at the original lens aperture setting suggested by the table. If a background photograph is required a second exposure of the negative is made before or after the chronocyclegraph is taken in the usual way.

A stereoscopic picture should be taken wherever possible and viewed for purposes of analysis through a stereoscope. For group work stereoscopic photographs can be projected on a screen. If the light from each picture is polarised in opposite directions they can be viewed stereoscopically through polarised spectacles. If no method of three dimensional photography is practicable, an ordinary photograph can be used and most of the information can be obtained from it, though less easily. The print should be of a reasonable size or should be projected on to a screen so that the spots can easily be counted if necessary.

The Uses of the Chronocyclegraph

The standardising of the means of making chronocyclegraphs has made them so much easier to take that they can now be used freely to assist in the recording and measuring of movements which is the first stage in any motion study investigation. Because of the very specialised nature of the technique it has not as universal an application as process charting or even micromotion study. But once a motion study investigator has made and analysed chrono-cyclegraphs he tends to want to use them for a variety of reasons in part at least of almost any job he studies. Chronocyclegraphs are extremely useful in the following ways:

1. In Recording an Unrestricted Movement

A chronocyclegraph is of assistance in the development of a new method particularly in cases where there is no definite workplace layout or fixtures to shape the movements, for example, in the folding of a garment.

2. In Analysing a Complex Single Purpose Movement

If a very extensive movement has only one purpose, it will be described in micromotion study by a single therblig such as "use" or "position." If its path is of greater significance than its purpose, it cannot be properly recorded except by means of a chronocyclegraph which should be used in addition to micromotion photography to obtain a complete record. In the same way, a single operation on a process chart may be studied more fully by means of a chronocyclegraph. The chronocyclegraph of the folding of a towel, Fig. 27, illustrates these two points. It shows a particularly extensive path of movement since the work cycle is made up of sweeping arm movements. There are no fixtures and the work place consists only of a flat table. A simo-chart would describe the whole operation under the therblig "assemble" and would give no idea of the direction of the folds.

3. To Record a Very Fast Movement

Where micromotion has already been used and some sections, filmed at 16 frames per second have proved to be too fast for the camera, a chronocyclegraph will make it unnecessary to retake these sections at 64 frames per second and will give more useful detail.

4. In the Experimental Stage of a New Method

In the experimental stage of developing a new method by means of any of the motion study techniques chronocyclegraphs of the whole or any part of the work cycle may be of considerable assistance in obtaining a really satisfactory result. They are particularly useful in the following circumstances:

(*a*) *In the Arrangement of Machine Controls.* It is often possible to show by means of a chronocyclegraph not only that existing controls are wrongly placed but also how the shape of handles or levers can be modified to allow an easier grasp.

(*b*) *In the Placing of Hand Tools.* Such tools as the screwdriver used in assembly work or the scissors of a sewing machinist can often be so placed at a point directly in the path of movement of the hands that they can be picked up without any change in the direction of the movement. In many cases this path of movement may be complicated and a chronocyclegraph is needed to check the position chosen. This chronocyclegraph will not only check the position of the tool in the work area but will also show whether the hand can pick it up without hesitating. If a tool is lying or hanging against a flat surface a marked hesitation will be seen as the hand approaches it. Fig.22 shows a chronocyclegraph of a hand picking up a small screwdriver which is lying flat on a bench. There are eight spots at the point where the hand is in a position to grasp the screwdriver and before it is ready to carry it away to position it in the slot of the screw. This shows that there is a hesitation in grasping the handle which is caused by an unconscious fear of striking the surface behind the tool at too high a speed. If the tool is arranged so that its handle is free on all sides, the hand will pick it up easily. Fig. 22 also shows below the effect of placing the same screwdriver on a raised support with the handle projecting about an inch above the bench. In this chronocyclegraph only three spots are seen at the same point where there were eight before. This particular tool-rest was designed for small screwdrivers used in instrument assembly work and the fact that it has been in continuous use over a

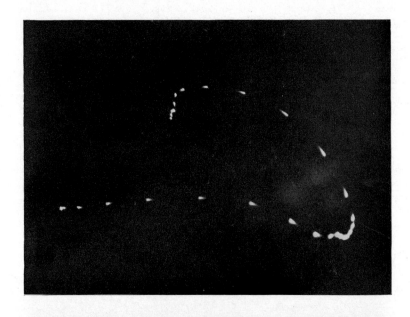

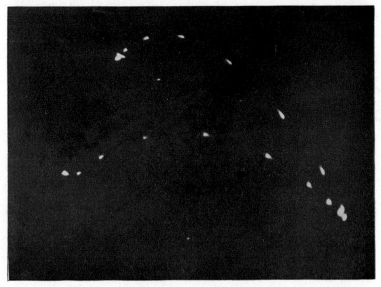

FIG. 22. PICKING UP A SMALL SCREWDRIVER

Upper: Old Method, screwdriver lying flat on the bench

Lower: New Method, screwdriver on a raised tool-rest on the bench

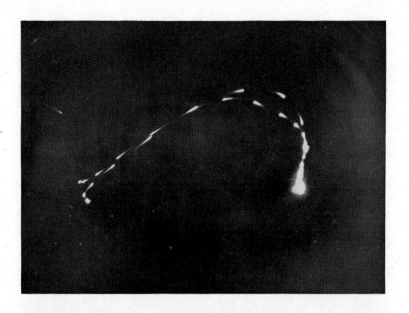

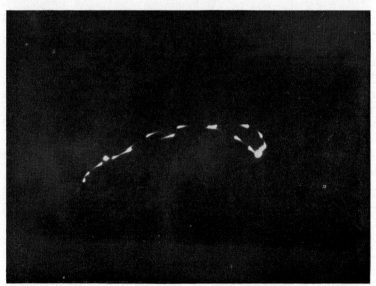

FIG. 23. PICKING A SCREW OUT OF A CONTAINER

Upper: The container here was a square tin 3 in. deep

Lower: This container was a correctly designed work-bin of the type
shown in Fig. 35

number of years shows its success. Other means of pre-positioning tools are described in Chapter 6.

(c) *In the Arrangement and Placing of Material*. Light materials such as washers, screws and nuts involve considerable handling. The design of suitable workbins and containers is discussed in Chapter 6 but certain points in their design are very easily checked by means of chronocyclegraphs. It is frequently found in small assembly work that the workbins provided are not used, the operator preferring to work from a small pile of material on the bench. He may not be fully conscious of his reason for doing this but his action should never be dismissed as a bad habit or as lack of co-operation until the containers have been tested. This is easily done by means of a chronocyclegraph which may show that the entrance is too narrow and causes hesitation in entering or that there is an unpleasantly sharp edge on the bin that makes the fingers over cautious and slows them down unnecessarily. Fig. 23 shows a hand picking a screw out of a half-filled tin box measuring 3in. x 3in. x 3in., while below a screw is being selected from the same quantity of screws in a properly designed material container (*see* Chapter 6).

The handling of heavier materials which have to be moved individually and which are not heavy enough for lifting tackle to be used can also be studied and checked by means of the chronocyclegraph technique. The path of movement of the material is of great significance here, particularly because of the physical effort involved in moving it. Chronocyclegraphs have been used in this way to study the movements of heavy packages in cotton spinning mills.

5. As a Check on the Training of Operators

Chronocyclegraphs made at each stage in the training of operators will act as tests of progress. They can also be used to explain their movements to trainees to encourage them to aim at better and easier movements. It is possible, in the final stages of training operators, to discover when the movement path has become habitual. This can be achieved by superimposing a number of chronocylegraphs of different cycles of work and finding whether the paths of movement are uniform.

6. As a Teaching Device

Chronocyclegraphs can be used in training motion study investigators to observe movements. They can also help those whose previous experience has been limited to time study to develop the habit of seeing the shape and character of a movement instead of concentrating largely on the time it has taken to perform. Neither process charting nor micromotion study will be as effective in this respect since their elements are easily timed. The chronocyclegraph contains no comparable time element and leaves the mind free to concentrate on other aspects of movement.

It has been found in training motion study investigators that much better results have been obtained by teaching the chronocyclegraph technique first.

From the beginning, students are then conscious of the path of movement and they interpret the other techniques in the light of this awareness. In this way they acquire a knowledge of movement which is much more fundamental and they are unlikely to fall into the error of thinking that a movement is simply a mathematical summation of elements.

As a means of demonstrating motion study to a wider circle such as supervisors, workers' representatives and management, chronocyclegraphs made of every day jobs are helpful. The chronocyclegraphs of loading and unloading a typewriter described below (Figs. 25 and 26) are suitable for this purpose and they demonstrate the complexity of the movements involved in comparatively simple work. The contrast between new and old methods is obvious and requires little detailed explanation.

Examples of Chronocyclegraphs

Although it is true to say that most of the improved methods shown in the following examples might have been developed from the analysis of a micromotion film or in some cases from a process chart, they are shown as examples of chronocyclegraphs as they are simple enough to give a clear demonstration of the technique. These particular examples have proved very useful in teaching motion study investigators to observe the path of movement. They are also very interesting as a means of showing the comparison between old and new methods and are much more quickly understood by the uninitiated than process or simo-charts. They show a picture of the jobs as a whole which cannot be given by a chart and they are factual evidence of improvement.

An experienced motion study investigator learns to recognise movement sequences that are good and that are easy to perform but a good movement is very difficult to define in words or to explain to the inexperienced. A chronocyclegraph makes it self-evident which of a group of movements is "good." For example, in the methods shown in Figs. 24 and 25 there is no possible doubt which are the best movements even if the chronocyclegraphs are viewed without any previous knowledge of the work.

The analysis of a chronocyclegraph is based on the same principles as the analysis of the two techniques already described. The investigator follows the same plan, questioning first the whole pattern of the movement, then, if necessary, each section within the whole, and finally, if a satisfactory new method has not yet been found, each group of spots within the sections. The questioning again takes place under the same four headings as are used in micromotion and process chart analysis.

By applying this scheme of analysis to the chronocyclegraphs (Figs. 24, 25, 26 and 27) the new methods illustrated can be developed.

They are particularly useful as an introduction to motion study because they show instantaneously a series of movements which have occurred consecutively over a period of time.

SORTING THE SHEETS OF A DUPLICATED REPORT OF FIVE PAGES

This is work that is done in any office but only at irregular intervals and for short periods of time so that no permanent set-up or fixtures can be justified. If a special fixture were to be designed it would fall into disuse almost at once. No one would take the trouble to get it out and set it up after the novelty had worn off. The improvement must therefore be sought in the actual handling of the papers. The path of movement is easily divided into sections made up of the part of the movement involved in picking up each sheet of paper. Any further subdivision into groups of spots is not likely to be very fruitful in this type of job. When the upper chronocyclegraph, Fig. 24, is examined as a whole, three points are immediately obvious:

1. The right hand is moving each sheet a considerable distance and the spacing and shape of the spots shows that the speed of movement varies along the path followed in picking up each sheet of paper. The round, closely spaced spots indicate how the movement begins slowly as the sheet is picked up. They then spread out and elongate as the hand gains speed, contracting as it slows down to allow the left hand to take the paper. As the hand travels down to pick up the next sheet they become long and thin, showing that this is the fastest part of the movement.

2. The left hand moves in jerks and the congestion of spots shows that it travels much more slowly than the right hand.

3. Both hands travel over a considerable distance from the moment when they pick up the first sheet to the point at which they shake the sheets together before the right hand puts them down and moves back to pick up the next sheet.

In beginning his more detailed examination of the path of movement the investigator next questions whether any part of it can be eliminated. He sees that the left hand movement would be unnecessary if each sheet were put directly on to the table instead of being passed from the right hand to the left to be shaken together with the rest of the report before the whole is laid on the table. If the left hand were freed in this way, each hand could pick up a separate sheet of paper and the distance moved by the sheets could be greatly reduced. By seating the operator in the centre and using the left hand to pick up a sheet of paper at the same time as the right, the body movements could be eliminated. The movements of bringing the sheets together and then putting them on the table could be combined by bringing each sheet on to a centre pile.

At this point it becomes necessary to make practical experiments with the sheets of paper to try out some of these ideas. It is found that the sequence of picking up the sheets must be reconsidered if they are to be in the correct order in the report. Sheets 4 and 2 are therefore arranged on the left of the operator and sheets 1 and 3 on her right with sheet 5 in the centre. In trying out this layout the operator begins by picking up sheet 5 with the left hand.

FIG. 24. SORTING SHEETS OF A DUPLICATED REPORT OF FIVE PAGES
Upper: Old Method. *Lower*: New Method

She next picks up sheets 4 and 3 with left and right hands simultaneously and lays them on sheet 5, followed by sheets 2 and 1 in the same way. As she goes on from here to pick up the next sheet 5 with the right hand, the left hand will tend to pick up sheet 4 so that the next movement with both hands picks up not 4 and 3 but 3 and 2. If this goes on, there will be a slightly different work cycle each time and the movements will be neither satisfactory nor balanced. The investigator will also find that under this arrangement there is no way of separating one assembled report from the next. Until these two objections have been settled, the new method cannot be successful and it is here that students examining this job as an exercise find their greatest difficulty. The solution is to make page 5 project beyond pages 4—1. This makes it possible to pick up a complete report merely by lifting page 5. To make sure that page 5 always projects the operator is taught to use her left hand to knock sheets 4—1 of the last report towards her body as she lays sheet 5 on top with the other hand. This left hand movement balances the cycle and also provides an emphasis or beat separating the cycles and helping to mark a rhythm. Any other solution within the same limitations, and many can be suggested, always involves more movement. These other solutions can be tested, if necessary, in the same way as the old method by making further chronocyclegraphs and analysing them. In the end it will be generally agreed that the method shown in the lower chroncyclegraph (Fig. 24) is the most satisfactory since no special equipment can be allowed for a job that is done only occasionally and as part of the general office routine. This new method involves nothing more than a rearrangement of the piles of numbered sheets and it is no more complex than the old method.

In this analysis, conclusions have been drawn from a general examination of the chronocyclegraph. There has been no need to count the spots either to find exactly what is happening or to compare one section with another. Indeed, a really experienced investigator would probably follow the path of movement in his mind in a job of this kind, without actually making a chronocyclegraph. To the less experienced, however, the taking of a chronocyclegraph is of great assistance and further chronocyclegraphs should be taken to test proposed methods.

This analysis can be summarised as follows:

Necessity:

(a) The use of the left hand to hold the collected paper is eliminated by piling the sheets on to the table.

(b) The walking along the table to pick up each sheet is cut out by using both hands to collect them and arranging the sheets in a semi-circle round the seated operator.

Sequence:

The sheets are picked up in the reverse order starting with 5 and piling 4 and 3 and 2 and 1 on to it. Their sequence on the table is changed from 1, 2, 3, 4, 5, to 2, 4, 5, 3, 1.

Combination:

The bringing of the sheets together is combined with laying them on the table since each sheet is laid on top of the last directly on the table. Two sheets are picked up at once.

Simplification:

The shaking down of the assembled report in the old method is changed to a single handed knocking down of sheets 4—1 when they are on the table. Sheet 5 is arranged to project beyond sheets 4—1 to simplify the ultimate selection of single sets of sheets.

LOADING A TYPEWRITER WITH PAPER AND CARBONS

The chronocyclegraph of loading a typewriter with paper and carbons (Fig. 25) by the usual method shown in the background photograph falls into three obvious groups of movement which must be analysed. The first group consists of the movements made when lifting each sheet of paper and drawing a carbon under it. The second is the shaking together of sheets and carbons and the third the lifting of the assembled pile into the typewriter carriage. The investigator questions the necessity of each group and discovers that the second, which is almost non-productive, is mainly necessary because the movements of the first group are not efficient in arranging the carbons squarely between the papers. The third group performs a necessary function but the papers travel an excessive distance before reaching their destination. There is no criticism to make about the sequence of operations at this stage nor can any two groups be combined.

There is, however, plenty of scope for simplification, especially in the first group. In considering this section, the investigator sees that if there were only two sheets of paper which were placed on shelves one above the other, they could be drawn out together. This principle could be applied to a number of sheets if there were a shelf for each and as each sheet would move over the same path as its carbon, they would not get out of alignment as in the present method. This would almost eliminate the shaking down movements. Accepting these suggestions, the investigator goes on to examine the third group once again and finds that if the shelves were placed immediately above the carriage of the typewriter the movement of the assembled carbons and papers would be much reduced. They could be dropped straight into the carriage from the shelves in one movement, as pulling them out of the shelves would bring them into the right position. Here the sequence of placing the papers in the carriage and shaking them down would be reversed. They would be dropped on to the carriage before being shaken down and wound round the typewriter roller.

When all these ideas have been tried out experimentally and seem likely to be successful a chronocyclegraph (Fig. 25, lower) is taken of the new method to test it. A comparison with the old method chronocyclegraph shows that the operation has been considerably simplified.

The analysis and the development of the new method can be summarised as follows:

Necessity:

(a) The movement of the carbons over the papers in inserting carbons between the papers has been eliminated.

(b) The lifting of carbons and papers four times to accommodate the carbons underneath has been completely cut out.

(c) There is no journey for the assembled papers and carbons from table to typewriter.

Sequence:

The papers are shaken down in a modified way after being dropped into the typewriter instead of before.

Combination:

The lifting of papers and carbons into the typewriter carriage has been modified and combined with the arranging of the carbons between the papers. The pulling of papers and carbons out of the shelves performs both functions.

Simplification:

The use of shelves for carbons and papers simplifies the placing of carbons between the papers.

In deciding that the most satisfactory method has been devised for loading the typewriter, consideration must be given to its unloading and the replacing of carbons on the shelves of the fixture. It is therefore necessary to make a complete analysis of the unloading operation.

UNLOADING PAPERS AND CARBONS FROM A TYPEWRITER

An examination of the chronocyclegraph of the customary method (Fig. 26) shows that it can be divided into the same kind of groups as the chronocyclegraph of loading a typewriter. The first group is the pulling out of the batch of carbons and papers from the typewriter carriage. The second is the concentration of spots where the left hand is holding the papers and the third is the selecting by the right hand of the individual carbons from among the papers. There is a fourth group of spots covering the carrying of the papers across from right to left, laying them down to the left of the typewriter. The second group is similar in appearance to the second group of spots in Fig. 25 of the loading of a typewriter since the movements are very much the same. Here, however, the spots spread further afield as it is a less exact set of movements.

Although none of these groups can be wholly eliminated, the movement across the typewriter to lay down the typed sheets becomes unnecessary if sheets and carbons can be separated as soon as they leave the typewriter carriage. If this is possible, the second, third and fourth groups can be combined. By using carbons which are a size longer than the papers and which have the left hand top corner cut this can be done. The left hand then holds the batch of papers by the top left corner and the right hand grasps the protruding carbons at the bottom right hand corner. Since the left hand is

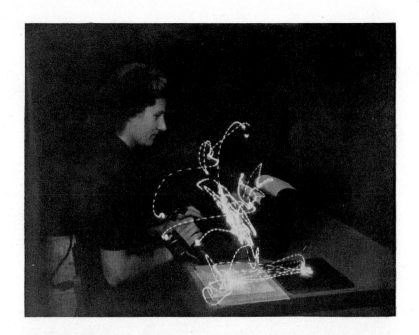

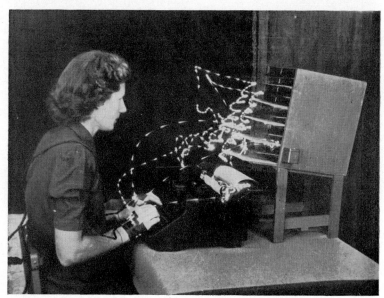

FIG. 25. LOADING PAPER AND CARBONS INTO A TYPEWRITER

Upper: Old Method.　*Lower*: New Method

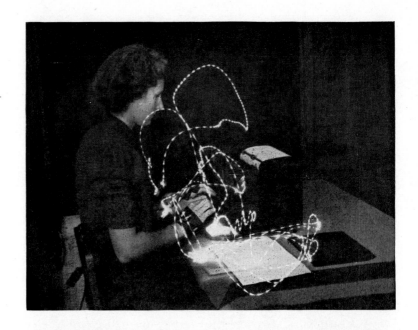

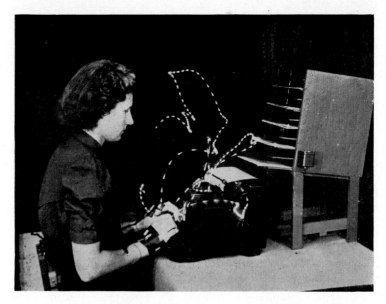

FIG. 26. UNLOADING PAPER AND CARBONS FROM A TYPEWRITER
Upper: Old Method. *Lower*: New Method

grasping the pile where the carbons are cut at the corners the right hand can pull out the carbons without restriction and go on in the same movement to place them on a shelf of the fixture. The left hand proceeds to lay the papers to the left of the typewriter. Carbons are laid in a different shelf in the fixture each time so that it is kept evenly filled. When a chronocyclegraph (Fig. 26, lower) is taken of the new method, it is clear that a considerable simplification has taken place in the path of movement and it is obvious that the new method is much easier. This analysis can be summarised:

Necessity:

(a) The handling of separate sheets and carbons has been eliminated.

(b) The movement of the papers from the typewriter carriage to the right side of the typewriter and from there to the left side is no longer necessary.

Sequence:

The separating of papers and carbons now takes place when they leave the typewriter carriage and before any other movement.

Combination:

(a) The withdrawing of the carbons has been combined with placing them on the appropriate shelf.

(b) The withdrawing of the papers has been combined with laying them to the left of the typewriter.

Simplification:

By redesigning the carbons, the combination detailed above has been made possible.

FOLDING A TOWEL

This chronocyclegraph (Fig. 27) is an example of a path of movement not controlled by any definite external limitations such as the shape of a machine or a particular layout of tools or material. The operator has developed her own method, controlled only by the number and position of the folds she has to make.

This whole path is much more clearly identified when it is viewed stereoscopically.

On looking at the chronocyclegraph as a whole two enclosed and overlapping figures are seen. These are the paths of the right and left hand. The close concentration of spots at the beginning of the right hand cycle and the spots at the extreme right of the chronocyclegraph near the left hand corner of the table indicate the point at which the operator picks up the corners b and c of the towel and brings them together at 1 and 1^1. It can then be seen that she slides her right hand along the edge of the folded towel, moving the left hand a little in the opposite direction to stretch the towel between the two hands. Both hands then lift the towel clear of the table to position 2 and 2^1 and shake it to make it lie flat on the table with the hands at 3 and 3^1. At 3^1 the concentration of spots shows that the left hand remains stationary while the right hand makes the second fold to 4. The diagram on the right of Fig. 27 (upper) shows how these folds are made.

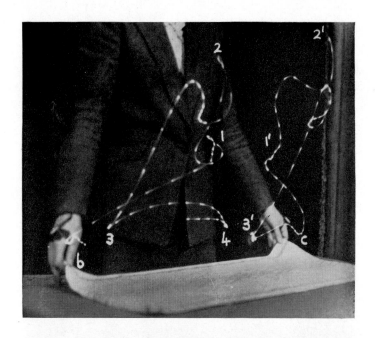

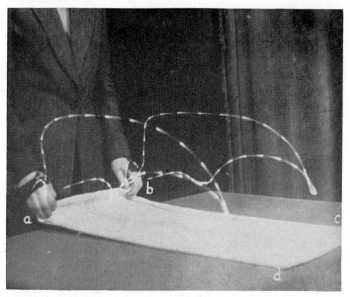

FIG. 27. FOLDING A ROLLER TOWEL

Upper: Old Method.   *Lower*: New Method

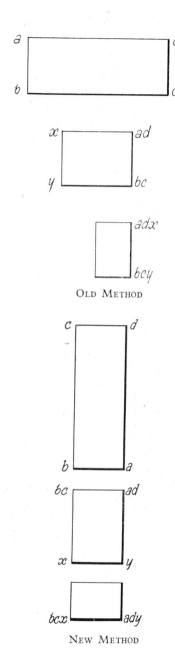

OLD METHOD

NEW METHOD

When close examination of the chronocyclegraph has decided the implications of the various groupings of spots, the investigator makes a detailed analysis of the path of movement and immediately observes the contrast between the complex movements required to complete the first fold and the much simpler movements of the second fold. This appears to be due to the fact that the towel is unsupported in making the first fold in mid-air and therefore becomes disarranged. The rest of the movement path up to point 3 is only necessary to put this right and contributes nothing productive. It appears that if the towel could be folded without lifting from the table not only would the movements of picking it up and returning it to the table be eliminated but also much of the disarrangement. When this idea is put into practice the two hands grasp *a* and *b* on the table, bringing them across to *d* and *c* and *bc* can then be brought back again to *x* and *y* to make the second fold in one more movement, eliminating the stretching and the shaking of the towel. These movements are, however, awkward, since one hand is much further from the body than the other and moves unsymmetrically. To simplify the movements the towel is turned through a right-angle and the folds are made according to the diagram on the right of the lower chronocyclegraph using both hands simultaneously and symmetrically to pick up *a* and *b* and in the same movement to lift them a little, drawing the towel nearer to the body and bringing the corners *d* and *c* closer to receive *a* and *b*, forming the corners *ad* and *bc* which are next brought back towards *x* and *y* to form the second fold by making corners *adx* and *bcy*.

The comparison of the two chronocyclegraphs in Fig. 27 leaves no doubt as to the effectiveness of these changes.

String Diagrams

Just as the light attached to an operator's hands traces a path on a photographic plate to produce a chronocyclegraph and provides an accurate picture of a movement or sequence of movements that has occupied a period of seconds, so less detailed movements performed over a wider area and over a longer period of time can be shown in the form of a string diagram. Direct observations are first made in code form. When these are complete they are plotted by means of string wound round pins driven into a scale drawing of the working area. The string follows the path of movement of either operator or material and the resulting pattern shows the investigator which parts of the job are causing the largest number of movements. These will be the parts that should receive further detailed investigation. At the same time, the amount of concentration of thread between the various sections of the layout will show the closeness of the relationship between them and suggest changes in layout or routine to shorten the path of movement.

Making a String Diagram

When it has been decided that an operation or series of operations can best be studied by means of string diagrams, certain preparations must be made. The investigator should watch the operator's movements carefully before making any written observations and it will usually be wise to make a preliminary process chart of the sequence of operations. He must then decide which places on the working area are visited by the operator. Each of these points is then given a code number. This may be one of a simple series or, where the points are more numerous or complex, it may be built up from three or more digits each representing a different class of object or place on the machine or in the workshop. At the same time the various operations can be referred to by means of letters. For example, observations of drawframe tenting (Fig. 28) were made by means of a code in which one, two or three figure numbers were used. The first digit represented the number of the frame concerned, the next referred to the number of the drawing head on that frame, and the third to the slivers running into the drawing heads. Each number was prefixed by a letter describing the type of operation performed so that, for example, B156 meant that the 6th sliver had been pieced at the 5th head of No. 1 frame; L44 that the rollers of No. 4 drawing head on No. 4 frame had been cleaned, and F3 that the full cans on the third frame had been doffed.

When a satisfactory code has been developed to provide for all foreseeable contingencies, the investigator uses it to record each movement of the operator. When the observations are complete he drives pins or nails into all the numbered points on a scale diagram of the layout with extra pins at the corners

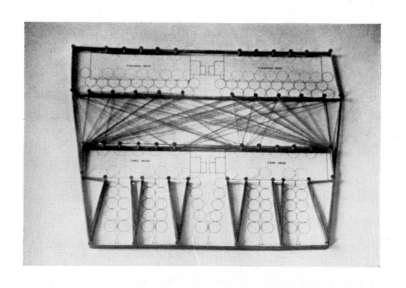

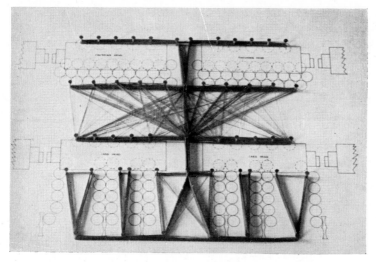

FIG. 28. DRAW FRAME TENTING IN COTTON SPINNING MILL

Upper: Machines placed together with passage at either end.
Length of string in diagram 169.5 yd.

Lower: Machines separated by passage. Length of string in diagram
135.6 yd.

String diagrams showing difference in path of movement of operative
when machines are placed together or separated by passage-way.
A centre passage gives a reduction of ten per cent on the path of
movement without any other alteration in method.

of the machines and anywhere else where there may be an obstruction in the path of movement. String or cotton, previously measured or marked off into yards or feet is wound round the pins following the operator's path of movement as recorded in the observations. If the thread is not measured or marked before beginning this part of the work, the diagram will have to be unwound after it has been made so that the thread can be measured for comparison with a diagram made of any future improved method. If it is measured or marked before use, the investigator can subtract the remaining length from the original figure and know at once how much he has used. It is usual to quote the actual length of thread used when comparing one string diagram with another. If the figures are converted according to scale to the actual distance walked by the operator there is a tendency to underestimate the result. For example, in thinking of a mile there is a tendency to visualise it as lying along a road; an easy fifteen or twenty minutes' walk. A mile under factory conditions, on the other hand, might consist of 880 two-yard movements; a very different picture.

The information on the observation sheet has other incidental uses as well as its part in the making of string diagrams. For instance, it is often helpful to know how many times a day each machine is stopped or what is the proportion of the different operations. The observations made of a new method will frequently show surprising contrasts with old method observations and these may be invaluable in planning further improvements.

Use of the String Diagram

The completed diagram is used by the investigator to examine the movements as a whole and to find where the greatest concentration of movement lies. It shows him which sections require further study. He makes his analysis in the same way that he analyses methods recorded by means of the other motion study techniques, questioning in exactly the same way the necessity, the correctness of sequence and the possibilities of combination or simplification of each part. He will seldom complete an entire investigation by means of string diagrams. The technique will largely be used as a means of locating weak spots which need fuller analysis.

Typical instances of movement paths successfully investigated by the string diagram technique are found where the work is bulky or heavy. In one case of this type, the assembling of the bases of large instruments, because of the size of the material and the difficulty of handling it, the heavy bases were laid out along a bench. The operator walked from one to another adding one smaller component to each and returning to add the next until all the assemblies were completed at the same time.

This type of example is also to be found where material is not particularly large or heavy but where there is something in the nature of the process, such as drying or baking, which causes a pause in the assembly process and makes it necessary to work on several pieces at the same time. A process chart of this type of work puts the emphasis on the sequence of the movements although the really significant feature of the method is the path of movement of the operator as he goes from object to object. A string diagram will record this path and it can be used both to test the value of possible rearrangements of the work and to suggest the parts of the work cycle that will most benefit from further analysis by means of the other motion study techniques.

A second group of work particularly suitable for investigation by the string diagram technique is found in some forms of machine minding. Where one operator is minding several machines and performing a variety of different operations in an irregular sequence controlled only by the demands of the machines, a string diagram can be made to record his or her movements. This will reveal any irregularities or complexities in the operator's path of movement and will enable the investigator to see where some improvement in the organisation of the work can be made to reduce the length of the path and give the operator more opportunity to meet the demands of the machine. In this way string diagrams can also be used to assess the merits of different schemes of work or changes in layout. The report of the investigation into drawframe tenting (Appendix *B*) shows examples of the use of string diagrams in this type of work.

String diagrams are of particular value in the making of a department or factory layout where the movement both of material and of operators is of great significance. If an existing layout is to be modified, separate string diagrams should be made of all the movements of operators and materials before anything is changed. The diagrams should be compared and the changes that each suggests co-ordinated into a single theoretical modified layout, drawn to the same scale. The observations used in making the original string diagrams can then be plotted on copies of the modified drawing and these in turn can be compared. It may be necessary to repeat the process several times until a layout is found to suit all circumstances. (*See* Chapter 7).

In laying out a new department or factory, string diagrams can be useful but the path of movement traced can only be theoretical and the diagrams have therefore to be made from existing knowledge of the processes rather than from direct observations.

A further use of this technique in a layout problem is as a check to discover which of two particular arrangements is the better. Fig. 28 shows the comparison between the path of movement of an operator tenting drawframes arranged on either side of a central gangway with the path that would have been followed if the frames had been placed in pairs with gangways on either side. The centre gangway is unusual in the cotton industry but the management who had tried it felt it to be right and wanted proof. A drawing was made of both layouts and observations taken of the operator's movements using a central gangway were plotted on both as string diagrams. The centre gangway path of movement proved to be 10 per cent shorter than the path of movement of the same observations plotted on the side gangway drawing.

Conclusion

Though an investigation will seldom be completed by the exclusive use of either chronocyclegraphs or string diagrams, few investigations made by means of either the process chart or micromotion techniques can reach the best possible conclusion without some examination of the path of movement to supplement the information already obtained.

The chronocyclegraph presents this supplementary information in the most accurate and detailed form. Only the chronocyclegraph can put on paper the subtle difference between a good and a bad movement. This distinction can often be made automatically by an experienced motion study investigator but it is very difficult to explain to the inexperienced. The chronocyclegraph of a satisfactory movement combines a picture of the shape of the movement with a sense of ease and rhythm and until an investigator has learnt to see movement in this way he will not be capable of achieving the best results.

Before longer movement paths can be recorded with the same accuracy as shorter cycles further development is needed in photographic technique to develop a form of chronocyclegraph that will replace the string diagram which at present can only be used to make a general survey of the problem.

5

CHARACTERISTICS OF EASY MOVEMENT

IN using motion study to develop a new method of work the improvement is made directly from a careful analysis of present practice. No problem is approached with a ready-made solution in mind, since no two problems are exactly alike, each having its own peculiar background and circumstances. Nevertheless, there are certain similarities and common characteristics to be found in all good methods. These can be used to assist in the development of new motion study methods after an analysis of present practice has been made, or where, in a new job, there is no present practice to analyse.

Motion study investigators, from the Gilbreths onwards, have been conscious of this common background and they have listed various maxims which they have called "Principles of Motion Economy." The Gilbreths listed twenty and Barnes, at a later date, twenty-two. In a pamphlet published in 1944, an attempt was made to condense these principles to seven general principles of motion economy[1]. Since then further teaching experience has shown that the phrase "principles of motion economy" is not entirely appropriate and that "characteristics of easy movement" gives a more correct impression. A further revision of the material has reduced these characteristics to five : —

1. Movements should be simultaneous.
2. Movements should be symmetrical.
3. Movements should be natural.
4. The path of movement should be rhythmical.
5. The path of movement should be habitual.

The first three apply to detailed movements, the remaining two to the whole movement cycle. All five are interdependent and must not be isolated from one another. They should be interpreted on a broad basis. It will be found that the longer lists of Barnes and the Gilbreths do not contradict this list but are elaborations of it, or recommendations for the necessary features in the arrangement of a workplace or the design of tools which the characteristics demand. The advantage of the shorter list is that the characteristics are few enough to be considered at once and sufficiently general to be applicable in all circumstances.

[1] *An Introduction to the Theory and Application of Motion Study,* by A. G. Shaw. H.M. Stationery Office.

Simultaneous Movements

In working out the movements of a motion study method, it should be arranged that both hands and arms work together. They should, if possible, be performing the same operation at the same time. One hand should not be idle while the other is working and the left hand should never be used merely to hold something that the right hand is working on. At the same time, there is no advantage in working with both hands if they are allowed to move one at a time. Not only should both hands do useful work throughout the cycle, they should also begin and finish their movement sequences at the same instant. This is easiest to achieve when both hands are doing identical work and it may be possible to arrange for an operator to work on two units at once if the single unit does not allow both hands to do the same work at the same time. Where the single unit does not lend itself to identical movements of both hands and where it cannot be duplicated, it may be necessary for the two hands to do different work. This is less easy, since the different movements must be balanced so that the left hand completes its movements at the same time as the right hand. If one hand is allowed to finish earlier than the other, it may tend to start on the next operation too soon and the whole cycle will become progressively more unbalanced.

In building up a motion study method the simultaneity of each section must be planned so that the whole cycle presents a completely balanced pattern. The new method of making up a five-page report (*see* page 78) is an illustration of this point. The pages are uneven in number and there would therefore be a tendency for the hands to get out of balance unless the method gave one hand something to do while the other handled the odd sheet. To balance the operation, the left hand straightens the first four sheets as they lie on the pile while the right hand collects the fifth sheet. This extra movement is also useful in making the reports easier to handle at a later stage.

Symmetrical Movements

After planning the sequence of movements in a motion study method so that they occur simultaneously, they should be arranged as far as possible so that they can be performed symmetrically about an imaginary line through the centre of the body. Because of the symmetrical structure of the body, movements of the arms can most easily be made when they are symmetrical, each arm moving in and out from the centre. In most types of assembly work the arms should move away from the body to pick up material and inwards to the centre to assemble it. Fig. 29 shows an operation set up to ensure symmetrical movements.

When movements are performed symmetrically and simultaneously, they achieve not only a time balance but also a balanced equilibrium of the whole body which makes them easier to perform.

There are occasions, for example when the operator has to make a visual inspection of material as it is picked up, when symmetrical movements cannot be made simultaneously. Since, in making a work cycle easier for the operator to perform, it is more important that movements should be simultaneous than that they should be symmetrical, some compromise has to be reached. In such circumstances, material containers can usually be placed so that both hands can move to collect material in the same direction, both remaining in the operator's line of vision. (*See* Fig. 29).

FIG. 29. SYMMETRICAL MOVEMENTS
Assembling springs, plungers, caps and safety pins on to fuses set up in a work-place designed to allow the operator to work with symmetrical movement.

Natural Movements

A natural movement is easy and makes the best use of the shape and arrangement of all parts of the body. Just as symmetrical movements are easy because the body is symmetrical, so there are other types of easy movement depending on other features of the structure of the body. In developing a new series of movements these features must be kept in mind.

Natural movements are curved not straight (Fig. 30). This is easily understood if the structure of the body is considered. The hand, for example, moves in an arc centred on the elbow or the shoulder; the foot swings from the knee or the hip; the shoulders describe an arc as the body turns. Correctly designed workplaces, footrests and foot pedals allow for these curved movements.

In heavy work great care should be taken to use the mechanical advantages that the position and posture of the body can give. Obviously, as much heavy work as possible should be eliminated by the introduction of suitable

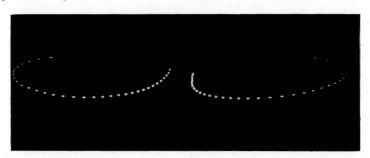

FIG. 30. NATURAL MOVEMENTS: PATH OF MOVEMENT OF FOREARM
The sweep of an operator's hand starting with hands crossed at centre. This illustrates the curves of natural movement.

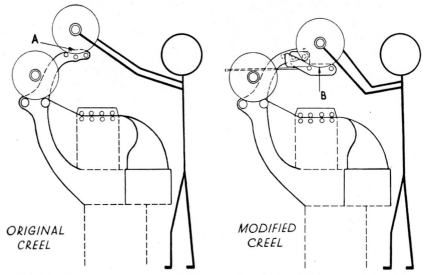

ORIGINAL CREEL

MODIFIED CREEL

FIG. 31. MODIFICATION TO THE CREEL OF A RIBBON LAP MACHINE IN A COTTON MILL: The original creel at (A) meant that the operative must lift a heavy lap of cotton into position at the maximum distance from the body. The modified creel (B) is 6 in. nearer to the operative's centre of gravity and 3 in. lower.

mechanical devices or lifting tackle, but there will always be some work that must be done manually. It should be remembered, for example, that a weight lifted at a distance from the body, which is the centre of gravity, not only feels heavier but actually puts more strain on the muscles. An example of an improvement made to bring the lifting of a weight closer to the body can be seen in Fig. 31, where a lap of cotton is lifted up into the creel of a ribbon lap machine in a cardroom. In the improved method the creel is six inches closer and three inches lower than in the original arrangement, both alterations bringing it nearer the centre of gravity of the operative handling the laps.

In designing detailed movements advantage should be taken of the natural shape and position of the hand and fingers. During assembly work or other fine work, individual fingers can hold small tools against the palm in a natural position for use at a later point in the work cycle. Again, the fingers move more strongly and accurately in towards the palm than in any other direction. This characteristic can be used to advantage in such movements as the operating of a cigarette lighter (*see* Fig. 32), which requires a

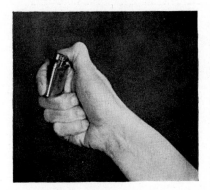 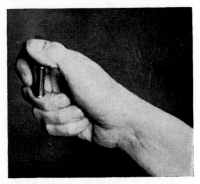

FIG. 32. NATURAL MOVEMENTS: OPERATING A CIGARETTE LIGHTER
Left: Restricted movement of thumb due to position of lighter. Note obvious strain. *Right*: Natural movements inwards towards palm.

downward pressure of some strength. If it is held in the right hand between the thumb and the first and second fingers and the thumb is used to operate it with a movement downwards in a circular direction towards the palm, it will light with less effort than if it is held with the thumb against the first finger and therefore operated with a restricted movement of the thumb.

In most motion study manuals arm movements are classified into five groups: —

1. Movements of the fingers.
2. Movements of the fingers and wrist.
3. Movements of fingers, wrist and forearm.
4. Movements of fingers, wrist, forearm and upper arm.
5. Movements of fingers, wrist, forearm, upper arm and shoulder.

It is often stated that hand movements should be confined to the lowest category that is consistent with doing the job properly. This must not be taken to mean that wherever possible finger movements only should be used.

Movements repeated at short intervals in cycles lasting from a few seconds to a minute or two should not involve the use of the whole stretch of the arm but in arranging smaller movements care must be taken to see that the operator does not feel cramped.   In longer cycles of work involving larger material and tools there may be advantages to be gained from introducing a range of movements to distribute the work between several groups of muscles to avoid strain and fatigue.

When a repetitive operation is of short duration and the movements used are comparatively small, there is some danger of monotony and a feeling of restriction.   To avoid this, it is better to introduce occasional larger movements, at intervals of an hour or a little less, rather than to alter the movement cycle.   In some cases these larger movements can be achieved by allowing the operator to replenish his own material containers from a store at a short distance from the workplace.

It is wrong to assume that fatigue will be reduced by the mere mixing of large and small movements.   While it is true that the unrelieved use of finger movements can be very fatiguing and can give the operators a feeling of restriction, it has been found in practice that large movements repeated at too frequent intervals simply amount to extra work which adds even more to the fatigue and irritation of the job.

If any doubt arises as to the merits of different sequences of movement, chronocyclegraphs should be made of each suggested series and the results compared to see which looks easiest.   Normally, the easiest movement will be the most natural but there is one danger in assuming that a movement that is easy and comfortable for one operator is the best and most natural for others.   Long practice may cause an operator to perform with ease and comfort movements which are neither natural nor easy.   It is always wiser for the investigator to begin by trying the feeling of the new movements himself to see that they are comfortable.   If in the next stage the operator complains of awkwardness, there will then be less danger of mistaking a difficulty in breaking old habits for a real fault in the method.   On the other hand, a very small amount of practice will often bring ease in the performance of movements which at the first attempt seem difficult and unnatural. Decisions should therefore be made only after a reasonable practice period and taking all these factors into account.

Individual differences between operators in the use of movements are not as great as is often supposed.   Allowance must however be made for them, though not until the standard movements have been taught and attempted, except in the very obvious cases of left-handed or disabled operators.

Rhythmical Movements

Simultaneous, symmetrical and natural movements are characteristics of detailed sequences of movements that are part of a full work cycle but no good motion study method is a mere addition of details.   It is a whole pattern in itself and one of the main characteristics of a good motion study pattern of movement is the rhythm it develops when it is repeated. Neither is a cycle complete in itself. The last movements of one cycle should run easily into the first of the next just as the movement sequences within the cycle are linked together. This smoothness and ease will be increased if the cycle has one point of emphasis to give a beat to the rhythm. For example, in collating the duplicated sheets of a 5-page report (*see* pp. 76 to 79) the old method involved not only putting together the sheets but binding them with a wire stitcher. This binding operation used a quite different type of movement from the rest of the cycle and the investigator therefore arranged it as a separate job even before beginning to develop a new method for the rest of the cycle. If it had been included in the new method, it would have spoilt the smoothness of the rhythm. On the other hand, without it, the new method lacked a definite focussing point or beat. The knocking together of sheets 1 to 4 by the left hand was therefore introduced to balance the sequence of movements and to provide the necessary beat to emphasise the rhythm. The chronocyclegraph (Fig. 24) shows how successful the arrangement was. In some industrial jobs it may not be possible to arrange for a change in the type of movement to give the necessary emphasis. A change in the velocity of the movements may serve instead and may be equally effective.

Any unnecessary change in the direction of movements tends to hinder a smooth rhythm. Changes of direction should be kept to a minimum in any case because slowing up, stopping and changing direction waste time and energy. Professor Barnes[1] has proved that from 15 to 25 per cent of the cycle time of picking up a small object is spent in this way. Too many changes in direction tend to make individual movements unnatural and jerky and spoil the rhythm of the whole cycle.

Habitual Movements

When motion study techniques have been used to develop a new method, the movement cycle will contain simultaneous, symmetrical and natural movements, and the complete cycle will be rhythmical. Since a method of this sort will be intended for frequent repetition, it must also be planned so that each movement can be made in exactly the same way each time. In developing a rhythm the operator will also develop movement habits. By making the movements habitual they will become automatic and require no conscious direction. Much mental fatigue and strain will be eliminated in this way.

The formation of movement habits is a process which will always occur whether a method has been studied or not, unless there is something in the layout that definitely prevents it. In a job which has not been studied, the movements will be only partly habitual because there will be certain sections in which material and tools come to hand in a different way in each cycle. These irregularities will be eliminated in a motion study method and the

[1] *Motion and Time Study*, Ch. 15, by Ralph M. Barnes.

workplace will be so arranged that every opportunity is given to the operator to form habits. In designing a workplace for simultaneous, symmetrical and natural movements, tools and materials will inevitably be given fixed locations as far as possible and the question of standardising material will have been considered. It will therefore be much easier for movements to become habitual in a motion study method than in a method which has not been studied.

Gilbreth's "Principles of Motion Economy"

Having considered the five characteristics of easy movement, it is interesting to see what Gilbreth considered to be the principles of motion economy. In 1923 Gilbreth laid down twenty principles which can be grouped into those which refer to movement, those which are instructions for developing a new method, and those which are suggestions for workplace layout or for the introduction of tools and gadgets. The following are Gilbreth's principles in his own words and with his own numbering, but grouped in categories : —

A. Principles which refer to Movements—

"1. Both hands should preferably begin their therbligs simultaneously.

2. Both hands should preferably finish their therbligs at the same instant.

3. Both hands should not be idle at the same instant except during rest periods.

4. Motion of arms should be in opposite and symmetrical directions instead of in the same direction and should be made instantaneously.

15. Sequence of motions should be arranged to build rhythm and automaticity into the operation."

B. Principles which refer to the Development of a Motion Study Method—

"5. Hesitation should be analysed and studied, its causes accounted for and, if possible, eliminated.

6. Shortest time demonstrated in one part of a study should be used as mark to attain, and reasons for other times required in other parts of the study should be known.

7. Number of therbligs required to do work should be counted; for the best way is almost always a sequence of the fewest therbligs.

8. The best sequence of therbligs in any one kind of work is useful as suggesting the best sequence in other kinds of work.

9. Every instance where delay occurs suggests advisability of providing some optional work that will permit utilising the time of delay, if so desired, or of making a fatigue study of the interval.

10. Variations of time required for any single therblig should be arrayed and causes recorded.

11. Lateness of various parts of the anatomy as compared with other portions should be recorded.

13. To reduce fatigue, motions should be confined to the lowest possible

classifications, as listed below, the least tiring and most economical being shown first.

    1st-finger motion.

    2nd-finger and wrist motions.

    3rd-finger, wrist and lower arm motions.

    4th-finger, wrist, lower arm and upper arm motions.

    5th-finger, wrist, lower arm, upper arm and body motions.

    16. Hands should be relieved of all work that can be done by feet or other parts of the body."

C. *Principles affecting Work Place Layout*—

"12. All material and tools should be located within the normal grasp area.

14. Tools and materials should be so located as to permit proper sequence of therbligs. The part required at the beginning of the cycle should be next the point of release of the finished piece from the former cycle.

17. Tools and materials should be pre-positioned as much as possible to reduce the ' search,' 'find' and 'select' therbligs.

18. Gravity feed containers should be used to deliver the material as close to the point of assembly or use as possible. This delivery point should be near the height at which it is assembled in order to eliminate any lifting or change in direction in carrying the parts to the assembly.

19. Ejectors should be used to remove the finished part.

20. Use 'drop delivery' whereby the operator may deliver the finished article, by releasing it in the position in which it was completed, without moving to dispose of it."

Barnes, in the 3rd edition of his *Motion and Time Study,* divides these principles of Gilbreth, with some additions and subtractions, into those concerned with "the use of the human body," "arrangement of the workplace" and "design of tools and equipment." He uses all the Gilbreth principles except those applying to the development of a new method, and number 19 on the use of ejectors. In his section on the use of the human body he adds three of his own (the numbering is his):

"5. Momentum should be employed to assist the worker wherever possible, and it should be reduced to a minimum if it must be overcome by muscular effort.

6. Continuous curved motions are preferable to straight-line motions involving sudden and sharp changes in direction.

7. Ballistic movements are faster, easier and more accurate than restricted (fixation) or 'controlled' movements."

He developed these from his experiments into the nature of various movements. He has added four more to the second group, the arrangement of the workplace:

"9. Definite and fixed stations should be provided for all tools and materials.

14. Provisions should be made for adequate conditions for seeing. Good illumination is the first requirement for satisfactory visual perception.

15. The height of the workplace and the chair should preferably be so arranged that alternate sitting and standing at work are easily possible.

16. A chair of the proper type and height to permit good posture should be provided for every worker possible."

Finally, under the heading "Design of tools and equipment," he has added:

"18. Two or more tools should be combined wherever possible.

20. Where each finger performs some specific movement such as type-writing, the load should be distributed in accordance with the inherent capacities of the fingers.

21. Handles such as those used on cranks and large screwdrivers should be designed to permit as much of the surface of the hand to come into contact with the handle as possible. This is particularly true when considerable force is exerted in using the handle. For light assembly work the screwdriver handle should be so shaped that it is smaller at the bottom than the top.

22. Levers, crossbars and handwheels should be located in such positions that the operator can manipulate them with the least change in body position and the greatest mechanical advantage."

It can be seen that everything in Gilbreth's principles referring to movement or in Barnes' on the use of the human body is covered by the five characteristics of easy movement outlined at the beginning of this chapter. These five characteristics are general and they are intended to be interpreted broadly. Originally[1], "minimum movements" and "change of direction of movements" were listed as separate headings. These are less fundamental than the rest and are really secondary to them. They have a basis of time saving rather than ease of movement and everything of value contained in them is covered by the statements that movements should be natural and that the path of movement should be rhythmical. They have therefore been omitted from the present classification.

Gilbreth's "principles" are chiefly intended to be applied when using the micromotion technique and for this reason they are rather minutely divided and therefore, perhaps, a little difficult to remember. Those that refer to the development of a new method are largely omitted by Barnes. This may be because Barnes makes use of motion study principles chiefly as a guide to workplace layout and the design of fixtures and tools. It may also, perhaps, be because there has been a feeling in recent years that some of Gilbreth's points are subject to misinterpretation. The five characteristics of easy move-

[1]*An Introduction to the Theory and Application of Motion Study*, by A. G. Shaw. H.M. Stationery Office.

ment, on the other hand, are not open to the same criticism and besides summarising the experience of the past in improving existing methods, they have a use in the development of a motion study method on new work where there is no existing method to record and analyse. Gilbreth may have been thinking of this when he laid down his principles, though their wording suggests that he used them to assist in developing any new method. The modern motion study investigator will find them helpful as long as he remembers that he must always work from his analysis of recorded fact in the first instance and never develop a new method from preconceived ideas alone. Gilbreth never made this mistake. He always held that each job must be analysed individually, and that it was never safe to assume that two problems, however apparently similar, could be solved in the same way.

Barnes' principles referring to workplace layout and the design of tools and equipment are specialised applications of some of the more general characteristics. They are useful as suggestions and they are applicable in all normal circumstances, but they are perhaps a little inflexible. Just as the best method of work arises from a new analysis of the facts of the particular problem and not from the application of lists of rules, so the layout of the workplace cannot be successfully standardised. A workplace and its tools and fixtures should be designed to facilitate a method of work already decided upon as the result of a thorough analysis of the facts. It should not dictate the movements to be used in it; it should make it easy to use a series of movements that have already been developed.

6

WORKPLACE LAYOUT

EVERY type of work has its own working area, whether this is temporary as in the changing of a motor car wheel at the roadside or permanent as in the packing of chocolates at a table in a factory. Whether it is planned or unplanned, this workplace always has an effect both upon the attitude of the worker to his work and upon his methods of work, just as his methods and attitude have an effect upon the workplace.

In analysing a poor method of work it is interesting to see how much the method is dictated by the limitations and design of tools and equipment and by the nature of the workplace. A badly designed workplace and clumsy tools will perpetuate a bad method of work and prevent its improvement. Conversely, where the workplace and tools are properly designed they can help to perpetuate a well-planned method. For this reason the layout of the workplace and the design of tools and equipment are of vital importance in completing a motion study method of work.

In developing a motion study method the movements should be worked out before the design of tools and workplace is considered. The workplace should then be built round the method of work and round the operator who is to use that method. An improved method will demand an improved workplace but the development of the method should come first and the design of the workplace second.

The Position of the Operator in the Workplace

Before studying the details of a workplace layout the investigator will check that the operator's position in it is as comfortable as possible. It will usually be found that he will become less fatigued if he is allowed to stand or sit at will. This can be arranged by making the working surface the correct height when he is standing and increasing the height of the chair to bring him into the normal sitting position at the higher working surface. A foot rest will be necessary if the chair is raised. As a general rule the working surface, which is not necessarily the table top but possibly a fixture attached to it, will be at the correct height if the operator's elbows are level with it when his arms hang from the shoulders with the elbows bent at a right angle

It is particularly important for comfort that the operator should be able to sit with the knees under the working surface. Anything in the design of the workbench, such as a very deep edge or cupboards placed beneath it, should be cleared away. Difficulty will nearly always be found in conveyor work. In many cases the conveyor is so arranged that operators cannot sit with their feet under it but must sit sideways or at a distance from it. They are often forced into a very cramped position. This should never be allowed in a motion study method.

There are many suitable chairs and foot-rests[1]. The main features to be considered are (a) that the chair should either be adjustable or be selected to allow the operator to sit at the correct height with both feet supported comfortably, (b) that the chair should be strongly built but light enough to move away easily when the operator decides to stand, (c) that the front edge of the chair seat should be well rounded so that there is no interference with the circulation of the blood in the legs, (d) that the back rest should support the lower part of the spine at a comfortable angle and (e) that the foot rest should allow the legs complete freedom and opportunity for changes of position. It is not enough to support the instep on the bar of a chair; the whole foot must be fully supported.

In addition to the chair and its foot-rest, each operator needs some place for personal possessions. Either a drawer in the workbench or a small locker built into the chair may be the solution. A cupboard at the other end of the room is not sufficient and, particularly where the operators are women, if nothing is provided in the working area, some part of the workplace which is intended for another purpose will inevitably be used to hold sandwiches and handbags or the results of the lunch hour shopping expedition.

When seating and the height of the working surface have been adjusted, the lighting of the workplace should be considered. A good diffused light is safer and better for most types of work than more concentrated individual lighting, though there are always certain types of work that require special conditions. Modern lighting is a specialist's job, and it is enough to state here that the best possible all over lighting should be installed so that there are as few dark corners as possible. All lights should be diffused or shaded to avoid glare.

The Extent of the Working Area

Having decided how the operator is to sit and having arranged for his comfort, it is necessary to decide upon the extent of the workplace; what area is available for the placing of tools, materials, fixtures and machines; what are the areas of the working surface most easily reached by the hands. These areas are called "areas of easiest reach." They are found by describing arcs with each hand pivoting on the elbows at the level of the working surface. Wider arcs are then described by the arms pivoting on the shoulders. In this way areas are mapped out (Fig. 33) in which the hands can most easily reach tools and materials. The smaller arcs enclose areas in which the hands can

[1] See *Seats for Workers*, published by H.M. Stationery Office.

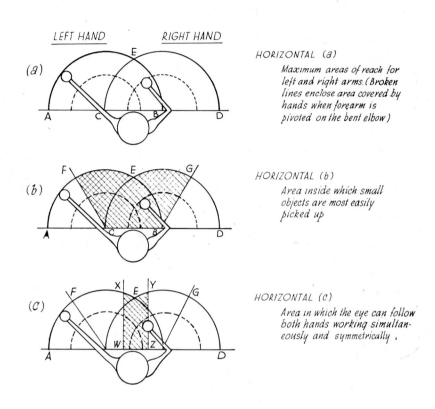

LEFT HAND   RIGHT HAND

(a)

HORIZONTAL (a)
Maximum areas of reach for left and right arms. (Broken lines enclose area covered by hands when forearm is pivoted on the bent elbow)

(b)

HORIZONTAL (b)
Area inside which small objects are most easily picked up

(c)

HORIZONTAL (c)
Area in which the eye can follow both hands working simultaneously and symmetrically.

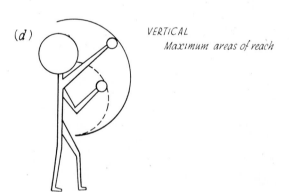

(d)

VERTICAL
Maximum areas of reach

Fig. 33. Areas of Easiest Reach

work without stretching the arms. The larger arcs enclose the areas which can be reached by movements of the whole arm. In Fig. 33a the arc AB encloses the area suitable for material to be picked up by the left hand and CD encloses the right hand area. Where they overlap, CEB is the area which is the easiest for both hands. These areas must be defined still more closely since in practice it will be found that, when material is placed in containers in the area AFC and BGD, the operator will feel that his movements are restricted and awkward. Professor Barnes and Marvin Mundel, in studies made at the University of Iowa[1], have discovered that lines drawn outwards at an angle of 60° from the position of the elbows at the bench edge (CF and BG in Fig. 33b) enclose the area inside which it is easiest to pick up small materials. Within this area again is a still smaller area, that in which it is easiest for the eye to watch the hands as they pick up small objects simultaneously. This is the area WXYZ in Fig. 33c. If it were always necessary for the eye to follow the movements of both hands, only this very restricted area would be available for the placing of materials and the building up of the job. Fortunately, in practice, most operations include large sections in which it is not necessary for the operator to look at his materials as they are selected and picked up. The workplace can therefore be arranged so that only those movements needing the assistance of the eyes take place in the area WXYZ, the remaining tools and materials occupying the wider areas convenient to the hands alone. If necessary, they can be placed in the area AFC and BGD but this should be avoided as far as possible since the nearer they approach A and D the more difficult it is to pick them up.

So far the working area has been considered as if it existed entirely on a horizontal plane. In fact it is three dimensional and extends into the vertical plane in the same way (Fig. 33d). In some circumstances it is particularly important to remember this and to realise that the "areas of easiest reach" cover approximately one half of a sphere with the workers' shoulders at its centre. The "areas of easiest reach" are not left behind by an operator when he gets up from his bench to perform a further operation in another place. They go with him and exist wherever work is to be done. For example, in a textile mill where an operative is responsible for three or four separate operations at various points on one or two machines or along a spinning frame, consideration must be given to keeping her work within the "areas of easiest reach" at all these points as well as to keeping as many points as possible within her "areas of easiest reach" as she stands in one place.

Contents of the Workplace

When the position of the operator in the working area and the extent of that area have been settled, attention turns towards the contents of the workplace; its equipment and furnishing. Before this equipment can be arranged to the best advantage its design must be checked. In changing from an old

---

[1] *Motion and Time Study Applications*, Ralph M. Barnes, pp. 56-8.

method to a motion study method some re-designing is inevitable. The new method will call for some alterations and well designed equipment will help to promote in a method of work the characteristics of easy movement outlined in the last chapter and to perpetuate the correct method.

The main types of equipment found in a workplace of any kind are material containers, tools, machines and fixtures. Each type of equipment presents different technical problems of design but the aim of the investigator is the same whether he is designing a tool, a box to hold material or a fixture to hold the work and free the hands. The equipment provided for a job that has not been motion studied is usually sound technically. It accomplishes what it is intended to do, but often with very little reference to the convenience of the operator. The motion study investigator in designing equipment must improve upon this. All equipment made for a motion study workplace must be as technically efficient as the equipment used in the old method but provision must also be made for the operator's requirements. These must receive as much consideration as the technical requirements of the job.

The first aim in designing equipment for a motion study method of work should be to make it so that it will not only allow the operator to use the right sequence of movements but will actually encourage him to do so. To achieve this, it is particularly important that all moving parts should be made to operate easily and that all tools should be pleasant to handle. Any preliminary stiffness of moving parts or roughness of a tool handle will tend to alienate the good will of the operator who is asked to use the device and will make the new method unpopular. Full use should be made of mechanical devices and of the effects of gravity. Mechanical devices must be handled with skill to be effective but the benefits of gravity are available to anyone and have endless uses, particularly in the design of material containers to bring material forward to the point at which it is to be used in the disposal of the finished product. Since motion study equipment is designed to save effort, it is essential that it should be as easy to handle as possible. It should be no heavier than is necessary for strength and it should have no rough edges or sharp corners. There must be nothing about it that can hurt the operator's hands. Any experience of friction or pinching will have an unconscious restrictive effect upon the operator's subsequent movements. Spring devices in particular should be watched to make sure that they are smooth working and that they do not jar the hands in use or when released.

It is not enough to design equipment that encourages correct and easy movements of the limbs. It is also important that the design should enable the operator to see what he is doing while operating the equipment. This is especially necessary during the learning period on a new method but even at a later stage difficulties will be much more easily overcome if the whole operation is clearly visible. This point should be remembered when designing fixtures intended to allow both hands to use simultaneous and symmetrical movements. If there is a point in the movement cycle where it is necessary for the eyes to follow the work of the hands, it will be necessary to see both hands at once and the points that are to be watched must therefore be very close together. In a two-handed inspection job, for example, two dials recording the measurements perhaps of a diameter, should be set side by side if both hands are to be encouraged to work together. If the dials are separated the hands will move alternately as the eye moves from one dial to the other.

It is also very important that all equipment should be robust. It must be strong enough to stand up to daily use without needing special care or maintenance. There is nothing more calculated to bring discredit upon a new method than tools and equipment which fail while the method is on trial. If they survive the trial period only to deteriorate as soon as the method has been handed over to the shop supervision, the result may be even worse. It may cause all kinds of unplanned alterations in the method and a general dis-like of the whole set-up. If it is unavoidable that some parts of a piece of equipment or tool will wear out before the rest, as may happen with location points, sliding pieces or adjustments, these parts should be designed for easy replacement and spares should be provided when the job is handed over to the supervisor. It may be possible to strengthen the parts which will receive the most wear with a reinforcement of a stronger material. The first set of any equipment should be closely watched for signs of trouble and should be rectified before the operator is put to any inconvenience. The design of all further sets of equipment should profit from this experience since the vulnerable points will be known and they can be strengthened or made replaceable before the equipment is issued for regular use.

Finally, equipment should be as simple as possible. Not only is a simple device usually stronger and easier to maintain but it is more easily understood by the operator. It is also more quickly made and installed. It is often easier to design elaborate equipment than to think of a simple device to serve the same purpose but the extra time and thought spent upon the design of a simple device is well worth while. Simplicity of equipment is particularly important in factories where other equipment is simple. It matters very little in an engineering works where there is a toolmaking department to make and service it but in a factory without skilled toolmakers much time will be wasted if equipment or tools recommended are too intricate to be serviced in the factory. Devices should be kept appropriate to the work they have to do. For example, it is absurd to use a vice where a bull dog clip is sufficient. It is wasteful to introduce a power driven conveyor if a gravity conveyor will serve the same purpose or a roller conveyor if the top of a polished table can be used instead. No advantage will be gained from using a power driven screwdriver for work which can be done as quickly by a ratchet screw driver. The more elaborate tool may even add to the fatigue of the worker because it is heavier.

These are the general requirements of all equipment and tools used in a motion study job but in designing or choosing them the investigator will think beyond these mere mechanical considerations and will bear in mind the characteristics of easy movement outlined in the last chapter. Every piece of equipment and every tool must be tried out in practice to find out if it does in fact allow and as far as possible encourage, easy movements. Only practice can show this satisfactorily; a drawing cannot be checked successfully.

In addition each type of equipment has its own particular problems of design.

1. MATERIAL CONTAINERS

There are two main points to be considered when designing material containers, the first being their shape and the second their capacity.

The shape of a material container must be so designed that each piece of material can be picked up from the same position whether a container is full or nearly empty. The bottom, which should curve slightly, should normally tilt forwards so that the material slides to the front of the container. The exact design will always depend on the shape and nature of the parts and on how they are to be used. Some components, such as unwrapped chocolates or radio valve grids, will be damaged if they are allowed to slide or fall forward. In such cases the arrangement of the material and the design of the containers must allow for this, perhaps by tipping flat trays containing the components to such an angle as to bring the furthest side of the tray as near to the operator as possible, without causing the material to slide. In the case of packet assembly, the trays should be designed to hold the parts in such a way that they can be picked up easily and in the correct order.

According to the nature of the material it contains, the lip of a workbin may be modified so that for example flat parts such as washers may be picked up from an extended flat lip or, if there is no need to lift them, drawn straight along the surface of the workbench[1].

At the point where the hand enters, containers should be wide enough to allow free access to the material without touching the sides and shallow enough to allow the hand to pick up a part without it being necessary to bend the wrist. If the entrance is too narrow, the operator will move too cautiously and will find the container irritating. He may even refuse to use it. Where a container is unpopular and frequently set on one side, a fault of this type is the most likely cause. A chronocyclegraph taken of the movement of selecting a piece of material from the container will show a hesitation if the entry is too narrow. If it is too deep, this will also be obvious on the chronocyclegraph. Rough edges or particularly sharp or cold edges will also produce the effect of hesitation, even if their contact with the hand is only accidental or occasional.

The capacity required of any material container depends upon the bulk and quantity of the material that it is to carry. It must hold the quantity that

[1]*Motion and Time Study*, R. M. Barnes, 3rd Edition, p. 158.

will allow the correct planning of production to be maintained. As far as possible, container capacity should be balanced so that all supplies of materials for one job run out together and all containers can be refilled at the same time. If sizes are not balanced, much time will be wasted by the operator getting up to fetch more material when each container is empty or waiting for fresh supplies to be brought. It is usually best to design containers to hold half a day's supply of material but in special circumstances, where the refilling of containers is used as a change of occupation for an operator on a repetitive operation or an operation demanding very close concentration (*see* Chapter 5, page 96), an hour or even half-an-hour's supply may be enough.

FIG. 34. STANDARD WORK BINS INCLUDING HOPPER FEED TYPE

Less than half-an-hour's supply will hardly ever be satisfactory. Where material is bulky, the capacity of containers may be increased without taking up too much of the working area by using hopper feeds if the nature of the material allows. In this way the bulk of the material can be stored out of reach of the operator and use made of gravity to bring fresh pieces forward as material is removed from the mouth of the bin (*see* Fig. 34).

Products made up of a large number of pieces and including fragile or valuable parts that need special handling may best be assembled from a tray arranged to hold all the different parts needed to make up a certain number of complete articles. Such trays are filled in the stores and delivered to the work benches complete.

The question of cost must be considered in designing containers for material. It is often uneconomic to design special containers for each job that is studied, unless the work is on a large scale and likely to go on for a long time, at least for the life of the container. More often a group of containers is needed that can be dismantled and used for different work of the

same general type when the first job is ended or suspended.   For small
assembly jobs in an engineering works, where each may only run for a spell
of a few hours or days and where few jobs are permanently in operation,
standard workbins are needed with a limited variety of sizes and modifications.
If they are to be used to their full advantage, they must be made so that they
can be easily stacked and as easily taken out again.   It may be possible to
design a stand to carry various combinations of these standard boxes (*see*
Fig. 35).   Stands may also be designed to convert for direct use at the workplace containers designed for storage purposes.   In short cycle machine work,
where a large quantity of material is needed over a comparatively short period,

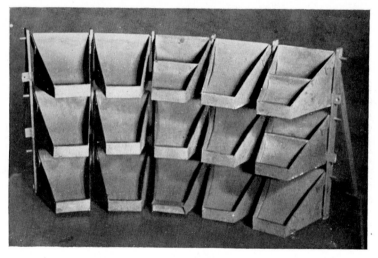

FIG. 35. STAND DESIGNED TO CARRY COMBINATION OF STANDARD
WORK BINS

this type of arrangement is often particularly satisfactory.   Because only one
or two types of material are required, there is enough space near the machine
to accommodate what may be a larger container than could be fitted into
the immediate working area of most assembly jobs.   The stand should be
designed to give to the stores container, when it is in position, the same
features as a specially designed container.   In a stores container there is
usually little difficulty of free access for the hand since it is large, but the
stand must give it the forward tilt that will make the contents fall to the
front.   So that the last few parts can be picked up easily it may be necessary
to arrange an insert to fill the bottom corner of the container or a detachable
lip fitted to its outside edge.   If containers can be adapted in this way, so that
one serves the three purposes of storage, transport and use at the machine,
there is a considerable saving in handling of individual parts.

An example of the use of a stand to adapt a storage container for use at a machine is the placing of small skips containing pirns at an angle above a bobbin battery on the looms in a cotton weaving shed. The skips are filled at the doffing of the ring frames and transported to the weaving shed. Stands and lip attachments are supplied to each loom and the skip is put directly into the stand. The pirns are then loaded one by one from the skip into the battery, using both hands. An arrangement of this sort is often made in weaving sheds but without properly designed stands to ensure easy access to the skip. As a result, the operative is obliged to take a number of pirns at a time from the skip, immobilising one hand to hold them. A further example comes from a biscuit works where a framework was designed to hold a varying number of biscuit tins containing different kinds of biscuits which could be rearranged for each assortment of mixed biscuits that was to be packed. (*See* Fig. 42.)

2. TOOLS

Each industry uses very different types of hand tools and the subject can only be treated very generally. A hand tool should be both strong enough to do its work efficiently and also as light as possible. There is some-times a tendency to use a larger and heavier tool than is absolutely necessary in the belief that it will last longer. The classic research in this field is that of F. W. Taylor at the Bethlehem Steel Works. His first investigation was into the shovelling of iron ore, coal, ashes and other materials in the yard. Some 500 men were employed and each man used his own shovel. In the course of a day each would handle several different materials and Taylor found that each was lifting shovel loads ranging in weight from $3\frac{1}{2}$ lb. in the case of rice coal to 38 lb. when shovelling iron ore. He established that the maximum total daily tonnage was moved when a load of $21\frac{1}{2}$ lb. per shovel was lifted. Large scoops to handle ashes and small spade shovels for iron ore were therefore designed and issued to the workers, and this change in tools resulted in a halving of the cost of handling materials in the yard. The influence of tools upon output is always considerable and careful experiments should always be made to find the best size and shape for each job[1].

The design of tool handles is an important side of tool design. Handles should be made to fit naturally into the hand and to allow the use of the easiest and most natural movements. Professor Barnes[2] has made some interesting experiments into the design of screwdriver handles.

Sometimes an investigation into a method of work will suggest that two or more tools should be combined into a single tool so that an operation can be performed in one sequence of movement instead of the two that would be inevitable if another tool had to be picked up. An example of a combination tool is a screwdriver with a box-key fitting on to its shaft. This tool was designed to tighten the locknut of a bearing screw (Fig. 36). When the

---

[1]*Scientific Management*, F. W. Taylor.
[2]*Motion and Time Study*, R. M. Barnes (3rd Edition), p. 301.

two tools were not combined the operator had to put down the screwdriver after it had been used to tighten the bearing screw to the required amount, loosening it a half-turn before leaving it. He then picked up a spanner or a box-key and tightened the nut, taking up the half-turn left by the previous operation. Using a properly designed combined tool in the new method the

FIG. 36. SCREWDRIVER BOX KEY
An example of a combination tool

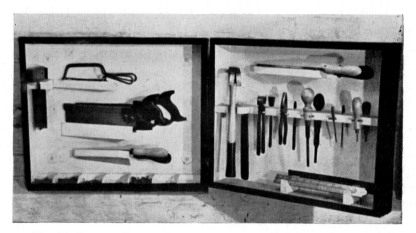

FIG. 37. GENERAL PURPOSE TOOLBOX FOR USE IN STUDENTS' WORKSHOP

screw is turned to the required tightness and held in place by the screwdriver tip, its handle gripped by the 2nd, 3rd and 4th fingers while the thumb and first finger are used to tighten the nut with the box key. This arrangement saves both the picking up and putting down of the tools and also does the job more accurately.

3. TOOL RESTS AND TOOL HOLDERS

The main object in designing tool holders and tool rests is to make it possible for tools to be picked up with the minimum of effort and in exactly the same way each time they are used and to remove all necessity for searching the workplace for them. It is comparatively easy to design holders from which tools can be taken quickly and easily; it is less easy to design a holder into which a tool can be returned without effort or wasted movements.

In a workplace such as that of a maintenance electrician or a jobbing carpenter where there are a large number of tools, some of which are only used occasionally, the main importance of a tool rack is to provide a place

FIG. 38. KITCHEN CABINET WITH RACK FOR COOKING IMPLEMENTS

for everything so that nothing is difficult to find. When a tool has been selected, it will not be put back in the rack until the job is finished. The tool rack here is for storage rather than for use while the work is going on. The rack shown in Fig. 37 illustrates one solution to a storage problem of this type. Here a simple set of tools was needed for use by an ever-changing group of students at irregular times and for many different elementary purposes. Much difficulty had been experienced in the past in persuading these casual users to replace the tools in a simple rack largely consisting of Terry clips or notches fairly carefully designed to suit each tool. The difficulty seemed to be that the students often could not remember where each tool belonged or how many they had taken from the rack. It was overcome by making a new rack consisting of a double box which could be closed against the wall when it was not in use. It was fitted with much the same clips and other holding devices as the original rack but each tool was silhouetted in crimson against a white background. This not only made its location quite clear but also showed very plainly which tools had not been replaced. After the new rack had been introduced, few students failed to replace their tools and to replace them correctly. This same idea has also been applied to kitchen

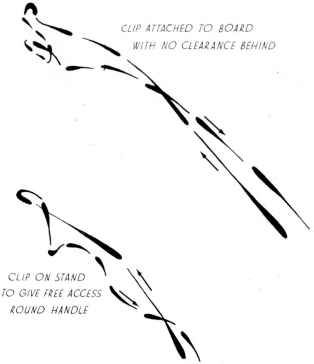

CLIP ATTACHED TO BOARD
WITH NO CLEARANCE BEHIND

CLIP ON STAND
TO GIVE FREE ACCESS
ROUND HANDLE

FIG. 39. REPRODUCTION OF CHRONOCYLEGRAPHS OF PICKING UP A RATCHET SCREWDRIVER FROM A HOLDING CLIP

implements (Fig. 38). Here a rack accommodated a tin opener, cork screw, strainer, scissors and other necessary devices. Each was hung against a painted silhouette, in a bright colour, which not only showed up at once if something was not replaced but also caused the user to put each article back in its appointed place, since to put a pair of kitchen scissors, for example, over the outline of a wooden spoon was so obviously incorrect and untidy. This is an important point where tools are used irregularly and by more than one person.

Tools used at shorter intervals and in smaller numbers require holders not so much as storage places but to present them to the worker so that they are easily picked up in the right position for use and as easily returned to the

same position. Freedom of movement in picking up a tool is of the greatest
importance and this is a matter for design. It is more difficult, for example,
to grasp a screwdriver lying flat on a bench than one resting against a
block (Fig. 22); or a screwdriver placed in a clip hard against the wall than
one held by a clip an inch or so away from the wall (*see* Fig. 39). In
designing tool holders or tool rests for special purposes practical experiment

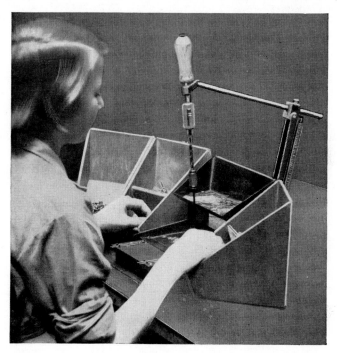

FIG. 40. VARIABLE RESISTANCE SPRING-BACK DEVICE
FOR SCREWDRIVER
This device holds an archimedes screwdriver and is used in
simple assembly work. When released the driver springs
back into a set position.

is used to discover the best design and chronocyclegraphs can be made to
test suggestions or to select the best from a number of ideas.
    The problem of tool holders for single tools or small groups of tools
used regularly in every cycle of a repetitive job, such as the screwdriver in a
small engineering assembly job or the scissors of a handkerchief machinist,
differs from the problem of tool holders for tools used less frequently and
less regularly but in greater variety. The movements of picking up such a
tool and replacing it are part of the whole regular movement cycle of the
job and must be considered together. Tools must be pre-positioned in such

a way that as far as possible they can be picked up ready for use in one movement and from exactly the same place every time. This pre-positioning can best be arranged, either by using particular care in replacing tools or by designing tool holders so that a tool automatically assumes the correct position when it is put down casually in the right area. Careful pre-positioning without assistance from the design of the toolholder may waste as much time and energy as it is intended to save, and will certainly be unpopular with most operators. The design of the tool rest must therefore be made to assist the hands. It may be possible to make use of gravity or some spring back device to return the tool to the correct place and position. There must, however, be no interference with the movements of using the tool or with the rest of the movement cycle. The mere suspension of a ratchet screwdriver from a spring for example is not enough. The tool must be made to spring back into a set position out of the way of the hands as soon as it is released. Any swinging or continued movement will interfere with the operator's later movements even if it ceases before the tool is needed once more. Again, a spring attached to certain parts of a tool handle may interfere with its proper use. A satisfactory spring back device is shown in Fig. 40.

4. MACHINE FEATURES

It is not often that a motion study investigator is so fortunate as to be called in on a job early enough to give advice about the external design of new machines. Many an excellent and ingenious machine which is most efficient technically is designed with very little thought for the worker and his movements in operating it. Switches are frequently fitted too high or too low for comfortable use or even outside the "areas of easiest reach" altogether. Starting levers are often placed where it is easiest for the makers to fit them rather than in the position best suited to the operator and arrangements for setting up or putting in fresh material are made without thought for the unnecessary trouble they may give to the operator.

It is not often possible to make major modifications in the design of machines but many minor modifications of external points often arise out of a motion study investigation. Switches may be brought into the "areas of easiest reach" and levers and foot pedals may be made easier to use or extended so that they can be operated by a worker standing or sitting in several different positions. Racks for material or finished articles can be re-designed and heavy controls or clumsy release mechanisms improved. Within the limits of mechanical efficiency the comfort and ease of movement of the operator should be the first consideration. A machine that is easy and convenient to operate will be more popular than a machine that is clumsy and difficult to handle.

An example of a simple modification of the externals of a machine is described in Chapter 5, page 95, showing the placing of a lap of cotton in the creel of a ribbon lap machine.

Motion study investigators should always check that machine controls are easy to operate. Complaints about the difficulty of operation should always be taken seriously. Controls operated, for example, by the knee or the elbow need a finer adjustment than foot or hand controls and can easily cause discomfort and fatigue. In one factory the knee lifts were removed from all sewing machines at the request of the operators. The management at first thought the objection arose out of prejudice but investigation proved that the controls were too stiff. So much force was needed to operate them that they were a definite source of fatigue and that was the real reason for the operators' request. Attention should also be paid to machine guards and safety devices. These are too often designed without thought for the obstacle that they may present in the path of the operator's movements. They may often be modified to satisfy both safety regulations and motion study principles and they are far more likely to be used properly if they are convenient to use.

5. Jigs and Fixtures

Although there are essential differences between jigs and fixtures, the general principles of their design as it affects the movements of the operator are very much the same. Both are devices for holding parts and both appear very frequently in a motion study method either as modifications of existing devices or as something newly introduced. A jig holds parts in an exact position and guides the tool that works upon them; a fixture is a less accurate device for holding parts which would otherwise have to be held in one hand while the other works on them.

In a motion study job when the general idea of a jig or fixture has been decided upon, the exact details must be worked out so that the easiest movements can be used in the loading of components into the fixture. The same attention must be given to the movements necessary to secure the component adequately and to eject it.

A jig or fixture should be designed so that components can be loaded easily with both hands and there should be no obstruction between the point of entry and the material containers. Small parts, such as thin washers, for example, are often most easily assembled into a fixture by a sliding action and the design of the fixture should allow for this if possible. If spring-loaded disappearing pins are used to locate components, particular attention should be given to strength of construction. Unless their design is robust, such devices tend to function admirably for a period and then have to be repaired or re-designed. This causes an unnecessary production delay.

If it is easy to introduce the component into the jig, it is usually also easy for the operator to maintain visual control over his movements. It is important that he should be able to see what he is doing at all stages if it is at all possible and this should be checked before any design is accepted.

Clamping devices should be as simple to operate as possible. Cams worked by foot pedals or compressed air mechanisms are worth consideration but where they are not justified economically a cam or toggle operated by the simple to and fro movement of a lever may be possible.   If two clamps are needed, they should be designed so that they can be used by the right and left hand working simultaneously and naturally, one turning clockwise and the other anti-clockwise (*see* Fig. 41).   If accuracy demands that the part

Fig. 41. Jig with Two-Handed Operation of Clamps
This jig holds a coil.   The clamps are operated by the thumbs, one turning clockwise and the other anti-clockwise to allow the most natural movement of the hands.

should be screwed down, suitable spanners should be provided and pre-positioned so that they can be used with minimum effort.

A jig should be designed so that the action of unclamping it also ejects the component without any additional movements.   It can sometimes be arranged that the lever which operates the clamps also opens the bottom or side of the jig so that the component falls away down a chute.   Where automatic or semi-automatic unloading is not possible, particular care must be taken to make sure that the operator will be able to remove the finished component with ease.

When the details of the jig or fixture have been worked out a full size model should be made so that it can be tried out in practice.   This is important since it is difficult to judge from a drawing the exact details of movement that will be needed for its operation. If the model is made very simply, in wood or modelling wax, it can be very quickly altered if a modification will make it easier to use.

The Arrangement of the Workplace

The arrangement of the contents of the workplace, like their design, is part of the third stage of a motion study investigation. In the first stage, the existing method is recorded and analysed and in the second the new method is developed theoretically. The third stage covers the experimental work of turning theory into practice and after the necessary tools and equipment have been designed it becomes necessary to arrange everything so that the set of movements that has been suggested can be carried out. In other words, the workplace must be arranged before the first operator can be trained.

It is only possible to give general examples of the arrangement of the workplace since the details must be worked out to suit the requirements of each individual job and operator but certain types of workplace have some common features and common problems.

In workplaces designed for assembly or packing jobs, the contents of the workplace are primarily the materials that are to be assembled or packed and the finished work. There may also be small tools such as screwdrivers, hammers, scissors, pencils, paste brushes or label wetting devices and there will be containers to hold the material. The material, in its containers, must be arranged somewhere within the "areas of easiest reach" so that it can be picked up easily by whichever hand the method requires, and in the correct order. If both hands are to be used, a supply of material must be provided for each and if it is necessary to use the eyes to select material the containers must be placed within the small area (*see* Fig. 33*c*) where it is possible for the eyes to watch the hands without causing the operator to turn the head. In a case of this type, it can be arranged that both hands collect material from the same workbin if its entrance is wide enough. Where all the material must be selected by sight and it is too bulky or varied for it all to be placed within the normal area for visual selection, this area can be extended by sacrificing the symmetry of the movements. The material can then be arranged so that both hands move together round the workplace, selecting material from the same or adjacent containers. An example of this arose during an investigation into the packing of assorted biscuits (*see* Fig. 42). The varieties were too many to be crowded into the small visual selection area so the tins containing each variety were arranged in sequence round the workplace and the operator worked from left to right round the semi-circle selecting the biscuits with both hands out of each tin or pair of tins in turn. Before coming to the decision that symmetry must be sacrificed in this way, it should however be remembered that in many cases an operator who tends to need to watch both hands and to turn his head from side to side in an attempt to do so on a symmetrical set-up may learn to select his material

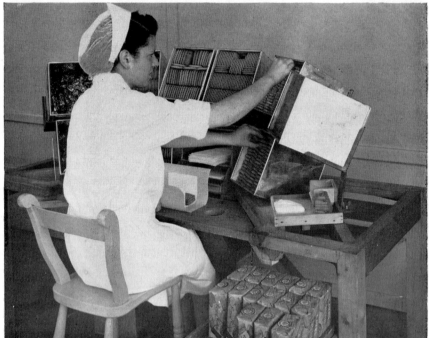

FIG. 42. PACKETING ASSORTED BISCUITS

Upper: Old Method. *Lower*: Motion study method showing adaptable stand for standard biscuit tins. *Note*: The workplace in the lower photograph is not set up for symmetrical movements because the operator has to look at the biscuits to inspect them for damage. She can move her hands simultaneously only if she can see both at once. This arrangement, therefore, although unconventional is easiest for the operator.

entirely by touch if he is allowed time to practice. The effect of practice should not be overlooked and an unsymmetrical arrangement should not be adopted until its necessity has been proved.

The particular nature and shape of certain material may influence its position in the workplace. For example, in a packing job that required two strips of paper to be laid at right angles to one another across a cardboard box, it was found that the best arrangement was to lay one set of strips parallel with the edge of the bench to the operator's left and the other at right angles and directly in front of the operator. The right hand could then grasp the end of one of the left hand strips and pull it to the right over the box with a movement that brought the hand across the body. At the same time the left hand pulled a strip from the other pile forwards towards the body and over the first strip. These were very easy, natural, pulling movements and were more satisfactory than the movements that would have been allowed by a more conventional arrangement of the material.

The primary consideration in deciding the position of hand tools must be that they should be picked up with the least disturbance to a smooth and rhythmical path of movement. As far as possible, an operator should be able to pick up a tool as his hand moves from one part of the work to the next, without making a special journey for it. Since natural movements are curved, not straight, the tool should not be placed on a straight line between the two extreme points of the movement but somewhere along an arc drawn between those points.

It is not enough to arrange tools so that they are easily picked up; it is equally important that they should be easy to replace in the same fixed position. If some form of automatic return is impracticable, the location of the next piece of material to be picked up should be arranged if possible to allow the operator to put the tool away as his hand goes towards it.

When an operation has been completed, the finished material must be removed. If it is robust enough to be dropped, it can be disposed of by releasing it through a hole in the bench or down a chute to fall into a container underneath. The chute or hole should be placed so that the finished article can be made to fall into it as soon as the work is completed. If for any reason this immediate disposal cannot be arranged, the hole or chute should be placed so that the hand can drop the article on its way to pick up the first piece of material required in the next cycle of work without using extra movements or changing its direction. Such arrangements for disposing of finished material are usually known as drop deliveries and a number of examples are quoted by Professor Barnes[1].

Where an article is easily damaged and the use of drop deliveries is not possible, or where a finished article is placed directly into its final packing, the hand movements involved in placing it in its container should be carefully considered so that the minimum of unproductive movements is used. For

[1] *Motion and Time Study.* R. M. Barnes (3rd edition), p. 251.

example, material placed on flat trays should be arranged so that the tray is filled from the back forwards, each piece reaching its place without being lifted over the others and with a single free movement. If during an intermediate operation articles are placed in containers which are to be passed to the next operator for further work, care should be taken to place them in such a way that they are in the right position for immediate use during the next operation.

The layout of an inspection workplace presents certain special problems. If gauges are used, their position must be very carefully considered. Many motion study methods call for the mounting of gauges in duplicate so that two parts can be inspected simultaneously. If they are mounted in a semi-circle or on a frame parallel with the edge of the bench, a very common arrangement, the movement of the hands in inserting and removing a part will be awkward. The upper photograph in Fig. 43 shows the position of the hands when using gauges mounted in this way. In most cases gauges should be mounted in a double line at right angles to the edge of the bench, as in the lower photograph, Fig. 43. This allows the easiest and most natural movements to be used because the hands then move freely in and out from the centre to the sides and parallel with the edge of the bench. This statement may appear to contradict some of the previous suggestions about workplace layout but there is good reason for the difference in treatment. The problem is the reverse of an assembly problem. Instead of a number of different materials to be incorporated into one assembly, there is one type of material to be fitted into a number of different gauges, and instead of movement from material container to assembly the bulk of the movement is from gauge to gauge.

In simple machine work, such as the operating of a press, the cycle will usually consist of loading, operating and unloading the machine. Instances of such work can be found in some form in nearly every industry. In this type of workplace, two points call for special consideration in the arrangement of the working area; the position of the material before loading and its disposal when the machine has finished its work. The operator should pick up his material in such a way that the movement that he makes with it towards the machine brings it into the right position for entry into the tool. This can be achieved by arranging the material in such a position that by grasping it in a uniform way no change of grip or alteration in the direction of the movement is needed to load it into the machine in one movement. If the material is in a pile, this should be at a height to make stooping unnecessary. Where a machine does not automatically eject the finished part, the action of loading a new part as far as possible should dislodge the finished part and provision should be made for containers to receive the finished parts as they are ejected. Where it has not been possible to combine the loading and unloading of the machine in this way, the same consideration should be given to the disposal of each finished piece as would be given to the disposal of finished work in an assembly layout. Since this type of machine work is nearly always

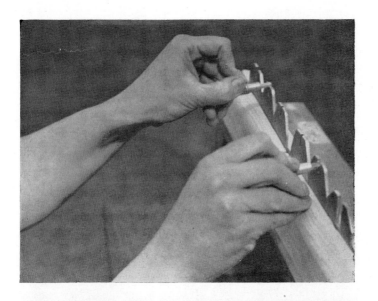

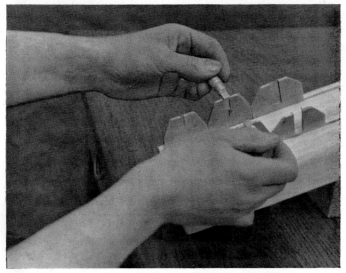

FIG. 43. INSPECTION GAUGES MOUNTED ON A BENCH

Upper: Gauges mounted on a framework parallel with the edge
  of the bench. Note the obvious strain on the hands.
Lower: Gauges mounted on a framework at *right angles* to the
  edge of the bench. Note the easy position of the hands.

one process among many others, particular care should be taken to ensure that finished parts are disposed of so that they are positioned for immediate use in the next operation.

The design of the machine controls and any jigs to be used will already have been settled (pages 116-9) before the arrangement of the workplace begins, but their incorporation into the working area and any necessary modifications must be considered at this stage. If, for example, there is to be a foot pedal, it must be adjusted so that it can be operated easily by either foot with the chair at the correct height and without stretching. Its range of operation should not be too great. The operator should not have to lift his foot too high or press too hard on the pedal. Chair and pedal should be adjusted together so that the operator can maintain with no effort a comfortable balance.

In planning the layout of a group of workplaces for a sequence of operations, the arrangement of individual workplaces should be planned before they are considered as a group. Whether the work is line assembly where parts are stacked between the different operations or conveyor assembly where parts are mechanically handled between operators, the disposal of material from one operation should be so organised that it reaches the next operator in the most convenient position for the next operation. Where there is no conveyor, work can often be passed between operators by means of chutes or turntables. In this type of group work, it is often better to arrange the workplaces on both sides of a bench. This allows more flexibility than a straight line arrangement as it makes it possible for two operators to take material from one operator. Such an arrangement often makes it easier to balance the line and it may allow extra operators to be put on to deal with sudden demands for increased output or to supplement the work of a slow operator or a temporary worker who is deputising for an absentee.

Individual workplaces on conveyors present some of the most complicated problems of workplace layout. They are very difficult to arrange satisfactorily. Because of the structure of most conveyors it is not easy to arrange a comfortable sitting position for the operator. There is usually insufficient knee room for the operators to sit facing the belt and, if they sit at right angles to it, they are obliged to turn to pick up material. Where the work is very simple such as the packing of small articles into boxes and the material comes quickly down the conveyor there is often a tendency to bend over the belt and therefore to sit all day in an unhealthy position.

The design of a conveyor and its use should be thoroughly investigated when an existing method of work is studied and the obvious difficulties of conveyor workplaces should be considered when recommendations for an improved method are made. If, after due consideration, it is still felt, as will often happen, that a belt conveyor is the most satisfactory form of transport between operations, very careful arrangements must be made for the comfort of the operator. The disposal of the finished work must also be considered.

In a simple conveyor packing operation it may be possible to direct the pieces that are to be packed from the centre of the conveyor where they may be at the limit of reach to the edge of the conveyor nearest to the operator. It may also be possible to supply packing material and containers above the conveyor and to arrange for the finished packages to be disposed of beneath the conveyor. Each arrangement will require a careful study of the individual circumstances.

The height of a conveyor is very important and where material is taken direct from the conveyor belt it should be at the correct working height. Many mistakes are made here and many examples could be quoted. During the war a conveyor was designed to transport bomb fuses weighing $4\frac{1}{2}$ lb. each. It was placed at such a height that each fuse had to be lifted down from the belt to a depth of $1\frac{1}{2}$ feet and put back again when the operation was finished. Merely by dropping the conveyor to bench level an increase in output of 25 per cent and a considerable reduction in fatigue were obtained with no other alteration in the method. But a complete study of the job at a later date, including a modification of the arrangement of the conveyor so that it delivered each part turned into the correct position for immediate work at the next operation, gave a further increase in output of more than 100 per cent.

Conclusion

Whatever kind of workplace is needed, whether it is the workplace of an individual worker or a group of workers or a conveyor workplace, its design should be based on the method that is to be used in it. The method must be developed first before any alterations are made to the workplace. When the new method is established the workplace should then be designed for the comfort of the operator, to enable him to use it with the greatest ease and the least fatigue. The workplace can be of the greatest assistance to the motion study investigator. If it is carefully designed, it can give the operator the necessary help and encouragement to use the new method accurately and can make it difficult for him to return to old habits.

7

FACTORY LAYOUT

THE criterion of efficiency in the layout of a department or factory is its effect upon movement; upon the movement of material between machines or processes, upon the movement of raw material and finished material and upon the movements of the operators as they go about their work and as they use such services as are provided for their welfare.

A workplace layout is made as part of the installation stage of any new method when the theoretical method is being adapted to suit the operator. It is at this stage that the operator is all important and it is wholly to suit him that the workplace is planned. It is his working environment, and everything in it therefore, should be designed with this in mind, but it is subsidiary to the method that is to be used in it, and it is designed to facilitate the use of that method. The layout of a factory or workshop on the other hand has a different basis. While the making of a good workplace is essential in finishing any kind of investigation, whatever techniques have been used, an investigation into the layout of a factory or workshop, though it may in some instances be suggested by difficulties that arise during the workplace layout stage of another investigation, is a problem in its own right. It is a separate investigation which will be carried out by means of a combination of the three motion study techniques described in Chapters 2 to 4. In most cases it is suggested to the investigator as a complete problem in itself, possibly because new machinery has been ordered or because the need for extra production has revealed departmental bottlenecks or transport inadequacies.

The following paragraphs describe the procedure for investigating and improving an existing layout. In laying out a factory for the first time the same lines are followed though it is inevitable that less accurate information will be available.

Recording Present Practice

As in all motion study investigations the first step is to record present practice. The facts to be recorded in a factory layout problem are: —

      1. The space and contents of the department or factory.
      2. The detailed processes which are involved.
      3. The quantity of the product.
      4. The variety of the product.

5. The number of operators making each product.
6. The flow of material through the factory.
7. The supervision and control system.

This information is collected by the investigator and recorded in four steps: First, a scale drawing is made of the layout showing the existing buildings and permanent fixtures, with particular reference to pillars or other obstructions; the position of external services such as electricity, gas and steam; the arrangement and nature of present workplaces; the location of the offices of the supervisory staff; the position of stores and areas used for the temporary storage of work in progress; the placing of the cloakrooms and time clocks; the position of light sources and heating and ventilating appliances, with notes as to their effectiveness; and the areas covered by each means of transport including external transport and railway sidings. Next, a survey is made of the products and of their quantity. In this survey, if there are a variety of products, those passing through the same processes are grouped together. Thirdly, process charts are constructed for each of the process groups, showing the flow of material through the department and recording very carefully any variations from the normal of the group. Finally, string diagrams are made from observations taken of the work of each group.

Once the available facts have been recorded in this way the investigator has an accurate picture of what is actually happening on the existing layout. This picture may show considerable variations from standard practice as originally laid down, but it will be the true picture, and the investigator will now be in a position to make an analysis of the facts just as he would make it in any other investigation. He will examine his process chart and string diagrams in the usual way, questioning each section as to its necessity, correctness of sequence and possibilities of combination or simplification, and he will collect information for developing a more satisfactory layout.

Analysing the Problem

In beginning to consider the new layout the investigator must first decide its focal point. This may well be a process that is causing particular difficulty in the existing layout or it may be something peculiar to the type of product. It will vary from industry to industry and even from department to department within a single factory. For example, the point round which a foundry layout might be built is the pouring, but if this were continuous the layout would be quite different from the layout of a foundry where it was intermittent. On the other hand the focal point of everything in any canteen layout is the service area, because in canteen work the service of dinner is the one operation that has a close time limit. Whatever the variety of the menu, everything that the kitchen produces has to be served at a particular place at an exact time and with the minimum of delay.

Other examples of the same sort will be immediately obvious to the reader though in some cases there may not be a single point of focus. The key to the layout may simply be the fitting in of a number of similar machines to allow the greatest amount of free space and movement in a workshop that has been overcrowded.

Whatever the starting point in making the new layout its objective will be to arrange the position of the machines and working areas to the best advantage and to ensure an unimpeded flow of material through the various processes in the factory. This flow of material must be assisted by an efficient stores or warehouse system, and this will mean that allowance must be made in the layout for adequate space for the stocks of material needed for the processes of the factory. In addition, the layout must be such that work is easily controlled by a suitable production system which arranges that material is in the right place in the right quantities at the right time. The problems of supervision can be simplified by a good layout. Finally, consideration must be given to the placing of the operator services so that they can function as comfortably and efficiently as possible.

Location of machines. The placing of the machines will naturally be very different for different types of product. Long processing machines such as those found in paper making for example, present a very different problem in layout from a group of machines in a general engineering shop and there are many different types between these two extremes.

Depending upon the type of production, machines and working areas may be arranged either in groups according to their function, or in production units consisting of a number of different machines or operations all required for the same product. For example, an engineering works may either group all lathes in one place and all milling machines in another, with presses and drills together somewhere else or, alternatively, several lathes, a milling machine and perhaps a radial arm drill may be gathered into one unit to produce one particular type of job, with other slightly varied groupings for other products. In a laundry, the choice would lie between placing all washing machines together, followed by all the hydros in one group, and the calenders, presses and sorting further on, or in single units working parallel with one another on different types of work, each unit complete in itself. The argument in favour of the functional arrangement is that each type of machine is then in the hands of experts, that the whole layout lends itself to use for an infinite variety of changing products, and that the organisation is easy, though there may be difficulties in the control of products. The argument for the unit system of grouping a variety of machines and workplaces according to product instead of function is that the control of the product is then much more efficient. There can be no general rule. The choice must depend upon the circumstances of production. Where there is great variety, machines are obviously more useful if they are grouped according to function and it is worth paying the necessary extra attention to the control of the product. On the other hand, where there is less variety it may be best to group the machines according to product, taking care that the layout is not too rigid to allow for a reasonable variation in product. Some form of compromise between the two systems is nearly always necessary and, as at all other points in a layout problem, the investigator must weigh every argument and make a final recommendation that suits the special circumstances of the particular factory or department, not relying on either system to solve his problem unadapted.

When the type of grouping has been decided the actual placing of individual machines and workplaces can be considered. Here four main points must be kept in mind. There must be sufficient space for the operators to work comfortably, a clear passage for raw materials to reach the machine, sufficient storage space to accumulate the necessary quantity of material that will keep the machine running steadily, and enough room for the finished job as it comes off the machine. Insufficient space for material is a very common fault in layout. Even small hold-ups in the internal transport system often cause two or three quite unproductive restackings which would be avoided if more space were allowed in the right place.

Before the final location of machines is decided, attention must be paid to the handling of material. Where any weight is difficult for an operator or operators to handle, consideration should be given to the possibility of using some form of mechanical handling. It is important to remember that a weight that can be lifted without hardship once or twice a day may easily be much too heavy to be handled at intervals of a few minutes throughout the day. If handling is to be mechanical it is essential to allow the right amount of space and the right placing of machines for this to be carried out economically.

After the location of the machines has been agreed and sufficient space in the right place has been allowed for the handling and the storage of material, the supply of power and other services should be checked. This is usually a question of making the necessary arrangements at the planning stage and should never be allowed to dictate the placing of machines. Even where it is more expensive and more difficult to run an additional cable or pipe to the location chosen than to make use of existing cables or pipes somewhere else, that expense or trouble occurs only once, while the extra or more difficult movements made by the operator on the machine, or in handling materials in the less ideal location, recurs and accumulates all the time, though it may be less obvious.

In arranging for power and other supplies to be available, consideration should be given to the maintenance of these services. All points that are likely to need attention should be made accessible. This also applies to the machines themselves. Space should always be allowed for their easy adjustment and maintenance.

Flow of Material. The most usual reason for embarking upon the study of a factory layout problem is to improve the material handling. There are many prejudices here and action sometimes follows the dictates of fashion rather

than of considered judgment. Conveyors, for example, are sometimes introduced more because they are thought to be up-to-date than because the
particular circumstances of the layout are best served by a conveyor or because
a conveyor will simplify the movements used on the job. A conveyor is not
by any means always the best answer to the problem of moving material or
finished work to and from machines and other workplaces. There are many
types of work where other forms of transport are more suitable. Where, for
example, a factory handles a large variety of product and there are many
changes and short runs in the production, flexible material handling is essential. This flexibility may often be best provided by some form of trucking
rather than by means of conveyors. Trucking, however, must be carefully
planned if it is not to cause confusion, untidiness and double handling. A
proper system must be devised and supervised to prevent material being
allowed to lie about on the workshop floor or in temporary storage areas
for more than the minimum time. If material of any sort is held up in
this way, or allowed to accumulate even for short periods, it makes organisation very difficult and adds considerably to costs by increasing work in
progress. It can be even more serious in such service industries as dry-
cleaning and laundry-work where it adds to the length of time the work is
in the factory. In such industries, delays in transport often account for the
major part of the whole time that goods are passing through the processes.

   Where the product and its components are heavy, cranes very often provide the best solution to the transport problem. The same is sometimes true
of bulky work even where it is not particularly heavy. In such industries as
airframe production, overhead cranes often justify the original cost by adding
greatly to the flexibility of the line.

   In a multi-storey building lifts should be adequate and consideration
should be given to their position. They should be suitably disposed along
the length of the building so that they serve each floor in such a way as to
allow the efficient handling of material. Many delays are caused by badly
placed or inadequate lifts. If the product is suitable the lift service can be
augmented and delays in waiting for lifts eliminated by chutes between floors.

   In all forms of production it is very important to adopt the most
suitable and economical type of handling. This will vary in different circumstances and it is impossible to attempt to give adequate examples of all
possible types in a book of this nature. Unsuitable forms of handling often
add very considerably to costs. The actual waste caused by a badly planned
system is often hidden and difficult to assess but the importance at the present
time of reducing such hidden waste cannot be over-emphasised. During the
war, indirect costs increased as a proportion of total manufacturing costs. At
the present time when manufacturing costs as a whole must be reduced
no possible means of reducing indirect costs can be ignored.

   A point in factory layout that is often given too little consideration is the
final disposal of the product. Since it is obviously impossible to anticipate

all the future variations in outside transport arrangements, a sufficient area should be allowed for efficient handling methods to be developed in varied circumstances. When making arrangements for the entry of outside transport into a department care should be taken to give operators adequate protection against draughts and cold. This may seem to be a very minor point but it is of major importance to the operators.

When all other means of moving material from operation to operation have been examined, the possibility of moving it mechanically should be considered. Conveyors have two distinct functions; they may carry a product through its various operations or they may serve as a substitute for a trucking system.

The type of conveyor that carries work through from process to process is normally part of a continuous production system and its use must be studied as part of any investigation into the working methods of the different operations that it serves. Reference has been made in Chapter 6 to the effect of conveyor workplaces on an operator's movements.

On the other hand, the conveyor that is a substitute for trucking is fundamentally a problem of layout and plays a part in most investigations into layout. Whatever its type, like all other forms of equipment that may be called for by an improved method, its cost must be very carefully measured against any estimated savings. As a substitute for a trucking system a conveyor has little effect on the ordinary operator's work and cannot do much to increase production directly, though it may save the work of one or two labourers. Its chief contribution to efficiency will be in simplifying the production control system and preventing the accumulation of material between processes.

Before a conveyor is installed careful thought should be given to its proper function and to its effect upon the detailed movements of the operators using it. It is very often better to employ labourers to deliver material where it is wanted and at the right time than to waste productive operator time taking it off a conveyor or waiting for it to come round. It is worse if an operator has to watch the conveyor and seize the opportunity to take material off as it passes him. This interrupts the cycle of movements and upsets the rhythm. It is not only irritating, but it has an adverse effect on production much greater than the actual seconds wasted.

All aspects of the movement of material must be studied before any means of transport is chosen and a conveyor should be installed only if it is really the best way of dealing with a particular transport problem.

Location of Stores, Production Control, and Supervision. When due consideration has been given to the placing of machines and workplaces and to the flow of material, the best location must be found for the stores, the production control system and the shop floor supervision.

The stores and warehouse system is much more elaborate and more important in some industries than in others. In engineering, for example, where there is always a multiplicity of parts and tools, it is of supreme importance. There, materials and tools are usually grouped separately in different stores or in different sections of the same stores and the main stores will usually have subsidiaries in each department. The actual organisation of each stores is a problem that must be studied as an independent investigation. Motion study can do much to improve store methods but in this chapter we are concerned not with internal stores organisation but with the location of stores as one of the essential services to production. This location must be very carefully planned. It must be chosen on the basis of an assessment of the exact function of the stores and planned so that this function can be fully carried out, giving the best services with minimum movement.

In considering the location of organised stores, areas for temporary storage must not be forgotten. Although any uncontrolled storing of material in a department is very expensive in indirect cost, sufficient space must be allowed for temporary storage. Too little space may be as expensive as too much, since it will cause much double handling of material in the attempt to find room for it. The areas allowed for temporary storage should be clearly marked out and obvious not only to those who use them but also to the supervisors concerned. This is the only way to keep them under control.

Linked with the stores system is production control. A product made to specification usually requires a much more elaborate scheme of production control than a standard product or a product made for stock. A review of the production control system must, therefore, precede any layout investigation. If there is nothing already in existence, a separate study should be made to determine the most suitable system before the layout is planned. The layout should aim at making all processes clearly visible so that at any time the production position can be seen immediately. A layout that conceals production bottlenecks may be a great comfort to the immediate supervisory staff but it leads to inefficiencies. If production hold-ups are immediately visible to anyone passing through the department they will tend to occur less frequently and to be dealt with more promptly.

Location of Operator Services. Finally, the position of the various operator services should be planned. If they are not well planned they may cause the operators to make many extra movements and to waste much time. For example, the cloakrooms should be as near as possible to the time recording clock, which should have plenty of space round it for free movement. Boards for clock cards should be placed at least a yard or two away from the clock on either side. This whole section again should be clearly visible from the supervisor's office to discourage people from waiting near the clock some minutes before stopping time. Lavatories should be situated as centrally as possible so that no one has too far to walk, and though men's and women's lavatories may be built side by side their entrances should be as far apart as possible. Again, the entrance for each sex should not be located directly in an area where the operators are mainly of the opposite sex. These points may seem to be rather remotely connected with motion study but they are too often overlooked in making a layout and they can cause so much dissatisfaction and so much unnecessary walking about.

The plan for the distribution of mid-morning and mid-afternoon tea is a further detail that may be important in the efficient running of a department. It is seldom considered when making changes in layout, but anyone who has had the courage to assess the loss of production caused by a badly-arranged scheme or to examine graphs of electrical power consumption will appreciate that the matter is well worth careful thought. The location of other employee services such as ambulance rooms and canteens should also be planned both for ease of supervision and also for the operators' convenience.

These are the general points to be covered in any layout investigation. To them must be added the consideration of any special points peculiar to a particular industry or organisation. After this the investigator is ready to gather his ideas together into an experimental layout.

Drawing Up the Layout Plan

The next step is to plan the new layout on paper. For this purpose the investigator will require templets which he can move about on a scale plan. These templets may be cut out of paper, cardboard or flat metal, or they may be three-dimensional blocks or models, according to the value and requirements of the job. The first experimental layout plan should be made without regard to the limitations of existing buildings or services, and then adapted to fit such existing conditions as cannot be modified. If the final layout is made in this way, first deciding the ideal positions for machines and equipment and only modifying them to allow for actual conditions, it will have as its basis the best arrangement of machines and equipment. There will be less danger of such obstructions as pillars or awkward spaces being made the excuse for faults in layout or being allowed to control the whole plan.

The approach to a layout problem is the same whether the factory is manufacturing a single product or a variety of products. In this latter case, a layout for each possible type of product should be planned on a separate layout drawing and a final compromise made between the requirements of each.

During this stage of a layout investigation, which corresponds to the development and experimental stages of an investigation into individual methods of work, obvious instances may arise of methods that must be studied and improved before the layout can be successful. If these individual investigations are not made, bottlenecks and delays may arise at certain points. Such subsidiary studies should, therefore, be made before the layout is finally approved.

When all possible points have been considered and the final layout plan has been evolved, it should be tested by making string diagrams of the flow of all the main products, to make sure that the best arrangement has been reached.

Finally, it is very important that all those who are likely to be involved in the new layout should be consulted so that they understand the reasons for each proposal. The plan should be thoroughly discussed so that agreement is reached about it before it is installed.

Installation

When the final layout plan has been agreed, its installation must be very carefully planned. It is difficult to suggest any exact rules to follow here as circumstances vary so considerably. In many cases the actual installation will not be in the hands of the investigator but will be the responsibility of some other department. Even so, the investigator should keep in close touch at every stage. This close contact is extremely important because no matter how efficiently the plan has been made, there may creep into the layout during construction modifications which those making the installation do not regard as important but which become of major importance in daily use.

Since there is such a variety in the layout problems of different factories it is difficult to give useful examples but it has been found in teaching and expounding motion study theories that one of the best subjects to choose for an example is a large-scale kitchen. It is a successful example for a number of reasons. With the shortage of domestic staff everyone tends to have some practical experience of the faults of kitchen layout and everyone is familiar with the type of material and equipment involved. Lastly, a kitchen is a manufacturing unit containing certain standard equipment which has to be arranged to give the best layout for a variety of processes, most of which have certain basic elements.

Example: The Layout of a Hospital Kitchen[1]

The continued scarcity of hospital domestic staff made a general study of kitchen work desirable. It was felt that such a study should reduce the fatigue of the workers and make the work more attractive, at the same time reducing the actual labour required.

So that there could be no question of blaming old buildings or old-fashioned ideas of kitchen management for any errors that might be found in the layout, a kitchen of recent construction was selected for study (Fig. 44). This, however, had been built during the war and its design suffered to some extent from shortage of materials and the need for economy and speed in construction.

A short preliminary survey indicated that the problem was primarily one of the layout of equipment.

[1]The author is indebted to the Department of Health for Scotland for permission to publish the material in this example.

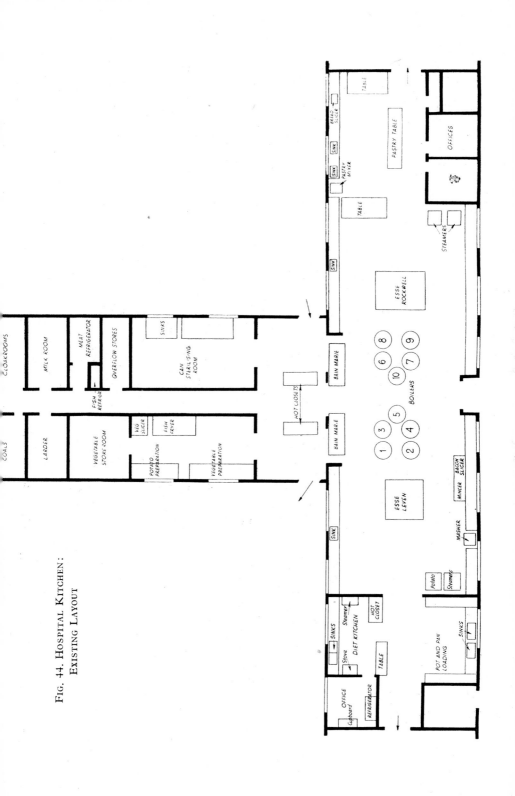

FIG. 44. HOSPITAL KITCHEN: EXISTING LAYOUT

Recording Present Practice. Present practice was recorded on the lines of the recommendations above. The facts to be considered in this investigation were : —

1. Space and contents: The investigation was confined to the kitchen itself and the stores and offices attached to it.
2. The detailed processes involved: These were the preparation and cooking of food for the patients and staff of the hospital.
3. The quantity of the product: This was virtually constant.
4. The variety of the product: There was considerable variety but the three main groupings were breakfast, dinner and supper. Each meal involved the routines of preparation, cooking and distribution of food and the clearing up that followed.
5. The number of operators making each product: Food was prepared in sections, meat, vegetable and sweet, and each had its own group of workers.
6. The flow of material: The flow varied in the different sections according to the day's menu which dictated the proportions of the various types of food involved, such as dry stores, vegetables or such perishable goods as meat, fish and milk.
7. The supervision and control system: A kitchen supervisor was responsible for the work of the kitchen. The "production control" was unlike most factories in that delivery dates were always the same for all products passing through the kitchen at one time. In most factories a delivery date may be postponed but in a kitchen, whatever else suffers or is altered in an emergency, the delivery date of meal times must be kept.

This information was recorded as follows : —

1. A scale drawing was made of the kitchen, including the stores and offices and recording the position of equipment.
2. A survey was made of all meals which were classified according to the amount of work involved in each.
3. Process charts were made of the work involved in the preparation, cooking and distribution of food, showing variations for the different groupings of menus and for each meal. Other charts were made of the distribution of food as far as the wards and dining rooms, and of the clearing up of the kitchen and the cleaning of the containers returned from the wards.
4. String diagrams (*see* Fig. 45) were made for 14 of typical routines. These records were carefully examined and analysed in the usual way, to find out which operations or movements could be eliminated as unnecessary, whether a change in sequence would improve matters, and which operations should be combined with others or simplified in some way.

Analysing Present Practice. The following points emerged from the analysis of the existing layout : —

1. The larder and cold storage rooms: These were placed at the end of a long passageway and all food had to be transported a minimum distance of 100ft. to the preparation areas. The passageway was narrow and could be reached only by passing between the hot cupboards of the servery. These features made the use of trolleys almost impossible.
2. Vegetable preparation area: The storeroom next to the preparation room provided a day-to-day stock. The preparation room was long and narrow and the whole area was unsuitable, both in location and shape and caused long transports of all vegetables between preparation and cooking.

In the preparation room itself all sinks and draining boards were arranged

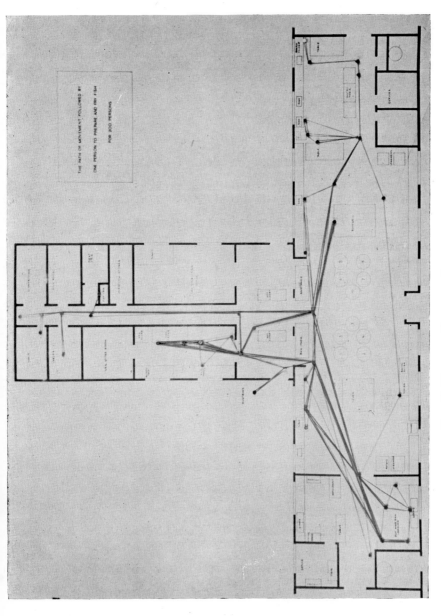

THE PATH OF MOVEMENT FOLLOWED BY

ONE PERSON TO PREPARE AND FRY FISH

FOR 200 PERSONS.

Fig. 45. Hospital Kitchen: Existing Layout

String diagram showing path of movement of cook in preparing and frying fish for 200 persons.

along the wall, restricting the working space at the sinks. For this reason part of the preparation had to be carried out in the main kitchen.

3. Servery for patients' meals: All hot food was put into containers at the two hot cupboards in the rectangular area between the main kitchen and the passageway to the stores. No provision was made for serving cold dishes into containers or for their preparation in the servery. The servery was not therefore used to full advantage and there was an enormous amount of wasteful transportation of container inserts to the food and back again to the servery for dispersal to the wards.

The servery was situated in a through draught and in addition, persons working there were standing in the only passageway leading to the stores and the vegetable preparation room.

4. Cooking boilers: The equipment included eight 40-gallon boilers and three smaller boilers, all arranged in a central block in the main kitchen. They were used for stewing meat, and for vegetables, soup, porridge, milk puddings and sauces. While this block arrangement was, without doubt, economical of steam piping and drain layout it resulted in much wasteful transportation of food from the preparation areas.

5. Steamers: The equipment included two potato steamers and two smaller steamers used for puddings and vegetables. These steamers were placed at the furthest possible point from the preparation areas: a distance of 100 ft. in the case of potatoes.

6. Special diet kitchen: The individual menus prescribed for those patients who were on special diets were prepared in a diet kitchen under the supervision of a dietician. She had the assistance of one cook and a maid and her unit was designed to be self-contained and independent of the main kitchen in cooking and preparation of dishes. Observation showed that this was by no means the case. The area was too small for the work required of it, and its staff made constant use of the main sterilising room, wash-up and servery. It was not sufficiently centrally placed and as a result the staff spent most of their time outside it, walking between it and the service areas.

7. Pan wash-up: The function of this area was to wash and store all cooking utensils for the whole kitchen, but its site was an average of 75 ft. from the preparation areas where the utensils were used. While the principle of centralised washing-up and storage has many advantages these were almost entirely offset in this case by the effort wasted in collecting and returning utensils.

Developing the Improved Layout. Figs. 46 and 47 show the changes in layout that were recommended. They show a saving of 70 per cent in the movements used in the preparation and cooking of one dish.

The principle modifications were: —

1. Larder and cold storage rooms: The string diagrams showed that these were most often visited from the preparation areas and it was obvious that they should be sited as close as possible to them, although this would mean that some of the less frequent journeys made to them would not be shortened or might even be lengthened.

It was decided to confine the meat and fish preparation to one end of the kitchen and to build on accommodation for meat and fish refrigerators in that area. The pastry and pudding preparation area was placed at the opposite end with the larder and milk store built on in the same way.

Table I shows the effect of these modifications on distances walked.

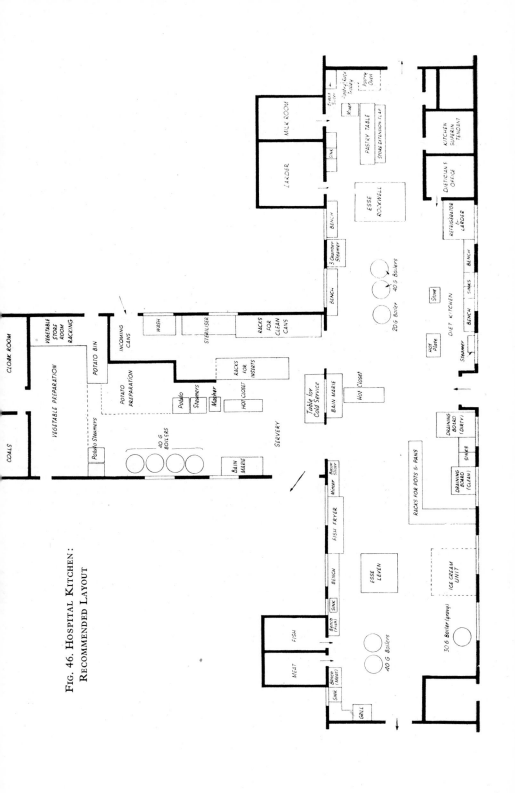

FIG. 46. HOSPITAL KITCHEN: RECOMMENDED LAYOUT

TABLE I. COMPARATIVE WALKING DISTANCES BETWEEN STORES AND
PREPARING AREAS.

From	To	Present Layout	Recommended Layout
Meat Refrigerator	Meat Bench	75ft.	10ft.
Fish Refrigerator	Fish Bench	75ft.	20ft.
Larder	Pastry Bench	110ft.	15ft.
Milk Store	Pastry Bench	110ft.	15ft.

2. Vegetable preparation area: In planning changes in layout for this area the following requirements were considered: —

(a) Food should move in a straight flow from storage to cooking. To allow this each piece of equipment should be placed in order according to its use.

(b) The sinks should be grouped in the centre of the area so that they could be used from both sides.

(c) Two units, one for vegetables and the other for potatoes, should be placed parallel to one another with the flow of work moving towards the servery.

To allow for these requirements considerably more space would be needed than existed in the original layout. It could be provided, however, by removing the larder and cold rooms, and it was recommended that the full width of the building should be used for the preparation area. This would involve the removal of inside walls and partitions and the placing of both units in the centre of the area to connect with two lines of cooking equipment running parallel towards the servery.

3. Servery: It did not seem necessary to change the site of the servery since it was a suitable collection point for the vans. A rearrangement of hot cupboards and bain maries was, however, recommended to relieve the congestion in the working space. A cold service table was planned to centralise the serving of cold dishes in the servery area and to eliminate the carrying to and fro of container inserts.

4. Cooking boilers: A policy of decentralisation was clearly indicated and the following recommendations were made: —

(a) Vegetables and soups: Four boilers to be placed along the outside wall between the vegetable preparation and the servery.

(b) Meat: Two large and one small boiler to be sited near the preparing bench (since stews formed a considerable part of the main meat dishes).

(c) Puddings: Two large and one small boiler to be allocated to that end of the kitchen.

This would distribute the cooking equipment according to the use that was made of it.

5. Steamers: Like the boilers these were required near the different preparation areas. Two were allocated to potatoes and placed between the potato preparation unit and the masher, one was placed between the slicing machine and the vegetable boilers and the last was sited near the pudding preparation bench.

Table II illustrates the effect on walking distances.

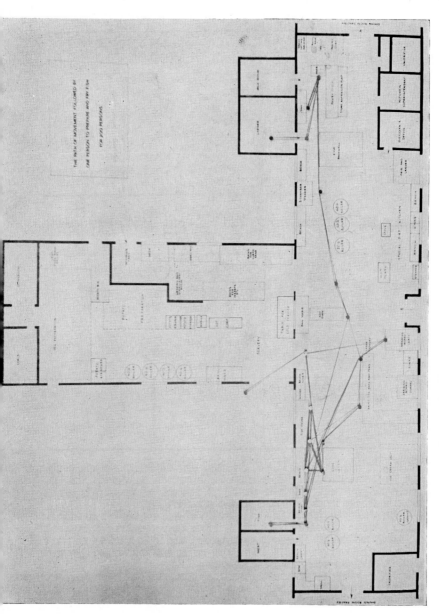

Fig. 47. Hospital Kitchen: Recommended Layout

String diagram showing path of movement of cook in preparing and frying fish for 200 persons.
A saving of 78 per cent in distance walked.

TABLE II. COMPARATIVE WALKING DISTANCES BETWEEN PREPARING AREAS
AND COOKING EPUIPMENT

From	To	Present Layout	Recommended Layout
Potato Sinks	Potato Steamers	60ft.	15ft.
Veg. Slicing M/c.	Boilers	60ft.	10ft.
Veg. Sinks	Steamer	90ft.	10ft.
Meat Bench	Boilers	20ft.	5ft.
Pasting Bench	Steamer	35ft.	20ft.

TABLE III. COMPARATIVE WALKING DISTANCES IN PERFORMANCE OF
PREPARATION OF ONE DISH

Operation	Approximate distance walked (units of thread)	
	Present Layout	Recommended Layout
1. Fried cod cutlets	1440	315
2. Bridies	1170	510
3. Bread and butter pudding	930	180
4. Soup	800	240
5. Stewed steak	450	133

6. Special diet kitchen: The observations showed that the existing area was
both too small and too remote from the remainder of the kitchen. It was
therefore recommended that it should be re-sited more centrally and connected with the block of offices in the main kitchen.

7. Pan wash-up: To retain the function of this section but to increase its
service value to the rest of the kitchen, it was recommended that it should be
re-sited more centrally. Its shelves were redesigned to be fixed round two sides
of the area and to give access from both inside and outside, so that utensils
could be collected without entering the area.

Synthetic string diagrams were made, plotting the observations of present
practice on an outline drawing of the recommended layout, modifying them
to include some replanning of the work. These diagrams were used to assess
the value of the recommendations before continuing to work out further
details of equipment or methods.

Table III illustrates the information presented by these diagrams.

Summary. The preparation, cooking and distribution of food were the main factors in this problem but the subsidiary activity of clearing up was not forgotten and was improved by the re-siting of the pan wash-up section. This clearing up had a very direct bearing on all other activities and a further improvement was made in the washing up of the container inserts that were returned empty from the wards. It was recommended that the door into the servery on the right of the kitchen should be closed and a further door made at the top of the sterilising room so that cans would move in one direction only. Dirty cans would not enter the main kitchen at all, and clean and dirty cans would not pass one another. This recommendation would have the incidental effect of curing the cross-draught in the servery area.

The investigation also covered detailed working methods and the design of equipment but no account of these can be given here.

Conclusion

No hard and fast rules can be laid down for the study of a layout problem but general lines of approach have been discussed here and it can be seen how these are applied in the example given above, which has many features common to every factory layout problem.

8

INSTALLATION

THE installation of a new method is the final stage that is needed to bring an investigation to a useful conclusion. It should always be the aim of the motion-study investigator once a method has been developed to install it immediately. It is only too easy to think that an investigation is finished when a solution to the problem has been found and tried out with an operator on an experimental set-up. There is a temptation to sit back and admire a fine piece of work and to forget that it is of no practical use whatever until it is in production. So often the final installation is postponed until a more suitable moment, or until some other changes have been made that may affect it. In this way much time and money can be wasted. For example, in the early days of motion study in this country, an assembly job was studied in an engineering works. The new method was tested and it was calculated that it would save £2,000 a year. In spite of this the installation was postponed because the designers announced that a change in manufacture was planned which would mean substituting rivets for bolts in the first operation. It seemed that this might materially upset the balance of the other operations in the proposed new method and so it was agreed to wait a little and make all the changes at the same time. When weeks ran into months and no progress had been made in the change of design, the motion-study engineer refused to wait any longer and installed the new method. This method ran for 18 months and saved £3,000 before the riveting operation was finally passed as ready for adoption. The further modification in method caused by the change from bolts to rivets proved to be much smaller than had been expected and caused very little trouble. The delay in installing the new method cost the firm £1,000 but this sum might have been four times as great if the motion-study engineer had hesitated any longer.

A more recent loss of the same type was incurred while waiting for an automatic machine to be delivered. An improvement could have been made in the hand method of production which would have saved fifty operators but because the delivery of the machine was promised in a short time the improved hand method was not installed. As a result for more than six months fifty more operators were at work than was necessary, earning an average of £3 a week each; a total loss of at least £3,750. If the cost of the installation of the motion study method had been compared with the estimated saving it would have been installed at once.

Experimenting before Installation

When a new method has been developed and details of fixtures and work-place completed, it should be tried out experimentally with the help of one of the operators who will be using it. This test should be made before the final installation of the method in its permanent place in the factory. If it is thorough, it will prevent a great many of the difficulties often experienced during the final installation.

Wherever possible, experiments with new methods should be carried out away from the main production department where the method will eventually be installed. There will inevitably be difficulties at first and the operator may feel awkward if he is asked to work among his normal companions. There will be endless jokes at his expense and he will be disturbed by the curiosity of his neighbours who will all make it their business to pass the experimental workplace to see and comment upon what is happening. It is nearly always possible to arrange for experiments to take place elsewhere, but where the method involves a large machine that cannot be moved it should be isolated within the department as far as is practicable.

Before an operator is asked to learn a new method it may be possible, in the early stages of an experiment, to try out the ideas with the help of a supervisor or chargehand who has been an operator on the job at some time in the past. This will help to show how practical the changes are. When this experimental stage is past the method is ready to go into production with a regular operator.

It is important to choose the most suitable operator to be the first on the new method. It is often suggested that it is best to train an entirely new operator who will not be prejudiced by any knowledge of the old method, but this is nearly always a mistake. The operators who are trained to use the existing method have a knowledge and experience of the work and its background which will enable them to make an invaluable contribution to the success of the new method. More important still, operators come to regard a particular job as their own property and this is an attitude to be encouraged if a stable labour force is to be maintained. It is obviously unfair to deprive an established operator of his job so that a newcomer may be trained to do the same work by a better method. It may be difficult to break old habits, but it is worth the effort and though it may be easier to train a new operator at first the later stages of training will often be longer and more difficult.

Before installation can begin there are many policy decisions to be taken and many problems to be solved. These problems are both psychological and practical and although the practical aspects are more obvious, the psychological implications are of equal or even greater importance. A merely practical approach may solve a particular difficulty at the time but unless it is based on an understanding of the psychological facts that lie behind the difficulty, ultimate harmony on the new method will not be achieved.

Arrangements for Dealing with Surplus Labour

The first of these problems is the question of the possibility of surplus labour. Experiment will show the increase in output that can be expected from each operator under the new method. If there is no shortage of material and an unlimited market for the goods this is no problem but if, as is more usual, there can be no very great increase in total output, it becomes necessary to decide how many operators can be used on the new method and what is to be done with those who will no longer be required. In times of labour shortage there is usually little practical difficulty in arranging suitable transfers to other work within the factory, but when there is already some unemployment in the district this is less easy. Even so, a reduction in intake will usually allow the ordinary wastage to absorb the surplus. Whatever changes have to be made must be made tactfully and with every consideration for the individuals concerned, but the problem must never be shirked. The interests of the individual must be balanced against the national interest. To manufacture goods using more labour than is absolutely necessary means selling those goods at unnecessarily high prices. This in its turn may mean losing customers and being compelled to reduce the labour force because of a shortage of work. This sequence of events is less likely in a sellers' market but such conditions are always short-lived and even in a sellers' market there is damage to the national interest; operators are employed unnecessarily in one factory who might be used more advantageously on other work.

This problem of surplus labour as the result of more efficient production is not, of course, new. It has arisen in the course of the centuries whenever technological improvements or new machines have been introduced and it has always caused controversy. It is perhaps more obvious and more challenging in this form because it arises out of an improvement in human efficiency rather than as a result of advances in mechanical invention. The effect upon the individual, however, is exactly the same and it is therefore essential that the difficulty should be foreseen and that plans should be made to deal with it before the improved method is installed.

Forestalling Opposition

One of the difficulties that will become most pressing at this stage may be general opposition to the new method. This will be more marked where motion study is not yet familiar to everyone and it will probably come more from the supervision and from inspectors and technical staff than from operators. From the beginning of the investigation, and even before it starts, efforts should be made on a concerted plan to forestall opposition and to build up goodwill by spreading as much knowledge as possible of the motion study techniques and methods. Some forms of opposition are particularly difficult to combat. There will always be those who do not directly oppose but who are completely unhelpful and indifferent, and others who cause trouble by disparaging the new methods and magnifying minor difficulties. It is unwise to be too much discouraged by such people or to take their criticisms too seriously but it is helpful to understand their point of view. Their behaviour is usually a very natural reaction against anything new or against anything that seems likely to upset their comfortable and well-established routine. In addition, because many motion study methods look so obvious when they are demonstrated, there is a tendency to be on the defensive and to expect criticism for not having thought of the improvement earlier. This attitude cannot be entirely prevented but a scheme of motion study propaganda and training, such as that described in Chapter 11, will help a great deal to emphasize that motion study improvements are the result of the application of complicated techniques and are not easy to make. No blame attaches therefore to anyone who has been unable to make the improvements without a knowledge of the techniques and the time to apply them.

Making Changes of Equipment and Layout

There will be certain physical changes to be made in a department before a new method can be installed. Penches or tables may have to be adjusted and changes may be called for in the arrangement of material, or in the position of machines and fixtures. On simple jobs these preparations will not normally be difficult, but even the simplest alterations should be planned in advance so that they cause as little interference with production as possible. A more complicated improvement involving a number of operators on a single operation, or on a series of operations, will need still more planning. In this case the steps in the plan must be prepared to the last detail and well in advance so that everyone concerned can know when his contribution is required. If this is not done the whole scheme may be seriously delayed as, for example, when a joiner or electrician is not available at the right time.

These physical changes may be made with the greatest possible efficiency and attention to detail but unless the individual operator's point of view is carefully considered he or she may be the cause of much ill-ease and unrest. There is always a danger, during a change of method, of interfering with those sources of satisfaction that have their origin in an operator's immediate surroundings. For example, a new piece of equipment may be quite efficient but may look rough or unfinished. This may hurt an operator's pride in his workplace. Again, if the new equipment is painted, a colour may be chosen that he dislikes or thinks unsuitable. All points of finish are particularly important when a method is installed. A good finish or attractive equipment may add to an operator's sense of prestige in the same way that an unattractive finish may spoil his satisfaction. A further point of the same type that often arises when a layout is changed, is that certain operators may be moved further from the door or the clock, so that instead of being first out at finishing time they are at a disadvantage. Such points seem trivial in themselves and it is usually difficult to discover their effect. They are not often raised by the operators but they may be the real cause of other complaints.

Maintaining Production during Installation

It will often be practicable to make changes of layout and equipment at a weekend or holiday period, to avoid interruption, but problems of another nature will arise that cannot be overcome in this way. Changes in methods and layouts will inevitably have a temporary effect upon the level of production and plans must be made to meet this difficulty. An investigation involving a number of operators will mean the re-training at this stage of those operators who have not taken part in the experiments. This will nearly always mean a temporary fall in output during the learning period, even where there are no adjustments or modifications to be made to the workplace after the job has been installed. Plans must be made to counteract this probable fall in output if the general output of the section is not to suffer. There are several possible solutions to this. Surplus production in the weeks before the installation is made may be banked as a reserve to be drawn upon in the transition period, or the production of the operator during the experimental period may be held back for the same purpose. The exact arrangement will be chosen to suit individual circumstances but it is important that the difficulty should be foreseen and that some provision should be made.

Conversely, when a new method begins to run smoothly, there is often a danger of an inadequate supply of material to each operator. This sometimes happens during the experimental period of an investigation, since it is nearly always difficult to convince those responsible that much more material will be needed than for an operator using the old method. If the improvement in method is at all considerable the operator may increase his rate of production very quickly and suddenly and to be stopped for shortage of material, or even to see that the supply is running low, just when he is getting into his stride, is upsetting to him. Several days supply should always be kept on the spot or immediately available, with arrangements for delivery of further material on call. Work should not begin until this has been settled satisfactorily.

In a motion study investigation into the work of a whole factory or department, or into a complex process involving a number of inter-dependant operations, special consideration must be given to the supply of material during the installation of new methods. There will inevitably be periods when the different operations are out of balance and where some temporary expedient must be adopted to prevent one operation from outrunning another and to allow operators to work at the new hourly output standard without fear of running out of work. Where no total increase in output is required from the new method, the problem can be solved by training only those operators who will eventually be required on the new method and gradually withdrawing the rest to other work when the newly-trained operators become proficient. This, however, is no solution where an increase in output is intended and where all the operators will eventually be needed. It will not often be possible to install all the operations simultaneously, since each group of operators in turn will need the undivided attention of the investigator while their operation is installed. In spite of this, an even flow of work from operation to operation must be maintained and no one must be discouraged by fear of shortage of material, from working at the new hourly output standard. The difficulty may sometimes be met to some extent by building up banks of work between operations, but the varying time taken to train different operators and to install different operations will inevitably cause unforeseeable variations in the flow of work. One solution to this difficulty, which has been used successfully, is to shorten the hours of those operators whose operation is outrunning the rest and to transfer them to some quite different work for the rest of the day. In this way they learn the correct hourly output standard from the beginning.

Safeguarding Inspection Standards

A further problem is that of inspection. It is always wise to increase the amount of inspection in the early days of training on a new method, but this policy has its drawbacks. There will always be a tendency for those responsible for inspection to increase their standards when they know that a method has been altered and, as they think, speeded up. They will have a very natural suspicion that any method that increases production per operator may lower the standard of work. The standard will not in fact be lowered; it is more likely to be raised; but in spite of this the percentage of rejects will probably increase. Faults that have existed but that have been overlooked under the old method will be noticed and rejected when the new method is known to have begun. Any increase in the number of rejects must be dealt with at once and thoroughly examined by the motion study investigator. Unless the matter is quickly and carefully handled and not allowed to develop, the operator will be depressed about his standard of work and may take a dislike to the new method. More serious still, motion study will tend to be generally condemned as encouraging slip-shod work. Although this is untrue it is very easy for the wrong impression to get round a factory and very damaging to future investigations. One of the possible ways of combating this difficulty at the experimental stage is to arrange for operators still working on the old method to act as a control group and to ask the inspectors to compare their work with the work of the new method operator. This will usually be enough to prove the case.

Setting Standards and Prices

Before the job goes into production the standard of output should be fixed; if possible by time study. This setting of standards presents few difficulties if no previous standard has been set, but there are many possible complications if existing standards have to be altered, especially where there is some form of payment by results.

Where a job that carries a piecework price is improved as the result of a motion study investigation that price must be revised. In most industries there is an agreement which allows for a revision of prices when a method is changed and, since a motion study investigation usually changes the method very considerably, the right to change the price is seldom challenged. There is, however, considerable difference of opinion about the basis of the new price. This point should be settled between management and workers' representatives before any motion study work is begun in a factory, and a definite policy should be laid down. It should always be part of the policy that workers derive some financial benefit from the change in method. The final results will be easier for the operators but they will inevitably have to make an extra effort to change their way of working and the change will call for considerable patience on their part. In addition, the success and smooth running of the method depends upon their co-operation. They should therefore derive some direct and immediate benefit from the change. These are minor arguments, however, compared with the fact that a correct motion study method, used by carefully trained operators, allows no opportunity to individuals to earn extra money by adopting better methods of work.

There are three possible ways of allowing workers to share in the financial benefits of improved methods. The most obvious is to give a fixed proportion of the saving to the operators. This arrangement seems equitable at first sight and is the first reaction of many managements to the problem because it makes an easy appeal to the workers when their agreement is sought. It can however lead to serious inconsistencies. While it may be satisfactory on the first improved method that is introduced, as soon as a number have been made it becomes unworkable. Increases in output may vary between such extremes as 15 per cent and 500 per cent on different jobs according to the number of movements that it has been possible either to eliminate or simplify and according to the previous efficiency of the method and the conditions of the job. Savings will usually be greater on a manual job than where a large proportion of the cycle time for each operation is controlled by a machine. It is therefore obviously unjust that a man working on a relatively efficient job yielding only a 15 per cent increase in output should get a smaller increase than a man whose job yields a 500 per cent increase. It is unlikely that the co-operative effort put into the investigation by either man bears any direct relation to the increase in output achieved. Even where differences are smaller, such an arrangement to pay a fixed proportion of savings to the worker will add substantially to the difficulties experienced by supervision in handling uneven prices.

There is a better alternative. The standard time for the new method is first established by time study as if it were a new job. The normal allowances for contingencies and fatigue are then added and finally a percentage for bonus earnings that is well above the normal percentage allowed for jobs that have not been motion studied. The amount of this percentage should be fixed before the first motion study job is installed and should be such that the operators are given every opportunity of gaining financial advantage from the change of method.

When a decision has been made on the policy to be adopted in re-setting prices there are other details to be settled. As soon as the new method begins, the old price must be cancelled and arrangements must be made to pay the operators' average earnings during the training period. There is often a temptation, especially where no very large increase in output is expected, to let the existing price stand and allow the operators to earn any extra money that they can make during the early stages of training. This is a dangerous practice, since it is very difficult to change a price once it has been applied to the new method. It will usually be found, in addition, that the old price acts as a brake on increased production after a certain point. Operators reach a stage where they are satisfied with their earnings and where they refuse to earn more. This difficulty is avoided if it is understood from the beginning that prices are cancelled as soon as a method changes. A further difficulty, however, often arises. Operators who are used to some form of payment by result may not work well when they are guaranteed their average earnings during a learning period. It may be necessary to introduce some form of financial incentive before they are ready to work to the final price. It is sometimes possible to meet this difficulty by setting a weekly price which gradually becomes more difficult until the final price is reached. This can be effective only if the weekly stages are decided beforehand and made known to the operators. The plan once agreed must be strictly adhered to if it is to be successful as an incentive.

It is important that final standards should not be set too soon. An operator will need a further period of practice to reach his full standard of output after he has learnt and mastered a new method. If piecework rates are set before this practice period is finished the potential increase in output from the new method may never be reached. The investigator should estimate the maximum output that can be expected from a new method and, setting this as a target, he should not be content until he has achieved it. The first operator on a new method will always tend to feel that the target is set too high and that it is unattainable (*see* Chapter 9) and it is the motion study investigator's business to prove that his estimate is reasonable. This will need his constant attention and it will be necessary for him to keep accurate hourly output records in the form of learning curves. If these records are accurately maintained there will be less temptation to set a final price before the operator has reached full efficiency. This close attention to records is tedious work for the investigator, but it is essential if maximum results are to be attained with piece work rates accurately and correctly set.

Where there is no form of payment by results, operators may still be allowed to derive some financial benefit from the new method. This can be arranged as an additional award given in two stages. The first increase is made when the training period begins and the second when training is complete, but only after the standard output has been maintained over a period of weeks (*see* Chapter 9).

When the operators' claim for some financial benefit from the improvements has been met, there are other claimants for benefit. The management can reasonably expect some repayment for the trouble and expense that the change has involved and finally some benefit should be passed on to the consumer in the form of a better or cheaper product. This in turn may eventually mean increased business for the company and benefits for all concerned in the enterprise.

Handing Over to the Shop Supervision

While a motion study job is being installed the investigator must take charge himself and accept full responsibility for all that is done, since the installation of the new method is the final stage in his investigation. This stage, however, is complete when the method is running smoothly and the time has then arrived for the responsibility to be handed on to the shop supervisors, who will rarely be at all anxious to accept it any sooner than they need. To make sure that there is no delay over this the investigator should fix a definite date for the final handing over and he should make every possible effort to complete the installation in time.

Before the job is handed over, careful provision must be made for the maintenance of the correct method in the future. This will include detailed instruction sheets (*see* example Fig. 48) for each operation, showing the operators' movements, the equipment required for the job and the workplace layout. The instruction sheet must also give information about the number of operators needed to produce a specific output, details of the standard of output expressed as hourly, daily and weekly figures, and piecework prices where they exist.

As the job will have to be maintained over a long period, arrangements must be made for the training of future operators when existing operators leave and are replaced by others, or when the production programme expands, requiring more operators. The type of training given will depend on the facilities available. If there is a training department, special films, diagrams and models, or other teaching aids can be developed. If only a very simple scheme is possible, full written and verbal instructions should be given to the shop supervisor who is in charge of the work, so that adequate training can be given in the department. These instructions should include diagrams of all the relevant movements involved in the work and any other teaching aids that are justified by the scope of the job.

The Report

Once the job is handed over to the shop supervision, a report on the whole investigation should be written and filed for future reference. This may seem unnecessary where the method is running smoothly but it may be found very useful later when many of the details have faded from the mind. The old method in particular will be forgotten very quickly indeed if it is

F R O N T S

OPERATION - ATTACH FRONT FACINGS.

**Equipment
per operator.** 1 Singer 241 type Flatbed machine on special frame.
Guide, swing out type.
Single frame for rail for work to be done, at back
of machine table extension.
Stand for facings, attached to machine table extension.
Movable frame with rail to collect completed work,
operated by foot pedal.
Flap on machine table operated with movable frame.
Spare single frame to hold left fronts while rights
being worked.

**Equipment
per team.** Rack and rails for work to be done.
Rack and rails for completed work.

Layout.

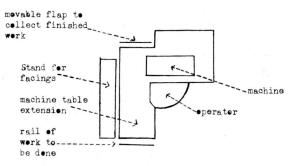

movable flap to
collect finished
work

Stand for
facings

machine table
extension

rail of
work to
be done

machine

operator

Thread. Top - 30 6-cord left twist
Below - 60 6-cord left twist

Stitch. 8 per inch.

**Seam and
turnings.** Single line of stitching, $\frac{3}{8}$" from edge

**Supply of
work.** Right fronts on rack from eyeletter, wrongside up. 1-30.
Left fronts on rack from labeller, right side up 30-1.

Facings placed on rack with left fronts. Both left and
right facings wrongside up 1-30.

Method.

Right fronts.

1. Obtain right and left fronts and facings from racks
behind operators (keep rails in the buddle).

2. Put left fronts on spare rail and place
rail with right fronts (eyelet side) on

Contd. overleaf

FIG. 48. FIRST PAGE OF INSTRUCTION SHEET FOR A MACHINING
OPERATION (*See Report No. 6*, Appendix B).

not recorded.   This report of the development of the method will be particularly helpful when any future change in design involves a modification of the motion study method.   A well-written report includes not only a description of old and new methods and an account of the arguments that led to the development of the new method, but also an account of those experiments which were tried and rejected.   This will prevent any time being wasted in the future on the same points.

The report may also have value from the trainer's point of view.   It may be suitable material for supervisors' courses or for the training of investigators.

Follow-up

It is not enough to develop a method, install it and hand it over.   During the first months of its independent existence it will need a regular check to see that it continues to run smoothly.   The investigator should see that he is kept informed about its progress and that output figures are given to him weekly.   He should also ask to be told at once of any changes in personnel or in the design of the product but he should not depend on this. He should, as a matter of routine, visit the job fairly frequently at first, reducing his visits gradually until they are made at quarterly intervals only.   It is almost impossible to make sure that all changes and troubles are reported.   Some quite major changes in method may arise out of a series of incidents themselves so insignificant that they do not seem worth mentioning.   The only safe way of ensuring the maintenance of correct methods is to check them regularly.

Conclusion

The installation of a motion study method is as essential a part of the investigation as its development.   Because it is often troublesome and less interesting it is frequently left half finished, but if motion study is to assist production to the fullest extent the investigator must not be discouraged by the difficulties of installation but must aim at leaving the job in such a condition that it is not only easily maintained by the shop supervision but also yielding the maximum output.   Some investigators have been known to be entirely satisfied with a 25 per cent increase in output where exactly the same method might have shown a 50 per cent increase if as much attention had been paid to the installation of the method as was given to its development.

9

INCENTIVES

AT the present time a great deal of thought is being given to the problem of incentives in work. Detailed studies of certain aspects of the problem have been made by scientific investigators but a comprehensive scientific study of the whole field has yet to be undertaken. In the absence of such complete knowledge, the present chapter is offered as a contribution to this study, particularly where it is related to the work of the motion study investigator. It can make no claim to be the result of a thorough scientific research but it is based on a wide industrial experience over a period of years and aims at assisting those who must make decisions now in the light of existing knowledge, however inadequate that may be.

The term incentive is used to cover all the factors that influence a worker's desire to produce. The word has too often been used very narrowly to mean some form of payment by results. A system of payment by results can certainly act as an incentive but it is only one of many possible incentives.

It is obvious that there are more reasons for working than the desire to earn money. A man digging his dahlia bed or practising a golf stroke may work very hard and persistently with no prospect of a financial reward. He knows other satisfactions in his work than the hope of material advantage.

There are many sources of satisfaction in any work which can act as incentives to stay on the job or to work hard, but these are only potential incentives and their actual incentive effect varies from time to time and as a result of changing economic conditions and even of changing fashions. Again, its effect on any one individual may vary at different stages in his life, quite apart from external circumstances. For example, an ambitious young man will often be much more interested in work offering chances of advancement than in a job promising security, though the same man, in middle life, would normally react in exactly the opposite way.

Since individual reactions are so different, it follows that it is important that every management should create as many potential incentives as possible and that each should be applied to the fullest advantage. It is not always easy to select for a particular job the operator who will react most favourably to the incentives that it offers. In practice no two people will get exactly the same satisfaction from the same work. One man's reason for choosing a particular factory or working hard at a particular job may make no appeal at all to another man who will find some quite different incentive in the same work. An incentive may even act as a deterrent to the wrong person and what attracts one worker may be positively disliked by another.

The problem of incentives in industry can be divided into two distinct parts. The first part is made up of those influences which get a worker out of his home and into the factory to do work of any sort. The second covers the more complicated influences which persuade him to do his work to the best of his ability when he is there. The first in fact, takes the horse to the water; the second induces him to drink. It is of the very greatest importance that these two groups of incentives should be carefully analysed and fully understood.

In examining possible sources of satisfaction the incentives that make men go to work must be considered before the inducements to work hard and well.

Before a man reaches his bench in a particular factory he has three decisions to make; first that he will go to work at all, second that he will do a particular kind of work, and third that he will work in that factory.

Incentives which make Men go to Work

There are three main reasons why people work at all. The first is the need to earn enough money to support themselves and their dependents at the standard of living that they regard as a minimum. At first glance it would seem that this must always be the main reason for going to work, since for the vast majority there is no alternative. Where, however, there is an alternative such as adequate private means or a sudden acquisition of wealth, perhaps from a large football pool dividend or the Irish Sweepstake, it is noticeable that very few people stop work altogether. The winner of a football pool dividend may give up his original job and take up other work that he prefers but he will hardly ever choose to do nothing at all. He will regard his private means not as an opportunity to live in idleness but as a chance to do the work he likes; to choose his job. In the same way, very few girls nowadays, whose families are willing to support them, are content to stay at home instead of taking an outside job.

There are, in fact, other very strong reasons for working. One of these is that it is the normal thing to do. This means that most people are at work every day and that therefore the best way of getting outside the narrow confines of the immediate family circle and making friends and finding wider interests is to go to work too. This is an incentive to work which influences women perhaps more than men. It is not just a case of exchanging unpaid work at home for paid work outside. For example, girls often choose work at a financial disadvantage because they see an opportunity to meet a particular group of men. Again, married women may be very glad of a part-time job, even if the financial gain is not very great, because it gets them out of the house. They like the company that they find in the workshop. This was very obvious in war-time among part-time married women workers, particularly where a factory was near a new housing estate or a scattered suburban district where normal social amenities were inadequate. Among men too, social contacts at work are regarded as important and there is often something of a club atmosphere about a well run workshop.

There are also ethical or religious reasons for choosing work rather than idleness. To work is considered meritorious and good, while to be idle is felt to be anti-social or positively bad. Most people feel ashamed of not having enough to do and prefer to create the impression that they are busy whether it is true or not. They may talk of work as a curse but they are not happy if they are idle for too long. There may also be a feeling of duty to the community; that everyone should contribute something to the common good; a dislike of being a drone in a busy hive. The post war outcry against "spivs" was, in part, a manifestation of this feeling.

These are the main general incentives to do work of some sort but it is necessary to elaborate them further to see why a man chooses a particular kind of work in a particular place or factory.

There are many reasons for taking up a particular type of work. Chance and opportunity or the absence of either may play a large part. Not everyone is in a position to choose even broadly what he will do. Circumstances force him into a particular line as the only type of work available and once he has started work economic reasons may prevent him from changing. The more fortunate may be able to choose their line because it interests them and because they have certain abilities that make it particularly suitable. Others again have such definite inclinations and talents that a particular type of work is to them a vocation and they will overcome all kinds of obstacles to reach their objective.

Many boys and girls have suffered in the past from a lack of knowledge about the occupations less usual in their district or from the type of family pride that forces a boy into clerical work as being more respectable than the farm or factory work he may prefer. A farmer's son, on the other hand, may be prevented from becoming an engineer or a clerk because there is no one else to inherit the farm. Very often, even now, boys or girls will be forced to take up work that is not best suited to them because the occupation they might prefer would mean living away from home or accepting a lower starting wage.

When a boy or girl or a man or woman have decided upon a particular occupation, the question arises as to where the work is to be done. Again the choice may be limited by the local opportunities and the economic and personal situation of the family, or a particular factory may be chosen because it is near home or because it is convenient to work the same hours as another member of the family who is already employed there. These reasons for choosing a factory are outside the control of the factory managements and need not be discussed here. There are however many incentives to choose a particular factory which are within the control of a factory management.

They may not all appeal to everyone and their relative importance will depend upon the economic circumstances of the moment and the tastes of the individual. They arise out of and are dependent upon the management policy of the firm which manifests itself in many different ways to those inside and outside the organisation.

Within the framework of the general management policy there are certain features which may act directly as incentives:

Good Human Relations. One of the most important incentives to come to work in a factory and to remain at work there is a good relationship between management and work people. A good relationship can only grow out of a careful consideration and handling of all the individual problems that arise in the day-to-day work of the factory. It is not easy to build up and it is very quickly lost but it is worth a great deal of effort to achieve it. It can only be based on a sound general management policy of treating each worker as an individual and not as a clock number or a 'hand.' In all dealings with individuals there must be a standard of fairness and justice and that standard must be consistently maintained. A reputation for fairness is one of the greatest incentives to recruiting labour and keeping it at work. This policy must not only be laid down; it must be implemented. The higher management must make certain that it is understood and followed right down the line of responsibility from manager to chargehand. Departmental supervisors should be given definite instruction about this side of the personnel policy of the firm and they should be taught how to carry it out. The attitude of the supervisor is accepted by the average worker as the attitude of the management. His supervisor is his chief contact with the management. A bad supervisor therefore can undo all the efforts made higher up the management line. For this reason, if for no other, supervisors should be carefully selected and trained and kept fully informed of all details of management policy. As part of their training the T.W.I. Job Relations programme may be used as a beginning. It must not be expected to act as anything more than a beginning. The teaching of good human relations to supervisors obviously cannot be completed in ten hours instruction, however good that instruction may be. There must be a fuller scheme devised to suit the needs of the particular factory and to go beyond the limits of the T.W.I. Job Relations programme.

The larger the factory the greater is the need to establish good human relationships. In a small factory of from fifty to a hundred employees, each worker is known to everyone and appreciated as a person with individual characteristics. His contribution to the work of the whole is obvious and it is easy to give him the feeling of belonging to a group and at the same time to allow him to retain his status as a person. As the size of the unit increases, this becomes more difficult and it needs a more definite effort to ensure that workers are not only treated as individuals but are also given as much information as possible about the organisation so that they may feel that they have a real personal share in its work. Here all forms of joint consultation can play a very valuable part but they must be properly organised and used in the right spirit.

If the management policy of a firm succeeds in establishing and maintaining good human relations, a happy, contented and reasonable working group will grow up and this will do more than anything else to attract the right type of labour and keep it at work. It will also make easier the solving of all the inevitable day to day human problems that arise even in a well run factory.

A Fair Wages Policy. A policy of high wages might seem to be the most effective means of attracting labour and of maintaining an efficient labour force but, although high wages are a powerful incentive to get people to work in a particular factory, mere high wages are not enough. It is even more important, provided that the rates paid are not excessively low, that the wages system should be equitable. This means that a wages policy to be effective in attracting and holding labour must be linked with good general industrial relations and a good personnel policy well administered. To achieve equity the different grades of employees must be clearly defined and distinct. The grading should be based on some scientific measure of the work and responsibility involved in each job. In the United States, Job Evaluation following upon a thorough Job Analysis has been used very successfully as a basis for the grading of jobs. Several organisations in this country are using it in the same way but any widespread application is difficult in our highly organised old established industries where there is a traditional wage structure and complicated machinery for wage negotiations. Most managements can only make such innovations in their wage policies as come within the general agreements that cover their industry as a whole.

If a wages policy is to be a successful incentive, a decision must be reached about the basis of payment; whether this is to be time or output. This is a very controversial point and it is not possible here to go into all the details of the various methods of payment by results and the advantages and disadvantages of each. The incentive effect of any payment by results system is more directly connected with an operator's particular job and is discussed later in this chapter under the section on incentives which make people work well.

Security of Employment. The knowledge that a firm can offer security of employment will act as a powerful incentive to some people to join that firm. Security may not have seemed very important immediately after the end of the war, when work was abnormally easy to obtain, but it will have an increasing value as an incentive as industry settles down. In a condition of full employment it may not be as strong an incentive as during a trade depression under the threat of unemployment, but it will always appeal to the more stable type of worker who usually makes the most valuable employee.

Chances of Advancement. Clear lines of promotion and opportunities to learn new and better jobs will always attract a certain type of worker. If a company can build up a reputation for offering good opportunities for self-improvement and chances of advancement to those who take those opportunities, it will be in a position to attract the best and rarest type of worker, the man or woman who is ambitious and willing and able to take responsibility. This is not an incentive that will appeal to everyone. It is a long term incentive offering no immediate advantages but it makes a greater appeal to some very good types of worker than any of the more obvious incentives and it is worth the attention of every management for this reason.

Suitable Hours of Work. The number of working hours and their distribution over the days of the week can act as an incentive to work in a particular factory. The first few managements who offered a five-day week were able to attract labour, particularly female labour, more easily than their neighbours who still worked on Saturday mornings. The difficulty always experienced in arranging shift work shows how unpopular hours of work can have the opposite effect.

Good Working Conditions. There is an incentive value in good working conditions. Pleasant workrooms with good heating, lighting and ventilation and factories which look attractive from the outside may offer a certain inducement to come to work there though it is easy to exaggerate the significance of working conditions. Their positive value is not very great, though the reverse side of the picture, the deterrent effect of very poor conditions, has some importance. In the past, some industries such as textiles have acquired a bad name for conditions of work which has been felt to be a hindrance in recruiting labour. The bad reputation is often not deserved, being a legacy from the past, but opinion can act as a deterrent whether or not it is based on fact. It would therefore seem that a management must not only maintain good conditions but must also see that they are given good publicity. It will help to dispel local prejudice if all applicants and everyone sent by the local employment exchange for work are shown the actual conditions of the factory and the work that they have been submitted for and are not merely interviewed in the employment office. Some firms have held successful "open" days on which anyone interested can go through the factory and see conditions for themselves. Where these conditions are adequate but offer no positive inducement some innovation such as, for example, the introduction of an unusual colour scheme will do more to improve a reputation than the mere maintenance of a good general standard. Employees will talk about it outside the factory. Ordinary good conditions arouse no comment.

Employee Services and Welfare Measures. Good canteens, sports clubs, recreational facilities, ambulance rooms and other welfare projects are a definite inducement to work in a particular factory. Here again their importance as an incentive is often exaggerated but no management can afford to ignore them. There is no doubt that they do attract a certain type of worker and, if they are well run, they contribute to the good working atmosphere of the factory. They are also a source of satisfaction to those who choose their work because of the desire to be one of a social group.

The incentive value of welfare facilities must not be over emphasized. It should only be their secondary aim. They must first be soundly administered both economically and from the point of view of human relations. There have been many cases where services provided by a factory would have been better and more economical if they were run by other authorities for the benefit of a wider community.

Reputation of the Firm's Product. If a firm's product is well-known or of a particularly high quality, this may be an incentive to some people. During the war many workers found an immense satisfaction in working in a factory which was making a famous type of bomber or tank. In normal times the reputation of the firm's product can give something of the same satisfaction. It is stimulating to a worker to see his product displayed in a shop window or advertised on a local hoarding for everyone to see. This may not be an important single incentive but, if other incentives exist, it adds to their force. Many firms who might make use of it to attract and hold labour do not exploit it as much as they might.

All incentives that arise out of the management policy of a firm can play their part in making a worker choose a particular firm. They will make a different appeal to each individual and some may make no appeal at all to some types of people. No management, however, can afford to ignore any of them. They will exist in some form whether they are recognised or not and there is a danger that uncontrolled they may degenerate and have a deterrent effect; not only failing to attract labour but actively keeping it away.

The first of the two main groups of incentives, those which get the worker out of his home and into the factory, have now been examined and it remains to consider the influences that play upon him inside the factory and persuade him to work to the best of his ability; the sources of satisfaction that are inherent in his actual work.

Incentives to Work Well

It is at this point in the scheme of incentives that the motion study investigator ceases to be an onlooker. He must understand the broader incentives but he has not much power to influence their application. He is, however, actively concerned with the application of incentives inside the factory where they are directly connected with a worker's job. Since many incentives are inherent in the job itself, he must know what he is doing when he changes a method or he will run the risk of taking something of incentive value out of the job and putting in nothing to take its place. This will affect the results that he will get from a new method and he will have trouble with the operators who will tend to prefer the old method with its incentive to the new method without it. An operator may himself be quite unconscious of an incentive that has influenced him and, if it is removed, he may be unable to explain what he has lost. The motion study investigator may therefore have to make his own analysis of the situation without any help from the operator. On the other hand, it will often increase the satisfaction that a worker obtains from his job if its incentive possibilities are explained to him.

Although it is generally agreed that other factors than the immediate pay packet influence the choice of employment, very little attention has been given to non-financial incentives to work well. Payment by results is generally advocated as the only way of inducing workers to produce more when in fact the financial reward is only one of a number of incentives. Indeed, except in the case of straight piecework with no guaranteed minimum wage, an arrangement uncommon today, the financial incentive has less effect upon the decision to work well than it has upon the more fundamental decision to go out to work at all or to choose a particular type of work and a particular factory. The economic pressure is less since minimum needs are often satisfied by the basic wage and a bonus for additional production may be regarded as extra money to be spent on less necessary goods and services. This money may or may not be worth the extra effort that is needed to obtain it.

Before discussing financial incentives and the merits and drawbacks of payment by results as a means of increasing output, there are many non-financial incentives to be considered. These sources of satisfaction will exist independently of any scheme of piecework or payment by results.

Certain jobs contain special sources of satisfaction which are not common to other work but there are some which are found in many different types of jobs. The order of their importance will vary from job to job and each operator will be satisfied or dissatisfied with them, or indifferent to them, according to his individual temperament. Something which is a great source of satisfaction to one operator may positively irritate another.

Quantity. There is often a great satisfaction to be gained from seeing finished work pile up. This can be appreciated by anyone who has done a dull job such as addressing a large number of envelopes, darning a basket of stockings or chopping firewood. The growth of the pile of finished work is an incentive to make it grow even faster. This is a satisfaction which is quite independent of any material reward and it plays a powerful part in industry, especially where the work consists of a constantly repeated short cycle of movements. It can be seriously diminished in line or conveyor production where each finished part moves at once to the next operator.

The sight of a pile of finished pieces may be the particular satisfaction of operating a press. It may seem more efficient in some cases to allow the pieces to fall directly from the press on to a belt to be conveyed to the next operation at once instead of removing them to a pile at one side, but because a source of satisfaction to the operator has been eliminated, such an improvement may not achieve the increase in output that is expected from it. The visible growing pile was an incentive to the operator and its removal may have made him lose interest. A suitable substitute for the lost satisfaction might perhaps be found by introducing a column with an automatic marker operated by each stroke of the press. This might help to restore interest.

This quantity incentive appears in another form in the presentation of material to the operator. The size of the pile of unfinished work may either be an incentive to the operator or may discourage him. An over large pile may be overpowering but too small a pile may make him feel that material is scarce and cause him to decrease his effort. Between these two extremes a supply based on the standard output figure for a limited period will provide the best incentive; enough material perhaps for an hour's work. The figure will vary in different circumstances and, in deciding it, the motion study investigator must consider the particular type of material and product and the effect on the individual operator.

Quality. There is a satisfaction to be gained from the quality of workmanship; from the thought, effort and skill that an operator puts into his work. This may be quite independent of the nature of the finished product. It is easy in thinking of quality to consider only the work of the skilled craftsman but the quality satisfaction is not confined to skilled work. The window cleaner may take as much pleasure in the shine that he puts upon a window as the craftsman in the work of producing a fine piece of furniture.

In an engraving department it was observed, on occasions, that certain operators engraving figures on black material would, as they completed a plate, cover it with chalk or polish it. This was not essential for inspection but it allowed them to admire their handiwork. Although it called for extra movements, it would probably have been unwise to interfere with it since it gave the operators a satisfaction in the quality of their workmanship.

During the development period of a new method the introduction of this type of quality satisfaction may be made deliberately. A dirty unpleasant job such as cleaning a car or a machine may be made more attractive by the use of new polishing techniques but these will be more effective if the work is done in sections so that the constant comparison between the clean and the dirty sections will be an incentive to further effort.

Speed of Movement. Many people take pleasure in moving quickly and enjoy working under conditions which allow quick movements. To them anything which prevents speed is a serious source of irritation and frustration. This can be seen in its simplest form in the annoyance caused to a fast walker by a crowded pavement or a slow companion. In industry, one speed satisfaction lies in the power to control the pace, to work in short bursts of great activity interspersed with slower spells or periods of inactivity. Some forms of work make variations in speed very difficult by controlling it within definite limits. In conveyor assembly work for example, each operator must work at the pace of the slowest and there is a constant speed which rarely gives the greatest satisfaction to anyone.

The satisfaction to be obtained from speed of movement is independent of the satisfaction of reaching and passing a set standard of output or the satisfaction to be gained from exceeding an hourly production target. Very often those who like to work fast will produce no more in a given period than slower workers. They will work very fast for a time, until they have reached some private production figure of their own and will then rest for the remainder of the period. Their satisfaction is not in exceptional output; in setting up a production record; it is kinaesthetic. They enjoy the sensation of fast movement. They feel frustrated and ill at ease on work that is restricted and inactive and they will not tolerate a fine job involving slow controlled movements and a high degree of accuracy.

Rhythm of Movement. The actual movements that make up a method of work can be a source of satisfaction in themselves because of the rhythm they develop. Many operators obtain a real physical satisfaction from a smooth flow of co-ordinated well-accented movements. This satisfaction will be found in very many motion study methods but particularly in short cycle operations where the path of movement is simple. Operators who particularly enjoy a rhythm in their work will not find a short cycle job dull.

Physical Activity. One of the sources of satisfaction most frequently eliminated in the change over to a motion study method is the physical activity demanded by certain types of work. Some people, particularly when they are young, have an immense amount of surplus physical energy which they like to expend upon their work. On the other hand, most operators dislike great exertion and the motion study investigator should never hesitate to eliminate as much heavy work as possible, wherever he finds it. There will always be some work which calls for energy and it can be reserved for the minority who really enjoy using their strength. The expenditure of physical effort is not a source of satisfaction to the majority, except for occasional short spells in special circumstances, but the few who find it satisfying must be remembered and provided for when a method is improved.

Personal Prestige. Most people react favourably to anything that adds to their personal prestige, either in their own eyes or in the opinion of others. From babyhood onwards, people glow with satisfaction when anyone praises them or thinks well of their actions. Children always want to be noticed and to have their importance recognised and, if they consider they are not being given enough attention, they will do their best to attract it. Adults are not as open about their feelings as children but they are equally anxious to obtain attention and approval. This desire for prestige can often be satisfied in a factory job if those responsible for planning realise its importance. All executives who are dealing with subordinates should remember this. A foreman, in his dealings with his operators, should remember how important it is to give praise where praise is due and blame where blame is due. Workers very soon lose interest if their supervisors treat them with indifference.

In addition to the attitude of the supervisor or the executive to the worker there are often certain definite sources of prestige in the job itself or which can be introduced into the job. It is not possible to make a complete list but the following are some that have given satisfaction to many operators.

There is an almost universal tendency among workers to want a workplace or a machine that can be identified as their own. They feel that it adds to their personal prestige. This desire is recognised more in the United States than in Great Britain. There, such workplaces as desks, lifts and booking office windows in railway stations are labelled with the clerk or operator's name for everyone to see. More might be done in this way in this country.

The product itself may add to an operator's feeling of importance. Some operators obtain a great deal of satisfaction from working on a product that is obviously useful. An example of this is the dialmarker who maintained that his work was the most important operation in the whole process of making an instrument, because it was the first part seen by a customer and because, without it, the instrument was useless. He was able to build up his own importance in this way and he took a real pride in his work. An operator's pride can often be stimulated if the use and importance of his product are explained to him and if he is able to identify his own contribution to the finished whole.

During the war many exhibitions were held inside factories to demonstrate the finished product to the workers who made the components. It was very often found that the workers took an increased interest in their work and worked much better when they realised that they were making, for example, parts of radar equipment and not merely turning out pieces of metal shaped to a particular size. An example of this came during the war from the training department of a large industrial concern in this country. The trainees were working on small parts for equipment which could not be described to them because it was then on the secret list. Although they were told of the importance of this work in general terms, when the job of assembling dummy rifle bullets for use by the Home Guard was brought into the department, all the girls wanted to do that work. They knew the other was really more important and that the bullets were dummies and, in addition, that the job was less interesting to do, but they could talk about it at home and it made them feel of some account. A further extension of this source of satisfaction is obtained by an operator working on a much advertised product which has a good name. This reputation not only gets him to come to work as we have seen above, but it also makes him take a pride in the quality of his workmanship. He feels a reflected glory from the reputation of the product and a responsibility for it.

Many people enjoy handling powerful machines such as aeroplanes or high-powered motor cars because they are able to feel that the power of the machine is transferred to themselves. This is a further example of the prestige satisfaction. If an operator seems to be obtaining this type of satisfaction from his machine and it is necessary to alter it in any way, the satisfaction must be provided by some other means. In a certain press shop in an engineering works where the existing machines were large and noisy and gave the impression of great power, a new type of machine was introduced. These new machines were smaller and comparatively silent, although each exerted a pressure four times greater than the old type. At first all the operators believed that the larger machines were more powerful and they were therefore more popular than the others. When it was demonstrated that this was a mistaken idea, everyone began to prefer the smaller machines and to want to work on them instead of remaining on the old type. The same kind of satisfaction may be found in operating a special machine that is the only one of its kind or in using a device that stands out in some way from the rest of the equipment in the department. Many examples can be quoted of satisfaction derived from operating a unique machine. In one case an operator had for many years used a special machine which was much larger than the others and was the type of machine that visitors were brought to see. During the war, work was maintained on it but at the normal pre-war piecework rates. The operator was offered the chance of being temporarily transferred to one of the wartime departments where he could have earned greatly increased wages but, although he knew that after the war he would get his old job back and there was no lack of security, he refused the opportunity as he could not bear to think of someone else getting the prestige value of the unique machine that he considered to be his own.

Variety. Variety of work does not appeal to everyone. Some operators like to do the same thing all the time and dislike any form of variety. There are many more people of this type than is often realised. As a group they do not dislike monotonous work though much unnecessary sympathy is often wasted on them. They are perhaps only too willing to like an apparently monotonous job because they do not have to give very much attention to it and are free either to think of something else or to allow their minds to rest. They obtain the necessary incentive to work well from some other source of satisfaction.

A further group of operators like variety in a job provided that they control it themselves. When they feel a need for it they are able to find it by noticing small points of difference, for example, between one piece of material and the next, but it must not obtrude itself when it is not wanted. There are many jobs which appear full of subtle variety to those who look for it but which can be considered either pleasantly unvaried by those who would be irritated and worried by variety or positively monotonous by those who want a constant obvious change of work and are not satisfied by small variations in pattern or method. An example of this comes from a clothing factory. Among the machinists one girl found the work entirely monotonous because the product was always the same. Another, on the same work, found a perpetual satisfaction in the changing designs and colours of the materials. A third saw the variety of colour and pattern, but preferred to ignore it so that she might attain the thought-free repetition that she preferred. She was merely irritated if one design needed more careful handling than another. The first girl was indifferent to variety in colour and design, wanting the broader variety of changes of work; the second made the best of the variety that the job offered, and the third shunned variety in any form.

Within the group of workers who love variety in its broader and more obvious forms and for its own sake are those who like the unexpected and welcome interruptions which would be extremely irritating to those who prefer an unchanging routine. Others again cannot settle to routine work, even where it is broken up by irregular interruptions. They are only satisfied when they are constantly moving from one type of work to another. They dislike repeating any one job or forming habits.

The variety satisfaction is inherent in some jobs. The attitude of the operator may increase or diminish its effect but it can arise directly out of the nature of the work. There may be little variety inherent in an entirely repetitive small operation such as the single pressing operation required to make a simple cigarette tin. But at the other end of the scale, such work as that of a jobbing shop in an engineering works offers infinite variety. In the jobbing shop no two operations are the same and there are a large number of different products. In between these extremes, every type of work offers a different amount of variety satisfaction. It must always be remembered, however, that not all variety is a source of satisfaction. While it is true that the variation found in some work can be irritating or stimulating according to the attitude of the worker, there is a certain kind of variety which is a source of irritation and frustration to almost every type of operator. It is found in work which demands unceasing concentration of thought and attention but which does not occupy the mind quite fully. A job such as the mending of worsteds is an example of this. Pieces are examined and mended away from the loom and although the mender will be rectifying only about six well-known types of fault, because of the variety in weave and design she must think about every stitch and follow each thread of the design. Her attention must never wander but the work is not sufficiently interesting to hold it without some considerable effort of will. She will need other incentives if she is to enjoy her work and keep up a good standard.

The variety satisfaction offered by any one job may arise out of the varied nature of the product itself or from the number of different operations performed by each operator. This type of variety can be controlled to some extent. During the war, as the result of introducing unskilled labour into the factories there was a tendency to break every job down to its simplest units so that often an operator was only assembling one part and then passing it on to the next operator. This, carried to excess, is bad motion study practice, not only because it means extra movements in picking up and putting away but also because it reduces scope for variety of movement. An instance of this was seen during the study of the making up of a garment. The process had been broken down into seventeen operations performed by seventeen different girls. The motion study method built it up into four operations and arranged the girls in teams of four to do the whole job between them. These four operations properly studied showed an increase in output of 55 per cent. Part of this increase was due to the fact that the operators greatly preferred the more varied work and felt that they were each taking a larger share in the whole product.

There is a further possible source of variety in the movements made by individual operators but, in practice, operators who have worked at one job for any considerable period do not vary their movements from cycle to cycle. In a method that has not been motion studied there is often a great variation between one girl and another but this does not affect individuals since each girl has her own set of movements which she usually repeats without variation. To alter such a set of movements merely for the sake of variety is rarely worth while. Most operators find that constant alteration on a repetition job is much more fatiguing than the development of one habit and rhythm which demands no thought once it is established. They therefore decide upon the method that they think is the best and most comfortable and repeat it indefinitely. Motion study does not, in fact, make their work more monotonous individually, though it is often accused of doing so. It merely standardises a method between one operator and another. There is less variety of movement between operators in any section or department engaged on the same work but the effect upon the individual operator is simply to change a personal habit for a standard set of movements which can be adapted where necessary to suit individual peculiarities.

One further source of variety in a job may be found in its external conditions. These may include the attitude of supervisors, variations in the demand for production or the provision of artificial variety, such as the morning cup of tea or "Music While You Work" at certain periods of the day. "Music While You Work" may not do all that is sometimes claimed for it, but it can often be used successfully to add interest to work which contains little inherent variety.

The motion study investigator should remember that variety is more important to some operators than to others and in establishing a new method of work he should find some means of introducing opportunities for variety if it is, or might become, a significant source of satisfaction to the operator with whom he is working.

Output Targets. It should be a recognised practice in modern industry to set a standard output figure and use it as a production target. This is often a very effective means of obtaining a required output. Its effects can be seen in their most obvious form in the works canteen. It is true to say that the only department in most factories that is never late on its production schedule is the canteen. It is virtually unknown for workpeople to arrive in the canteen at lunchtime and be told that dinner will not be ready for another half-hour. There is normally no payment by results in canteen work and the labour is only too often of the type that, because of difficult domestic circumstances, is very irregular in its attendance. Absenteeism and bad time-keeping is therefore as great a problem as in a manufacturing department but the knowledge that dinner must be ready by a certain time, whatever the difficulties, is a very strong incentive.

During the war, group production targets were used very widely. They were effective for a period in each case until the novelty began to fail. This will always tend to happen especially if the target is set for the whole department or works and is only remotely connected with the work of individual operators. The nearer the target comes to the operator the more lasting will be its effect. If it is set for each operator or for very small groups of operators and its importance is continually emphasised by the supervisor concerned, it can have a permanent effect.

It is very important that the operator should fully understand what is the standard expected of him and work evenly towards it. It is much easier to maintain a good standard of output if the target for the day or week is split up into smaller targets for each hour of the day or for some other short period. Any motorist will appreciate the effect of hourly targets. On a long journey where time is short and he is scheduled to reach his destination at a definite time a driver will set himself the target of averaging a certain number of miles each hour. Unless he checks his achievement at hourly intervals he may find this average difficult to maintain. It depends upon extra concentration in one hour to make up for the miles lost in the previous hour.

In setting targets for operators it is important that each should know the target figure for the week, the day and the hour. The hourly figure is the most important since hourly production must inevitably vary because of tea breaks and other interruptions and time lost in one hour must be made up in the next. The target must be such that the operator feels that it is possible to reach it. If it is too high and he finds that he can never attain it, it will be a source of irritation rather than an incentive. On the other hand, too low a target will be reached too easily and may cause the operator to be content with too small an output. A compromise between these extremes must be found in a target which will give a sense of achievement if it is passed but which is not too difficult to reach.

It is also important that operators believe that a target is reasonable. This is a difficulty in teaching a new method as there is no visible proof at this stage that the target set is attainable. It is probably much higher than the old method target and it is difficult for the operator to believe that the alteration in method will have such a tremendous effect. For this reason he will take much longer to complete his training period than any subsequent operator using the same method. An instance of this occurred in a laundry. A girl was producing an average of twenty-two articles an hour working according to the old method and this was already a much higher figure than the output of any other operator on the same work. The target for the motion study method was thirty-eight an hour and she achieved it eventually after nine weeks of training and practice. After this she maintained an average of thirty-eight an hour, very frequently producing as many as forty-two in single hours. She continued to do so for six months until she left the laundry. Her successor reached the figure of forty-two in an hour after only two days of training. She knew the target was reasonable. The motive for maintaining or attempting to exceed a target output figure will vary with different operators. Some will feel a desire to achieve the standard for its own sake while others will be affected by external considerations such as the fear of losing their jobs or the hope of attracting favourable attention and the chance of promotion.

The incentive effect of output targets, the last of the common non-financial incentives to be examined here, leads on to a consideration of financial incentives.

Financial Incentives. The financial incentive to work well is probably the strongest single incentive though it may not be as powerful as a combination of other incentives. The term "financial incentive" is here used to mean some form of additional monetary reward for work that is above the minimum standard. It may be a system of direct payment by results, with or without some form of guaranteed minimum rate, or a system of money awards either based on a scheme of measured day work or on some scale of individual merit rating.

(a) Individual Merit Rating Schemes. Many schemes for individual merit rating are open to the criticism that they are too subjective. This criticism is often merited when awards are made entirely at the discretion of a supervisor since personal prejudice will inevitably influence the rating, but it is possible to devise a scheme which can be administered objectively and fairly. A rating scale can be worked out and weighted to cover points of importance such as quality of work, special knowledge, adaptability and co-operation. If ratings are made by individuals working independently, checked by a group, and finally published, personal prejudices or tendencies to favouritism cannot affect the results.

Schemes of this type have often been successful and in many cases they have led to increased output, though increased output is usually only a secondary consideration.

(b) Money Award on Measured Day Work: This form of financial incentive has received much less attention than it deserves. It is much less well-known than the other types. There are various schemes for arranging such a system and a plan should be adopted that suits the needs of each particular factory. All the existing schemes follow much the same broad lines though some are more complicated than others.

The general principle of all such systems is that wages are paid on a time basis, standards of output being set for each operation. Before standards are set, the work is studied and the best methods are laid down and taught to the operators. Some form of time study is normally used to set the final standard. The work of each operator is then recorded and measured against the set standards and a carefully regulated system of merit awards is arranged for those who achieve and maintain the standard output.

When a motion study investigation into work that has previously been paid on a day rate has reached its third stage and the first operator is being trained, a financial incentive of some kind will help to maintain his interest. It will also establish confidence that he is likely to gain financially from the introduction of motion study. It is easy to adopt a scheme of merit awards to meet this need. Each operator is given a definite and pre-arranged merit increase from the moment that he begins training on the new motion study method. He then receives a further increase when he has reached the required standard of output and maintained it over a reasonable period, perhaps two weeks. To safeguard the incentive effect of the increases, those trainees who are not co-operative and who do not reach the standard within a reasonable period are warned that their progress is unsatisfactory. If this warning has no effect and there is no reasonable explanation for their failure, they are transferred to work which does not carry a merit award. These conditions will, of course, be made clear before the operator begins to train for the job.

The final merit award at the end of the training period is permanent and does not vary week by week according to an operator's output record. If, however, there is a significant fall in output, below the standard set, and there are no external circumstances to account for it, the operator should receive a warning that he is not maintaining a satisfactory standard. At the same time, the job should be carefully examined to discover if anything is wrong and, if the operator still fails to maintain the standard after he has been warned, and no real reason is found for the failure, he should be transferred to work not qualifying for a merit award. In practice this situation arises only in exceptional cases. Once an operator has reached and maintained a standard over a period he very rarely produces a lower output without a valid excuse.

The system can be further adapted to encourage the exceptional operator. If the standard output is exceeded over a period by more than 25 per cent the operator can be given a further increase in his merit bonus.

The actual amount paid as a merit award should be agreed with the workers' representatives and, once agreed, it should apply to every operator on a particular job without discrimination.

The main advantage of the system is that it maintains a standard output that does not vary to any extent.   At the same time it allows for the exceptional operator.   It does, of course, pre-suppose a motion study investigation of each job to find the best method, and the careful training of operators so that a sufficiently high standard can be attained.   As far as is known, it has never been tried except under these conditions.

It is no more difficult to set output standards than it is to set piecework rates.   Where it is difficult to set output standards, because of the diversity of the work, it is equally difficult to set piecework rates.   The standards have however an advantage over the piece rates in that an error in a standard can be corrected more easily and with less opposition than a mistake in setting a piece rate.

A system of merit bonuses on standard day work demands supervision of a high quality carried out by well-trained supervisors, but given a good standard of management it is possible to maintain output at as high an average level as under a piece rate system, and without many of the disadvantages inherent in any form of direct payment by results.

(c) Direct Payment by Results: The introduction of a system of direct payment by results must be accompanied in the same way by the careful setting of standards of output.   In assessing the benefit resulting from the introduction of piecework payments it is difficult to estimate how much is directly due to the money incentive and how much to the setting of standards or to the simple fact that the work has been the subject of an investigation. In few cases have standards been set and tried out thoroughly before the introduction of direct payment by results.   In general it can be said that the first advantage to be gained from a direct payment by results scheme is a definite increase in output, most marked at the beginning of the scheme though less certain in its later stages.   Another advantage is that the best operators are recognised and receive a greater reward for their efforts.   In addition, the required standard of output can often be maintained with less supervision.   These advantages are, however, offset by certain very definite disadvantages inherent in any system of direct payment by results.   The most important of these is the bad feeling among the operators that any form of piece work is liable to arouse.   Piece work often leads to ill-feeling because there are always variations in yield between one job and another however carefully prices are set.   Everyone who has had experience of systems of direct payment by results knows that some prices always prove easier than others; that some get the reputation of being "good" and others "bad."   This means that, where there is a variety of jobs in one department, elaborate arrangements may have to be made to give each operator a fair share of both in each pay period.

An example of this comes from a factory stitching a number of styles of the same article.   Because the amount of work involved in making each style varied, each had a different piece work price.   Inevitably some of the prices were slightly easier than others and therefore each operator was given a share of each style. Because the cotton had to be changed in the sewing machines for every style and because the type of stitching varied, it was obviously more efficient if operators concentrated on one style only. This suggestion was given a trial over a period and everyone earned considerably more than the previous average. Unfortunately the increases varied. The "bad" prices yielded a smaller increase than the "good." To meet this difficulty it was suggested that there should be a compromise between the two methods; that the different styles should be moved from one operator to another but over a long period, so that eventually after a number of weeks everyone would have worked at each style and have received the same advantages and disadvantages. Because this would not have produced equality over the short period, the operators preferred to lose the increased earnings and return to the more apparent equity of the original plan. They would not agree to the new plan even with the suggested modification and it was dropped.

This disparity between prices where rates have been set carefully is often caused by an accumulation of very small changes in conditions, none of which, taken separately, justifies a change in the rate. It can arise even when the rate has been accurately set on a method that has been properly studied and improved, and where operators are given full instruction in the use of the correct method. In the majority of cases this careful preparation for rate setting is not made and the disparity is very much worse. It will always be a source of friction and ill-feeling and it can have far reaching effects which are difficult to estimate.

A further difficulty is the tendency among operators to limit their earnings to a maximum set by themselves. This may happen because they are afraid that easy prices may be cut if they become too obvious or because of a definite policy not to earn more than a certain maximum percentage or to allow any one worker to stand out as exceptional. The tendency is accentuated by the common practice of most wages departments of checking exceptional piecework earnings in order to prevent error or dishonesty. Many operators prefer to avoid the check by keeping their earnings below the level at which it operates. This happens even when no just claim for high bonus earnings is ever refused and where a management assures its workers that there is no limit to piecework earnings.

The limitation of earnings is not always a true limitation of output. It sometimes takes the form of a manipulation of the record of hours spent on various jobs so that, although prices vary from good to bad, the same percentage of earnings is claimed for each. This practice need not be in itself dishonest since, unless hours are carried over into another week, the total bonus claimed is the same that would be paid if it were claimed correctly. It is, however, a hindrance to costing and makes an accurate assessment of hours spent on a job impossible. It also reacts unfavourably against future operators when they claim that a particular price is bad and the records show that it has given as much bonus as any other job. In addition, it wastes an operator's time on making calculations and is bad for the general tone of a department or works.

Another disadvantage not always considered when installing a scheme of payment by results is the expense of its administration. Although standards of individual output should be set in any efficient factory, whatever the system of payment, the fixing of piece rates is an additional cost which must be charged against the piecework system. This is an expense which does not recur but there is also the considerable cost of the regular clerical work necessary to check workers' time cards and calculate individual earnings. A less obvious expense is the time spent by supervisors in arranging the distribution of work so that each operator has an equal chance to earn bonus, but this should not be overlooked.

A further disadvantage of direct payment by results is the difficulty experienced in maintaining the quality of the work. If quality can be measured or is a matter of accuracy, as in so many engineering jobs, it can be maintained by means of careful inspection, though this too adds to the cost of the system. If quality, on the other hand, lies in the finish of an article and cannot be measured exactly, it becomes merely a matter of opinion. In this case there is a considerable danger that the quality standard will deteriorate with the introduction of a piecework system.

Most exponents of direct payment by results list the advantages and disadvantages of that type of system. In almost every case the list of disadvantages exceeds the advantages numerically, but the usual conclusion is that the increased output that follows the introduction of a payment by results system is worth all the difficulties. Even where this conclusion is not entirely accepted, the demands of labour for extra earnings will often force a management into adopting that basis of payment.

When a scheme of direct payment by results is being installed, there are certain points that should be considered if it is to be fully effective. The system should be easily understood by the operators and rates should be set so that an operator can calculate his hourly target and can easily check how much money he is making. If circumstances allow, individual rates should be set and the operator should be free to work as hard as he likes and to make as much money as he can. This means that he must not be held up for material or too much dependent on the pace of the previous operators.

It is not possible to say definitely that one basis of payment is better than another. It depends on the individual conditions of each factory. It is however, important to make the choice carefully because a direct payment by results scheme once established is not easily changed for a timework system if it proves unsatisfactory. In spite of the difficulty changes in this direction have been made successfully in recent years. The demand for the adoption of systems of direct payment by results is still on the increase, perhaps because their advantages are often immediate and obvious while their disadvantages are less apparent, at least in the early stages. Nevertheless, it is usually wiser, in searching for the most appropriate form of payment for a particular organisation, to try other methods first which are easier to drop if they prove unsuccessful.

Conclusion

The foregoing has been a very general survey of incentives both to come to work and to work well. It makes no claim to be comprehensive. It is extremely important that the motion study investigator should understand the general background of incentives and that he should use this knowledge when he is developing new methods and installing them in the factory. In his relations with the personnel department it is also important that his job analyses should cover the incentives inherent in each job so that an operator can be selected for it who will appreciate the sources of satisfaction that it contains.

10

MOTION STUDY AND PERSONNEL MANAGEMENT

GOOD human relations are a necessary background to successful motion study work. Unless the motion study investigator has the confidence of all grades in the factory he will find it difficult to introduce his improvements. Motion study can only flourish as one aspect of a good management policy, where the other aspects are satisfactory. The main part of this book contains information about motion study techniques and about the training of managers, supervisors and operators to apply them and to carry out the methods resulting from their application. This chapter is concerned with the background against which all motion study work should be set; particularly with the personnel function of management. This more than any other management function can help or hinder the motion study programme.

It is important that the motion study investigator should work closely with the personnel officer, since so much of his work touches upon the personnel field. He must understand and co-operate with the work of the personnel department where it bears directly upon his own work. At the same time the personnel officer must be prepared to be advised by the motion study investigator about that side of an operator's work which is the concern of the motion study department.

The functions of the personnel department which are of direct interest to the motion study investigator are employment, operator training, the training of supervisors, joint consultation, the maintenance of the wage structure and financial incentives, and certain aspects of welfare, health and safety provisions. Each of these functions must be examined separately.

Employment: Selection and Placing

The motion study investigator will spend a considerable amount of time and trouble in fitting his new methods to the individual operator whose work has been studied. He will always be willing to adapt the method, the tools and the layout of the workplace to suit the individual differences or disabilities of existing operators. Where, however, an operator leaves and must be replaced, or where motion study has been applied to new work, good methods of selection and placing used by the personnel department will make motion study work much easier. A great many difficulties in suiting the worker to the job are not physical but mental and emotional. For example, an operator otherwise entirely suitable for a job may dislike it either because it is too isolated and he is unhappy without company, or, conversely, because it is group work and he can only work as an individual. The motion study investigator relies on the personnel officer to submit for the job an operator who is likely to be suitable in as many ways as possible. In turn, the personnel officer depends upon the motion study investigator for that accurate information about the work that will make it possible to select the right operator. This information is best obtained by means of job analysis.

Job Analysis. A job analysis, which is the first step in the successful placing of operators, is a tabulated summary of the special features of a job and a description of the qualities needed in the operator who is to perform it. Motion study has a direct bearing on the requirements of each job, and the introduction of a motion study method often modifies these requirements. The making of a job analysis is work for the motion study investigator in co-operation with the foreman concerned and the personnel officer.

In any well-organised factory some form of job description exists. A foreman, when he is requisitioning labour from the employment department, describes the general type of man or woman that he wants: a skilled man to operate a centre lathe or, perhaps, a tall girl for a big press. The employment officer adds to this his personal knowledge of the job and the conditions in the department, and is careful not to submit a rough type of operator to a department engaged on fine work, or a particularly sensitive person to a rough job such as work in a foundry coreshop. Between the foreman's description of his requirements and the employment officer's personal knowledge of the job or the department, there may be enough information to make it possible to place someone in the job who will be able to do it more or less adequately, but such information will be very general and it will not be possible to compare the requirements of one job with those of the other jobs in the factory. Since little will be written down, there will often be a danger of some of the relevant information not being available when it is wanted, perhaps during the absence of foreman or employment officer.

A job analysis sets out to make all the possible information about a job available in a standard presentation, so that one job can be compared with another. For this reason a form must be designed that will hold all the information that is likely to be of importance in filling any job in the factory. This form should be as simple as possible so that it can be easily used by a variety of people. Fig. 49 shows a job analysis form originally designed to collect information about every woman's job in an engineering works, as a preliminary to the setting up of a general training scheme for new entrants. This same form was also used to compile a list of the jobs which most needed further motion study investigation. It should not be regarded as an exact pattern for others since it was drawn up for a particular purpose and for a particular firm, but it is an example of a form that proved extremely useful in the circumstances for which it was designed. Each industry and each individual

Dept. Small machine Job. Mechanism   Operation Rivetting pillars on plate
Wage Rate   P.W. Price

General Description:

	Hand	Tools used — Machine	Fixture
Slide jig loaded by other operator under press		Townsend power rivetting press	Block Fixture for holding pillars with plate on top
Operate press			
Place completed jig on chute.			

Nature of Work

		Hand	Machine	
General:		Quiet sitting ✓ clean	Noisy standing dirty wet steamy hot cold	V noisy ✓
Ventilation:		good	average ✓	poor
Illumination:		good	average ✓	poor
Production:		continuous	recurring ✓	occasional
Length of Cycle:		long	medium	short
Muscular exertion required for:				
leg and body movement		much	average	little ✓
trunk and arm movement		much	average	little ✓
arm and hand		much	average	little ✓
Nature of Movement:		fine	medium	coarse ✓
Adjustment necessary:		simple & fine complex & fine	simple & coarse complex & coarse	none ✓

Operator's Qualifications

Physical:	Sex ... F ✓.. Age 14-16 ....16-18 .... 18-21 ✓... over 21			
	Height: under 5'3"	under 5'6"	over 5'6"	immaterial ✓
	Build: small	average	large	immaterial ✓
	Eyesight:		good	immaterial ✓
Mental:	Write:		legibly	immaterial ✓
	Add and subtract: ·		quickly	immaterial ✓
	Fractions:		necessary	unnecessary ✓
	Read specifications:		necessary	unnecessary ✓
	Read blue prints:		necessary	unnecessary ✓
	Quick observations:		necessary	unnecessary ✓
	Good memory:		necessary	unnecessary ✓
Personality:	Shy	average ✓	selfconfident	immaterial
	Patient	average ✓	impatient	immaterial
	Unsociable	average ✓	sociable	immaterial
Experience:	apprenticed	non-apprenticed ✓		
On similar work:		necessary	desirable	unnecessary ✓

Remarks:

Short cycle machine operation with operator assisting
on opposite side of bench by loading pillars and
plates in jig and unloading after rivetting

Is further investigation recommended? No. Motion study
investigation completed.

FIG. 49. JOB ANALYSIS FORM

This form was drawn up for the analysis of women's work in an
engineering works.

factory requires a form designed especially for it, to contain the information that is peculiar to that industry and that factory. In spite of this, however, the design of all forms will have certain points in common. Every form should be planned so that the main part of it can be completed merely by ticking each appropriate classification. If several copies are likely to be required it should also be laid out so that a typist can fill it in with the minimum of movements.

There are also certain general items and headings that are common to all job analysis forms, whatever the industry or circumstances.

"General description of job" is the first of these. Under this heading will come such information as "department," "name of job," "summary of the work required of the operator," and details about the type of hand tools used and the machines and fixtures involved.

Under the main heading of "General department conditions" information would be recorded about the surroundings of the job, such as the heating, lighting and ventilation, and about methods of payment, whether there is a standard rate paid by the hour, the day, or the month, or a financial incentive scheme with or without a guaranteed minimum rate.

"Nature of the work" will be the next general heading. Under it will be grouped information about the conditions of the work, whether it is clean or dirty, whether the operator sits or stands, whether it is an individual job or team work; an independent workplace or at a conveyor.

Such general information can easily be gathered and recorded by anyone but there are other more detailed classifications that must be made by the motion study investigator and which will always be revised when a method has been investigated and improved by motion study. They include some general assessment of the muscular work involved, the type of movements used, the degree to which parts have to be adjusted or machines set, and, in some cases, a classification of the accuracy required and the limits within which the operator is expected to work.

"Operator's qualifications" comes next. Here the sex, age, range and rate of pay would be listed. Physical qualifications would be classified under such subheadings as height, build, general physique, eyesight and hearing. Mental attainments might include arithmetic accomplishment, ability to read and understand specifications or drawings, quick observation, good memory and other qualities or attainments. Personal attributes might also be included, since for some work they are important. A receptionist, for example, must be considered very carefully in that respect. She would need self-confidence and decision. An inspector on the other hand would require patience and concentration, while some simple work might be best done by an impatient person anxious to get on quickly. It is also useful to know whether a sociable or an unsociable person will best suit the work. Some jobs are isolated and offer very little chance of social intercourse; others inevitably involve becoming one of a social group. There are many other personal traits that might be

5 og

listed but if this classification is made too complete there is a danger of its becoming too complex to be useful.

"Experience and training" is an essential heading; in many cases the most important of all. It is necessary to record whether the job requires an operator who has served an apprenticeship and has standard accepted qualifications, or whether an experienced operator is sufficient or even someone with no previous training or experience. Where no experience is necessary the details of the training that will be given to a new operator should be stated. Even where an experienced operator is necessary details should be recorded of any additional training that will be given either in the works department concerned or in a special training department.

When every kind of general and special category of information has been provided for, according to the needs of a particular factory or industry, a space should be left on the analysis form for remarks. Here the analyst can fill in any unusual points about the job that cannot be classified normally. It will usually be necessary to design separate forms for the analysis of manual, clerical and administrative jobs.

Job analysis has as its primary object the correct selection of operators, which is the first step in securing a contented and stable labour force. If an operator is assigned to a job for which he is technically and temperamentally suited he will give of his best and be well adjusted to his work and satisfied with it. Such a situation is necessary for the best motion study results.

A job analysis presents in a standard form the information necessary for the successful selection of operators. It can be used in its original tabulated form or a job description may be made from it, written in narrative style and in simple language. This job description may be illustrated by photographs of the job and of the workplace if it describes a manual operation. It will be useful for explaining the nature of the work to applicants for employment and since any employment interview should be two-sided, giving information as well as obtaining it, a job description should always be made and used wherever possible.

A second use of job analysis, which also concerns the employment function of the personnel officer, is as a basis for a scheme of job evaluation. Job evaluation is a comparatively new technique and has gained considerable popularity in the United States.[1] In this country it has been used by a few large companies[2] but its more general use has been restricted by our well established and somewhat complex wage negotiating machinery. It is not proposed to discuss it further here since it is normally outside the province of the motion study department.

Before a training scheme for new entrants is introduced, a comprehensive job analysis should be made of all the jobs in the factory to discover the

[1]*Practical Job Evaluation,* Philip W. Jones, Wiley (New York, 1948).
[2]*Job Evaluation and Merit Rating in Theory and Practice,* J. J. Gracie, Manchester College of Technology (May, 1948).

common features of jobs in the same broad working groups and the common simple skills and knowledge that they demand from the worker. These can then be included in the training of general workers who have to learn to undertake a variety of jobs within one general category. It will also be necessary to make a very careful analysis before planning the training of workers for specific jobs. (*See* Chapter 12).

Job analysis is also a valuable tool for the motion study investigator's own use. By making a job analysis of a wide variety of work in the factory it is possible to find out which jobs are most worth studying and improving and which should be studied first. This is particularly important when motion study is being introduced into a factory for the first time.

Selection. The use of a job analysis is only the first step in selecting a suitable operator for a particular job. There must be a corresponding personnel analysis made by the personnel officer. This should include for each individual interviewed, information about special skills and knowledge and about previous experience. Since the skills and knowledge acquired on one job will often have only an indirect bearing upon another, some assessment of aptitude must be made. Physical attributes should also be recorded so that there is no danger, for example, of a small man, otherwise entirely suitable for the work, being given a job involving reaches beyond his capacity. More important still is the mental attitude of a worker. This, too, must be estimated since a correct assessment will decide whether the worker, for example, will be more useful on machines or on assembly or inspection work, since each of these three types of work requires a different temperament.

The assessment of the peculiarities of an operator before he is assigned to a particular job is made by means of an interview which may be supplemented by aptitude and intelligence tests. The record of this interview will be more useful if it is made on a standard form designed for each particular factory. This will help the interviewer to record comparable information about every individual for use at any time.

. This is work for the trained personnel officer and although it is of the greatest importance the details are beyond the scope of this book[1]. It is only necessary here to emphasise that the careful selection of the operator for the job is always essential whether labour is scarce or plentiful. Where there are numbers of applicants for each job it is a matter of selecting the most suitable. Here the value of good interviewing and selection tests is obvious but they are equally important when labour is scarce. In a time of labour scarcity every operator must be helped to give of his best and he cannot do so if he is unsuited to his work. The problem becomes one of allocation rather than selection.

---

[1]For further information *see* the series of broadsheets issued by the Institute of Personnel Management. See also *Personnel Management—its Scope and Practice,* by C. H. Northcott (Pitman's).

Personnel Records and Statistics

The personnel department is responsible for all types of employment and personnel statistics. Among these, two are of special interest to the motion study investigator because of their value in dealing with particular problems that affect his work.

Labour Turnover. There is nothing more calculated to nullify the work of the motion study investigator than an excessively high labour turnover figure. Where the turnover is high there is the constant danger of a change of operator in the middle of an investigation or worse still at the installation stage of a new method. This is difficult enough when the job which is being investigated involves one operator only, and time is wasted in training replacements, but where a team of operators is involved constant changes in its personnel may make it impossible to finish the investigation or to judge its results. An unstable, constantly changing labour force will also mean that established good methods may lapse because it is impossible to give adequate training every time there is a change of operator.

Unless figures are kept and analysed the labour turnover may become dangerously high before it is realised. Even with a high labour turnover there is always a nucleus of permanent employees, and this may obscure the true position. Companies who do not keep statistics will often assert that they have a low turnover or even none at all. They are surprised and alarmed when the first figure is worked out to find that it may have been anything from 50 to 100 per cent per annum without any danger signal being recognised.

The figure is generally calculated by expressing the total number of leavers in a given period as a percentage of the average labour force in that period, i.e.,

$$\text{Labour turnover} = \frac{\text{Total number of leavers in given period}}{\text{Average number of employees on pay roll for that period}} \times 100$$

This is the simplest method of calculation and gives a basis for comparison related to the size of the factory. It should be calculated separately for men and women and for full time and part time workers. It is normally quoted as an annual figure but it may be useful to calculate it monthly. In this case the percentage after calculation should be multiplied by twelve so that it can be compared with other annual figures. Records should also be kept of the age of leavers, their reasons for leaving, and their length of service. In a large works figures should be taken out departmentally, as well as for the works as a whole.

An efficient personnel department will keep a very close watch on the labour turnover figures, analysing them carefully so that appropriate action can be taken before there is any danger of their becoming so high that the turnover is a hindrance to progress in the factory. Careful selection methods are the first means of building up a static labour force with a low labour turn-over but they are not the only means. It has been found that where a sound training scheme has been introduced new starters will settle in better and that the proportion that leave during first few months will be reduced. This training of new starters should be the joint responsibility of the personnel and motion study departments. It is often worth undertaking for its effect on the labour turnover alone and for the direct money saving that this means to a company, quite apart from the indirect saving which results from the smoother functioning of production departments and the uninterrupted work of the motion study investigator. For example, if in a firm of 1,000 employees the labour turnover is 55 per cent per annum (a not uncommon figure for women) the introduction of a training scheme may easily reduce it to 45 per cent per annum or less. A hundred operators are therefore retained who would have had to be replaced and since the average cost of replacing an operator is at a very conservative estimate £20, depending upon the type of work, the saving in this instance would be at least £2,000 in a year.

Attendance and Timekeeping. It is very important that records should be kept of attendance and timekeeping. A close control over absences and bad timekeeping cannot be kept without accurate records. This control is of vital importance to any form of production but even more so to a motion study method of work where every operator's job is carefully balanced and each plays an indispensable part in the whole. Here any hasty redistribution of the work of an absentee among the other operators must inevitably upset the balance and rhythm and overload the remaining workers.

Absenteeism upsets all forms of production. Even on work involving only one operator it can have serious results, though it is particularly dis-rupting on conveyor or team work, the more so when it takes the form of casual absence, or lateness at the beginning of the day. For example, in one factory where teams of twenty women worked on a belt conveyor the super-visor was fully occupied from 7.45 to 9 every morning reallocating the work of the absentees among those who had reported for work. The re-allocation could not be final until 9 o'clock when it was certain that none of the absentees would come in late. During more than two months of a motion study investi-gation of the work in the department, this happened every day, though the serious effect on production was not realised by the management until figures had been accumulated and analysed at the end of the investigation.

At all stages of an investigation lateness and casual absence are a hin-drance to progress but during the training period of a new method they may mean a set-back of many days. This set-back will last not only for the exact number of days or hours that have been missed but will be prolonged by the effect on progress of an interrupted training period. The installation stage of a new method may be retarded in the same way and, while this is irritating and inconvenient enough when only one operator is involved, it is again even more serious when the absent operator is a member of a team. Here the investigator has the choice between bringing in a fresh operator to complete the team or closing the work down. In either case training is interrupted, no progress can be made and, the irritation and disappointment may wreck the chances of a new method being acceptable to the operators concerned.

In general, longer absences, where the reason and the likely duration of the absence is known, are often less upsetting than casual short absences or unpunctuality. The average supervisor is too much inclined to accept bad timekeeping as inevitable in post-war conditions and it is too little understood that both lateness and absenteeism can to a large extent be controlled and reduced by good management on the part of both the personnel officer and the supervisor. The first step in gaining this control is to know the extent of the problem. This demands accurate and up to date statistics.

Initiation and Training

When an operator has been assigned to his job it is necessary, if he is to make his full contribution, that he should be properly adjusted to his work and conscious that he is a member of an organisation with an active individual part to play in it. His initiation, which should include information about the outlook and policy of the firm, should be part of the general training scheme (*see* Chapter 12) and should form the broad background for the more detailed instruction in work methods in the training school or during the training period. There must be close co-operation here between the motion study and employment sections. In every step in the selection and initiation of new workers the two must work together. Until the detailed training in work methods begins, the personnel officer has the primary responsibility with the motion study investigator in an advisory capacity. At the training stage the motion study investigator takes over the responsibility for the method training in liaison with the personnel officer.

Follow-up

When training is finished and a new operator is launched upon his regular production job, the motion study investigator and the personnel officer must again co-operate in a regular system of follow-up. Each new operator should be visited daily at first and then weekly for a period until it is safe to make only a quarterly check. To the personnel officer such a system gives the opportunity for dealing with weaknesses in human relations before they become major problems. The motion study investigator should co-operate to see that points of method are checked at the same time and that progress towards efficiency and full production is being steadily maintained. Full co-operation means that the motion study investigator must give the personnel officer very full information about the details of the movements and methods that have been taught and about the progress that should be expected. In the same way the personnel officer must give the motion study investigator warning of anything that is likely to impede progress or cause difficulty.

Where the personnel department does not arrange for a regular follow-up of new operators, the motion study investigator should develop a scheme of his own on jobs he has studied.

Training of Supervisors

The work of the motion study investigator is made very much easier when supervisors are properly trained. To the operator the supervisor represents the management, and except in special circumstances his words are the only expression of management policy that are heard by the operator. Where a supervisor has reached his position merely by growing up in the department and without any additional training he cannot reasonably be expected to implement policies that he does not fully understand himself. In spite of this, the operator believes that he acts under instructions in this respect and as far as the operator knows he is following a recognised plan and carrying out exactly the management policy. Good industrial relations in a department depend very largely on the attitude of the supervisor, and a wrong attitude, or even a wrong opinion expressed only once or twice, can do almost irreparable harm. If a supervisor receives a definite training it should be directed towards teaching him how to run his department smoothly. He should be taught to anticipate and solve the various difficulties that are inherent in production and to handle his operators carefully. To the motion study investigator this will be invaluable, since it will mean that his methods are likely to run smoothly and to be maintained correctly. A supervisor's ability, or his training and experience in handling operators, will also be important since the attitude of the operators to changed methods depends very largely upon the way the idea is put to them.

Apart from his general training in supervision, a supervisor will be in a better position to convince his operators of the value of the new methods if he fully appreciates them himself. He should be given further training in motion study so that he understands its aims and objects (*see* Chapter 11).

Joint Consultation

The term joint consultation should be interpreted in the broadest way. Too often managements take it to mean nothing more than the existence of a committee representing jointly both workers and management. The formation of a committee does not, however, guarantee real consultation unless there is a true spirit of co-operation behind it and a full intention on all sides to exchange information and ideas and reach agreement. Many committees of this kind have been formed only because joint consultation is fashionable. Such committees are worthless because they are wrongly founded. Joint consultation cannot be administered from above as a panacea for management ills. Successful consultation can arise only out of the desire of each individual to contribute everything within his power and capacity to the smooth running and success of the enterprise of which he is a part. Group discussion of a particular problem can achieve excellent results but only if the members of the group have a real common interest and are prepared to think in terms of a common good rather than of serving the self interest of the particular section they represent. If this spirit does not exist consultation will not flourish whatever the composition of the committee. Where it does exist, consultation may even take place in exceptional circumstances without a committee. This can, of course, be possible only in smaller organisations where it is comparatively easy for the individual voice to be heard. Larger companies can consult only through representatives and it is very important that there should be regular meetings between the representatives of all factory groups at all levels. It is equally important that each representative should keep those he represents in touch with what is discussed and that they in turn should be sufficiently interested to put up their ideas and suggestions for him to contribute to the discussions of the committee. It is comparatively simple to form a representative committee but much more difficult to make that committee perform its functions of joint consultation. Much research and experiment into methods of consultation is needed and the researches being undertaken at present by the Schuster Panel[1] will be very helpful, but there is also a great opportunity for everyone concerned with the subject to experiment independently and to try the fresh methods which are so badly needed to make joint consultation really work.

The organisation of joint consultation is normally the function of the personnel officer but the motion study investigator depends upon it in several ways. A well-established system is invaluable where new methods are to be introduced. Real consultation is very important to him since he is always seeking both to give information about his aims and objects and to teach everyone as much about his theories as they are prepared to learn. He is also anxious to know about any difficulties that may arise as a result of the changes that he makes and to receive suggestions from as many sources as possible, particularly from the operators who have a specialised knowledge of work methods.

New methods have a direct bearing upon the conditions of the operators in general and it is essential that not only the individual operators directly affected by the changes but also the whole body of operators and their representatives should understand what motion study means and what are its advantages to them. Most people dislike change and when to this dislike is added the fear that work may be made harder by the changes, some hostility towards new methods is inevitable. A motion study investigator will always try to consult both the operators concerned and their representatives before making changes, and some motion study training for operators will be included in any full programme of motion study (*see* Chapters 11 and 12) but this policy is more satisfactory and more certain of success where there is accepted

[1] Panel on Human Relations Affecting Productivity. Chairman, Sir George Schuster. Report published by H.M. Stationery Office (Com. 7665), 1949.

machinery for the discussion and explanation of difficult points. Where there is mutual confidence and understanding between management and workpeople fewer difficulties arise during the change to new methods, and those that do appear are more easily solved. To take two examples, if, as is often the case, a new method means that fewer operators are required on a job, the transfer of surplus labour to other work is more easily achieved where there has been free discussion of the necessity. Again, if a workshop operates under a system of payment by results, a change in method will inevitably mean a revision of the piecework price. In most industries such revisions are covered by agreements between unions and employers and there is usually very little dispute about the fact of the necessity for a revision of prices. Any disagreement that arises is usually about the amount of the change, but it is much less likely to be difficult to settle where joint consultation is real, not merely formal.

Joint consultation plays a special part in investigations and experiments carried out on behalf of a whole industry rather than for an individual company. Here it must take place at two distinct levels. There must be the usual consultation within the particular factory that is the scene of the experiment but this must be preceded by consultation at a higher level between the employers organisations and the trade unions of the industry. If this consultation is to be effective it must be based on a sound knowledge of the methods, application and results of motion study. Both sides need this knowledge but it is particularly important that the trade unions should have it, since they are being asked to commit their members to co-operation in an experiment that may well have a direct effect upon the work of each individual member. Before an experiment of this kind begins the motion study investigator must spend time and thought on the problem and be prepared to give all the help he can in spreading information about his subject.

It has been found invaluable in such experiments to have a trade union representative working in close contact with the investigator on the job. Since he will have the opportunity of following the development of the new method step by step, he will know the reason for every proposed change and he will be able to explain this to the operators, dispelling any fears of exploitation that may still be held and gaining their full co-operation. In all investigations the fullest trade union understanding of motion study is to be welcomed. Several unions are organising courses of background training in motion study, time study and the general principles of management. Such courses could be an excellent source of information if they were to be more widely adopted.

Rates and Wages

In most factories the wage structure is the result of national agreement and is common to the industry. The personnel officer's function with regard to wages is to advise his Board of Directors, before agreements are made and to see that, once made, they are fairly applied within the factory. The motion study investigator has a definite interest in this since any unfair or uneven application may become a source of friction that will hinder his work. He must also be thoroughly familiar with the whole wage structure so that he may avoid any violation of established practice when he is re-allocating work. For example, in the engineering industry he would have to be careful not to give, without modification, work graded as skilled to semi-skilled or unskilled labour.

Piece rates are usually set internally for individual factories but in some old-established industries they are set by agreement for the whole industry. In either case the personnel officer is concerned not in the setting of the rates but in their fair application, bringing cases of difficulty to the notice of the proper authority. Where rates have to be changed after a motion study investigation the personnel officer can be of great assistance to the motion study investigator, advising both on matters of principle and on the best method of negotiating and introducing the changes. The whole question of making changes in rates is discussed in Chapter 8.

Welfare, Health and Safety

A personnel officer may need reassurance that the changes made by motion study are in no way detrimental to the operator, either immediately or in the long run. That this is the case there is no doubt, since any movement that imposes undue strain cannot be good from a motion study point of view and will always be rejected by the investigator in developing improved methods. It is, however, important that the personnel officer understands and believes this, and the motion study investigator should be careful to explain his methods and aims as fully as he is able. Welfare, health and safety are particularly the responsibility of the personnel officer and unless he fully understands the meaning of motion study he may be tempted to support or confirm a complaint that a new method is too hard on an operator without first making sure that the new method is the real cause of the trouble or, indeed, that any real trouble exists. An example of this comes from a factory where a motion study investigation of a certain operation resulted in an improvement which called for an output standard which was 25 per cent higher than the standard set for exactly the same operation in a similar factory in the same neighbourhood which had not used motion study. In fact, the effort required from individual operators in reaching the lower standard without motion study was greater than the effort required to reach the higher standard on the operation that had been studied, but this was not at first obvious to anyone not trained in motion study. The operators, knowing the disparity in rates between the two factories but not mentioning it in their complaint to the personnel officer, asserted that the motion study method made the work too constant and therefore harder. One or two operators left, giving this as their reason. The personnel officer, without making any proper enquiry but feeling, very naturally, that at all costs the firm must not lose labour, sympathised with the operators and backed their complaint to the managing director. This not only made future motion study work infinitely more difficult but also caused that particular group of operators to take nine months to settle down to the new method compared with the two or three months taken by other groups on similar improvements in other parts of the same factory. If this particular personnel officer had really appreciated the difference between an unplanned method and a method that had been motion studied, the first grumbles of a few operators would not have been allowed to become a major complaint or the subject of a protracted negotiation which wasted much time and engendered considerable ill-feeling.

On the other hand, since the personnel officer is responsible for good human relations in the factory, it is extremely important that he has a sufficiently complete knowledge of motion study to enable him to recognise the difference between a genuine motion study investigation and a change in method, which though incorrectly called "motion study" is really some form of speeding up. In this latter case he must be prepared to hold his ground and fight to maintain fair conditions for the operator but where motion study has been applied correctly he must be equally ready to recognise this and careful not to support complaints that are not justified.

Conclusion

With the change of emphasis in the industrial outlook from the importance of the machine as the most valuable factory asset to the importance of the individuals who make up the factory team and who use the machines, personnel management is becoming one of the key functions of management. It is in factories which have recognised and accepted this change of outlook that motion study, by concentrating on the human beings who do the work, can obtain the best results. In this situation it is extremely important that the personnel officer and the motion study investigator understand and appreciate each other's work and realise the scope each has for improving efficiency in the factory.

11

A FULL MOTION STUDY PROGRAMME[1]

THE full application of motion study in any organisation or factory calls for the active co-operation of every group and individual. Motion study applications range from the full scale investigation, employing all available means and techniques to achieve the best use of the effort of the operator in every detail, to the making of small improvements without the use of the more exact techniques and the application of general motion study principles to every part of the daily round. Everyone in an organisation can use motion study in some way and a full programme must provide the information and opportunities that will help each individual to use it to the best advantage in his own sphere.

Making Use of the Full Range of Motion Study Application

There has been a tendency in the past to make only a partial application of motion study, to disregard its full range and to concentrate either on detailed investigations of specific problems or on the use of a simplified technique to make numerous smaller improvements over a wide field. It has often been argued either that motion study is work for the trained full-time specialist only, or, alternatively, that greater aggregate savings can be gained by training a large number of people to apply motion study in their spare time. In Great Britain, the first argument has largely been used in the past, with a few notable exceptions, though recently the "Training Within Industry Job Methods" programme has introduced the second type of application. This T.W.I. programme serves as an excellent introduction to motion study, though it is not adequate in itself. In the U.S.A., on the other hand, the broader simplified form has been more fully developed. There the term "work simplification" is often used instead of "motion study."

Each type of application has its advantages if both are used together, and its dangers and disadvantages if the two forms are separated. Used in conjunction with a more general form of application, detailed investigations, carried out by one or two investigators working full time, will result in new methods efficient in every detail, giving increased output per operator in its most direct form, on direct labour. Such detailed investigations show

[1] Some of this material was presented as a paper entitled *The Full Application of Motion Study* to the Institution of Mechanical Engineers in London, on March 24, 1950.

tangible and easily measured results and the savings which they effect are immediately attributable to motion study, giving them additional value as propaganda. They produce high percentage savings over a small area of work. On the other hand, the broader and less detailed applications of motion study work by a larger number of less highly trained people conducted in addition to their normal daily work, produce results which are, perhaps, less easy to assess. The savings made on any one job are usually small, since only the more obvious improvements can be made in the time available and with a limited knowledge of techniques, but, if these small savings are contributed in large numbers, the total savings may be very considerable. They are, in fact, low percentage savings over a large area of work.

Dangers of a One-sided Application

If the more detailed and the simplified forms of application are isolated, there are certain obvious dangers to both. The full-scale detailed investigation depends largely for its continued success on intelligent maintenance and the correct training of operators. It is likely to lapse if supervisors and operators do not know enough about motion study to realize the importance of carrying out the exact details of the methods laid down by the motion study investigator. In addition, the development of a new method, the training of operators to use it in the first instance and its final installation in the workshop will all take very much longer if supervisors and operators do not understand the principles behind the work. Where a foreman has been trained to use motion study himself, and where an operator has had a preliminary motion study training, investigations will run much more smoothly. Finally, to concentrate on single detailed investigations carried out by one person only is to overlook the reserves of interest, skill and enthusiasm to be found in the wider group of supervisors, technical specialists and operators.

On the other hand, if the application of motion study is confined to the simplified form that is suitable for part-time application by these wider groups, there is the danger inherent in any over simplified subject that, because it has no developing roots in experiment and detailed knowledge, it may tend to lose strength and die away when the first rapid growth is over. The belief may also be engendered that only simple operations can be improved by means of motion study and the potentialities of the more developed techniques will not be appreciated.

Planning a Full Motion Study Programme

A full motion study programme is not an end in itself. It is a means by which the greatest possible amount of production can be obtained with the least expenditure of effort. If this object is to be attained, there must be opportunities for all groups from top to bottom of the factory to use motion study to make their own contribution to greater production. The motion study programme must be planned to include them all, teaching them both to make their own work easier and to assist the investigator when a detailed investigation comes into their own field. Gilbreth demonstrated this when, in addition to carrying out thorough investigations of specific jobs, he taught all grades of employees to be " motion-minded."

The Motion Study Specialist — the Full-time Investigator. The specialist in charge of a motion study department and responsible for the full application of motion study throughout an organisation must divide his time between full-scale investigations and the teaching of simplified motion study to the other members of the organisation. He must never neglect the full-scale investigations in his anxiety to go forward with the wider programme. He should not attempt to teach motion study, even in a simplified form, until his own training is complete and he has had some experience of making detailed investigations. He should continue the detailed investigations all the time that he is running training courses for others. It is not necessary to discuss here the form that his own training should take, except to say that it should be as full as possible. The whole of this book is concerned with the more detailed techniques and the background knowledge needed for their application. It is obvious that the motion study investigator cannot know too much about these detailed techniques, or about the background of inter-related subjects against which they are applied in a factory.

The Main Factory Groups—the Part-time Users of Motion Study. In introducing motion study throughout an organisation a programme must be drawn up to allow all the main factory groups to play their appropriate parts. A factory can be roughly divided into four sections for this purpose— higher management, supervisors, operators and functional specialists, and each group can contribute according to its special experience and knowledge. The amount of direct motion study work to be expected from each will vary with the responsibilities and opportunities of its members and the time that they can spare for the work.

Since each group will use motion study differently, each must receive a different type of training, but this definite training in the use of simplified methods should not be begun until a general programme of motion study propaganda has been arranged throughout the factory. When real curiosity and interest have been aroused, and not before, it is time to arrange a series of training courses in motion study for each factory group. Finally, plans must be made for maintaining interest and stimulating continued motion study work; they must cover arrangements for bringing newcomers of all grades into the scheme.

The Three Stages of a Training Scheme

The programme for teaching the whole of an organisation to make full use of motion study should be planned in outline before any part of it begins.

It should be introduced to the organisation in three stages:—

    1. The arousing of general interest.

    2. Courses of motion study instruction for all factory groups.

    3. The organisation of reports, refresher courses and individual follow-ups to maintain interest and good methods and to stimulate individual work.

1. AROUSING INTEREST

There are a number of ways of arousing interest. Opportunities will vary from factory to factory but the following ideas have been used successfully.

(a) *Use of Sample Improved Method—Detailed Investigations.* Very few people believe that their own methods of work, or the methods used in their own factories or departments can be improved to any extent. However much they see examples of improvements made in the methods of others, they find it difficult to believe that their own work can be improved in the same way. There is also a general tendency to think that less familiar work is simpler and more suited to new methods. It is, therefore, very much more effective to use examples of improvements made in their own factory to arouse the interest of both workers and supervisors, and before making any attempt to arouse general interest in motion study in a factory or organisation, improvements should be made on one or two jobs as a sample of what can be done. Key people must be told of this work, but it is unwise at this stage to try to encourage interest and enthusiasm among those who will not be asked to take part in the first investigations. Those taking part should, of course, be given all the information they want and should be invited to make suggestions and to assist in developing the new methods.

The jobs to be studied and used as demonstrations should be carefully chosen. They should be generally recognised as efficient in their present state. This is more important than the possibility of effecting a spectacular increase in output which might be achieved if less efficient jobs were chosen. They should be methods which can be improved without the introduction of elaborate new equipment and which are unlikely to involve major modifications in existing equipment or layout, since these will inevitably delay the installation of the new methods. Where the necessity for such modifications arises unexpectedly in the course of a sample investigation of this kind, the work should be allowed to proceed but it should be supplemented by the investigation of another job in which a new method can be installed quickly. Films should always be made of both old and new methods of these first investigations whether they are needed for analysis or not. They are very effective in demonstrating improvements and are later useful for record and training purposes.

(b) *Articles and Lectures.* When the first new methods have been established and are running smoothly and when films have been made of them, all the material is available for a campaign to arouse general interest in motion study throughout the organisation. The first improvements will act as a permanent focus of attention and a demonstration of the potentialities of motion study in the organisation. They should now be supplemented by lectures and articles in the company magazine written with the object of making everyone talk about motion study and understand a little of what it means.

(*c*) *Exhibition*. In addition, an exhibition should be set up in the motion study department designed to demonstrate general motion study principles. This should be available to anyone at any time. It need not be large or elaborate and it should be informal. It will be more effective if it is shown to small groups or to individuals. It should contain a variety of simple exhibits set out in different ways, appealing to the sense of touch as well as to the eye and ear. Besides films and diagrams of old and new methods and the verbal explanations that are needed for them, there should be examples of improvements that can be tried and felt by the visitor. To compare two methods of work by doing both and feeling the improvement and the ease of the new method is often much more convincing than any other form of presentation. The impression tends to remain in the memory longer than ideas presented verbally or in the form of films and diagrams.

Just as the form of presentation of the exhibits is important in impressing motion study ideas upon the visitor to the exhibition, so the choice of subjects can also play its part. The function of the exhibition is not only to arouse the interest of those who visit it but also to make them carry the ideas away with them into their daily life. If some of the examples chosen are from the field of domestic work, the ideas will be remembered deliberately by the visitor to be discussed that evening at home. Domestic examples must, however, be chosen very carefully for their general application. They should emphasise the elimination of the unnecessary movements and obstacles in the path of movement that are such a source of irritation to the housewife and they should be simple, practical ideas that the visitor will immediately want to introduce into his own home. They should be demonstrated as examples of improvements made by applying motion study to everyday problems and the demonstrator should be careful to show how the new method has been obtained from a critical analysis of the old method and how it corrects the faults of the old method. Other examples can be chosen from a variety of fields provided that each is easily understood and unlikely to provoke technical arguments which might detract from the study of movements.

The following are typical of some of the examples and demonstrations that have been found useful in this type of exhibition: —

(i) *Professor Barnes's Pegboard*[1]. This consists of a square board with 36 holes in it and a box of metal pegs lying flat on the table. On one side of the board the holes are countersunk and on the other they are left plain

---

[1] *Works Methods Manual*, by Ralph M. Barnes, pp. 62-9 (John Wiley & Sons).

FIG. 50. ASSEMBLING PEGS IN BOARD
Upper: Old Method   *Lower*: New Method

The pegs are cut flat at one end and rounded at the other. This board can be used as a demonstration in a number of ways. The visitor can be asked to try several methods of filling the board and to feel the difference between them. In the first method, the pegs are put into the holes in the most usual way, taking a handful from the box with the left hand and using the right hand to select single pegs from it and put them into the holes, beginning at the top left-hand corner of the board and filling a row at a time downwards from left to right. It is easy to see that this method does not make full use of the left hand, and it may be suggested that both hands should be used to collect single pegs from the box. The visitor should be asked to try this method. If, however, he fills the holes in the same order, this arrangement, though making both hands productive, creates a further difficulty. After the first row there is an obstacle in the path of movement of each peg from box to hole. Every peg has to be lifted over the pegs already in the board. In the old method this only happened once or twice in a full cycle, when the left hand took a fresh handful of pegs from the box. The right hand in this method took its pegs from the left hand, in front of those already in the board and quite clear of them. If this difficulty is pointed out to anyone who has not much knowledge of motion study, the suggestion will nearly always be made that the bottom rows of holes should be filled first since they are the furthest from the box. But this is not the improvement that it seems as the pegs are now in the way of the hands. In putting in the second row and subsequent rows of pegs the hand will be restricted in its movements by the pegs already in the board.

The correct solution, which gives free passage to hands and fingers and a clear path of movement for the pegs, is to start at the two centre holes in the row furthest from the box and work up the middle towards the box, filling two rows of pegs at a time. The rows on either side of the first rows are filled next and finally the outside rows. In this way the hand has a clear path from first to last since the pegs are held in the fingers with the greater part of the hand lying to the outside, free from the pegs in the board. Finally, to make the grasping of the pegs easier and their transport shorter, the box of pegs is tilted forward to an angle of about 60° from the table.

Further points that can be discussed, if a visitor is particularly interested in the board, are the advantages and disadvantages of picking up two, or even three, pegs at a time and the difference countersunk or plain holes and rounded or flat-ended pegs can make to the ease of insertion[1]. This simple and non-technical example can be used in this way to demonstrate innumerable points in the development of motion study methods and it serves to emphasise that motion study results are based on a very thorough and detailed analysis of the whole problem and do not merely depend upon the use of two hands instead of one. (Fig. 50.)

[1] Further uses have been made of this pegboard by Harold Dunlap Hood, Ice Cream Co., Providence, U.S.A. He has demonstrated in particular the unloading of the board by setting it on a special table which he uses as an example of the use of fixtures where the job warrants it.

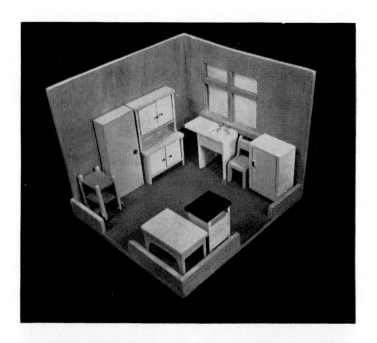

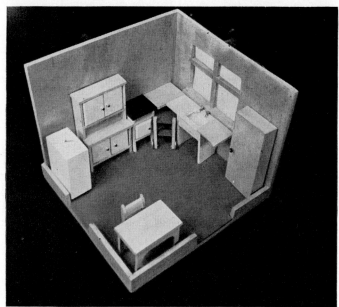

FIG. 51. KITCHEN MODEL

Upper: Old Layout   *Lower*: New Layout

(ii) *The Collating of the Duplicated Sheets of a Five-page Report.*
This example, previously described in Chapter 4, p. 76-9, can be used to
show how motion study can be applied to problems which must be solved
without the use of any special equipment. It demonstrates that an improvement
can be effected by altering movements only and that a new method does not
necessarily need a long practice period. This is important since the example
chosen is not a continuous job but one that arises for a short time at long
intervals. As a demonstration it has the advantage of simplicity. It is very
easy to set up as it needs only five piles of numbered sheets of paper and a
table and chair. It involves no technical problems and both methods can be
tried by the visitor. A film and chronocyclegraphs of the job can be shown,
if they are available, to demonstrate how the analysis has been made and as
an exact measure of the success of the improvement. (*See* Fig. 24 in
Chapter 4.)

(iii) *The Layout of a Domestic Kitchen.* This is a domestic example
that will always arouse interest. There should be a drawing of an old method
layout and a blank plan of the kitchen with templets cut to scale of the different
pieces of equipment that are to be rearranged. The visitor can move these
about on the plan to find the best arrangement. String diagrams of different
meals cooked under the old layout conditions may be provided to assist him.
When he has had time to try out his ideas, a new method layout should be
shown and he should be given reasons for its recommendations and be allowed
to discuss them.

If possible, a three-dimensional model (*see* Fig. 51) should be used instead
of a drawing and templets, as this is more convincing to those unaccustomed
to reading drawings and will be given much more willing attention than a
drawing.

(iv) *Plate Storage.* This is a further domestic example which provides
the solution to a small problem found in almost every household. In most
china cupboards and kitchen dressers, shelf space is inadequate and plates
of different sizes are piled on top of one another (Fig. 52). This means
that the whole composite pile must be handled every time a single plate is
removed or put away, if it is not one of the smallest in the pile. A small
supplementary stand (Fig. 53) solves the problem. It is placed in the corner
of the main shelf and forms two or three additional small shelves across the
corner. It is very easily made by anyone and removes the irritation that is
felt every time plates are taken out or put away under the normal arrangements.

In addition to these general examples, there should be demonstrations of
improvements on small jobs within the industry for which the exhibition is
intended. In engineering, for example, improved toolracks and workbins
can be shown, while in other industries contrasted new and old method layouts
or training examples might be displayed.

FIG. 52. PLATE STORAGE, NORMAL
ARRANGEMENT

Graduated Pile on deep shelf

FIG. 53. PLATE STORAGE, IMPROVED
ARRANGEMENT

Supplementary stand for shelf with corner
to divide sizes

2. Courses of Instruction for Different Factory Groups

Though separate courses will have to be arranged for different factory groups to suit the requirements of each, the general organisation and pattern of all the courses will be similar.

General Organisation of Courses. Some of the first courses to be organised in this country were held after working hours. This was found to be a mistake and although it is unlikely to be repeated now that all kinds of courses during working hours are a feature of industrial life, there are good and bad times to choose for meetings even during the daytime. The morning has been found to be better on the whole than the afternoon. To prevent discussions going on too long, it is as well to end at a time such as the lunch hour which makes a punctual finish inevitable. Meetings lasting one hour are long enough and this hour should be divided between instruction, discussion and practical work. The meetings should be held once or twice a week, and their conduct should be informal. Everyone should be encouraged to take an active part and the teaching should be more in the form of demonstrations than by means of straightforward lectures.

It should be remembered that most people whose work is practical rather than theoretical find it difficult to listen with concentration to a lecture. If it is broken by demonstrations and illustrations the attention will be held more easily. These demonstrations must be carefully prepared beforehand so that they run smoothly. Each session should include some practical work. For instance, if a method of work is to be studied as an example it should not merely be demonstrated. Each member of the group should be given an opportunity of handling the sample parts and feeling the movements. Where a layout problem is the subject, scale drawings of the area in question and templets of the equipment to be arranged on it should be provided for every one. The instruction given at the first few sessions should be illustrated by general examples and later each member should be asked to bring an individual problem. Each of these problems should be discussed by all the members in turn.

Written summaries of the lectures and any charts or diagrams, should be given to every member of the group so that there is no need for note-taking. These written summaries not only serve to drive home the subject of the lecture at the time, but can also be used as a source of reference in the future and they give the student the satisfaction of having something of his own to take away from the course. The first few minutes of every session should be devoted to a short verbal summary of the subject matter of the previous sessions.

Not more than ten people should attend at one time. A smaller group of about six is even better, as it allows everyone to take part more fully. Even if meetings are held in working hours, no one should be compelled or pressed to attend. One unwilling man in a group of this sort can spoil the work of all the others.

If a member of the higher management will address each course at its first meeting, this will impress upon the group the importance that the management attaches to the development of motion study in the organisation. At the same time, he can explain that the course will be followed up by regular quarterly reports on progress and that the management will watch this progress with interest and will take notice of the individual work that is being done. When the first complete motion study programme in this country was introduced into a large organisation, the works director took the chair at a meeting called to explain the plan to the foremen. He began by saying that they would see apparently very obvious improvements made in existing methods in their own shops and that they might feel upset because they had not made the suggestions themselves. He assured them that such results were not nearly so easy to obtain as appeared at first sight; they were the outcome of the application of techniques needing specialised training and expert handling. He said that he blamed himself that the improvements had not been made earlier, since he had not made the necessary expert advice available. No blame could be attached to the foremen up to this point, but there would now be a service available to them for improving methods and facilities for learning some of the techniques themselves. If, in the future, poor methods were found in their departments it would then be the fault of the foremen for not taking advantage of the new facilities. A statement of this type from the higher management will do much to gain co-operation.

The Special Requirements and Contributions of the Separate Groups. The four main groups, higher management, supervisors, operators and functional specialists, will each use motion study in a different way. They will each contribute differently to the main programme and each must therefore have a different training.

The content of the courses organised for each main group or sub-division of a group will vary considerably according to the needs of the group and according to the amount of motion study work expected of it. By keeping the groups separate the examples and illustrations used for each can be such as will be of special interest to the particular group. The emphasis of each course can then be directed towards training each group to make the best of its own particular assets.

(a) Higher Management. The management structure will vary greatly in different organisations. The top levels will normally have some knowledge of motion study since it is they who will have sponsored its introduction into the factory. No organised training scheme can be considered practicable for this group though the motion study investigator should take every opportunity to explain and report any developments in motion study.

The less senior grades of management should be given some opportunity to understand the theory, either by means of group meetings of short duration spread over a period or in the form of half-day conferences. The main emphasis should be on the width of the application with particular reference to the larger type of investigation such as layout and production schemes. Films should be used as much as possible and if time allows an improved method should be developed by the group.

(b) *The Supervisors.* After the higher management, the next group concerned in a full motion study programme is that of the supervisors, the foremen and chargehands. Their part is very important. Apart from any direct motion study work that they may do, they can either co-operate in or hinder the installation of a new method of work. Upon them also falls the responsibility for its maintenance. If they are made antagonistic, they can be more successfully obstructive than any other group in the factory. Unless their confidence is gained at the beginning, they may tend to take the investigations as direct criticism of their own work. If this happens they will find good reasons at every stage of the investigations for condemning all suggestions and experiments. It is upon them that the investigator relies for guidance in selecting operators for the experimental stages of developing a new method and they can make the work very slow and difficult by recommending bad workers or making those selected feel that their supervisors have no confidence in the experiments and expect them to fail. On the other hand, if a supervisor is interested and co-operative, his help is invaluable since he has an unrivalled specialised knowledge of his own department and processes and a direct influence upon the operators under his charge.

In drawing up a syllabus for a supervisors' course, the part of the supervisors in the motion study programme and the use that they will be expected to make of motion study in their own work must be carefully considered. Before beginning the training it is important to know exactly what results are required from the course and what are the limitations. Foremen and supervisors who have received motion study training will be required to co-operate with the full-time investigator in detailed investigations in their own departments; to suggest suitable jobs for full investigations; to make small improvements in the simpler methods used in their departments; to devise sound methods for small new jobs as they arise; to organise the work of their departments according to motion study principles, particularly with regard to the handling and movement of materials; to maintain methods that have already been studied; to assist in the training of operators to use motion study methods and, by showing enthusiasm for the subject, to encourage the operators in their charge to co-operate in the scheme.

To play their part fully, foremen and supervisors must first understand something of the techniques used in developing new methods. The course should therefore include a description of the steps taken in making a full investigation and an outline of the techniques used. It should include demonstrations and examples of old and new methods, showing how the new method is developed from the old. These examples should not be obviously easy to improve. A fairly full knowledge of motion study techniques is necessary to a supervisor, not because he will ever have time to make detailed investigations himself, but so that he can appreciate the work of the full-time investigator without feeling that he is being superseded or disregarded in his own department. He must also acquire an eye for seeing movement so that he can tell at a glance when a method is unsatisfactory. While supervisors should learn all the techniques theoretically, it is a mistake for them to spend time on the detailed analysis of complex jobs or to develop new methods which are more complicated than any that they will have time to do later. Having acquired a general knowledge of motion study techniques which will help them to co-operate in the more detailed investigations, to make their own small improvements and to read instruction sheets and maintain established motion study methods, foremen must learn how to train operators to use motion study methods. For this they must know a little about the learning processes, so that they can realise the stages through which operators pass before they are fully proficient. They should understand the significance of the learning curve theory (cf. Chapter 12) so that they remain patient when an operator shows a tendency to fall back or to progress too slowly.

In the typical course programme shown on page 209, which was originally drawn up for supervisors, all the theoretical work is covered during the first eight meetings. At the end of this period the supervisor should have a sufficient grasp of theory to be ready to put his ideas into practice. In the next section of the course, he should be allowed to try out the theory on various problems of the kind that he will be tackling in his own department in future. Each member of the class should bring a suitable problem which should be discussed and solved by the whole group working together. Most supervisors will find this much the most interesting part of the course, but the first section is equally essential as a background both to this work and to the other motion study work involved in co-operating in the more detailed investigations made by the full-time investigator.

The examples of jobs studied during the course should be of a type that supervisors can be expected to improve in their own departments. If they are trained to make longer and more thorough investigations, they will either be tempted to neglect their normal work, or they will do the motion study work superficially. It is important to remember that the average supervisor is a very busy man with many responsibilities and to realise that the time available to him for motion study work is extremely limited. It is easy to expect too much and to make him discouraged and dissatisfied. It should be made clear to him at the beginning of any training course that his capacity for learning and applying the more detailed techniques is not doubted but that he is not being asked to apply them because it is felt that his main job is so important that he must not be encouraged to neglect it for specialist work.

(c) *Specialist Groups.* Others within the organisation who can contribute to the development of a motion study programme are the functional specialists. Their type and relative importance depend on the nature of the industry and they will vary according to the structure of each organisation. It is only possible to list the most obvious. These may include designers, draughtsmen, tool engineers, planners, time study men, salesmen, personnel officers, administrators and others. If the factory is large, separate courses should be arranged for each group, giving special emphasis to those aspects of motion study which are particularly appropriate to their work. Like the supervisors, none of these specialists can spare much time for the direct application of motion study but they can use its principles in their daily work and, by understanding the contents and the objects of the whole motion study programme, they can make sure that the normal work of their departments not only does not hinder it but positively helps other groups to develop and maintain good methods of work. The designer, for example, will design his product not only for the convenience of the customer using it, but also so that it is easy for the operators in the factory to make or assemble it. He will listen sympathetically to requests from the motion study department that existing designs should be modified to improve working methods in the factory. The tool engineer will make jigs and fixtures which not only ensure accuracy in the finished product but are at the same time easy to use.

In the same way that the syllabus of a course for supervisors is directed at teaching them the aspects of motion study that will help them to play the part in the motion study programme that has been assigned to them, courses for specialist groups must also be based on an analysis of the motion study work which can be expected from each. For designers, for example, the course would follow the outline of the supervisors' course on page 208 until the end of the first five sections, though the illustrations and examples used would be specially chosen to appeal to designers and to emphasise the effect that the design of a product has upon methods of manufacture. They would be taught how a small change or improvement in the finished product may have a quite disproportionate effect in increasing the difficulties of manufacture. Sections 6, 7 and 8 of the sample syllabus would be omitted, or combined, as having very little relevance for designers. A section would be planned to emphasise how the design of a product can help to make it possible to assemble it according to motion study principles. A discussion section would be included dealing as far as possible with problems brought forward by members of the group but, if suitable problems were difficult to find, general problems would be discussed. As an example of this, a study of the best way to shave, which always tends to develop into an argument as to the merits of particular types of razor and is not suitable as an example for analysis by other groups in the first part of the course, is very suitable here. It can be turned into a very useful lesson about the effect of design upon the movements of the user. A course for designers should include an additional session for a discussion on the relationship between the designer and the motion study investigator and on the application of motion study to new products.

The standard syllabus would be modified in a similar way for other specialist groups. For tool engineers, the emphasis would be upon the design of jigs, fixtures and tools and their effect on the movement cycle. Extra sessions would be added to cover this part of the subject in some detail. The course for the personnel department will emphasise the importance of the selection and training of operators for work that has been motion studied and the importance of general operator training in motion study principles for every new entrant as part of the initiation course. In addition to the practical work, such as the design of forms and employment procedure, there should be discussions on the problems that may arise in the handling of operators during a change from old methods to new and on the question of changes of standards and piecework prices which an improved method will inevitably cause.

Courses for administrators and office staffs would be arranged with illustrations and examples of motion study applied to organisation problems, office systems and the design of forms.

Besides the courses provided for functional specialists, there should be co-operation between the motion study investigator and the education officer, or the department responsible for apprentices and management trainees, to ensure that any general management training scheme includes motion study instruction.

(*d*) *The Operators*. The fourth main group to be considered when planning a full motion study programme is that of the operators. Plans should be made to interest them both as a group, through their representatives and individually. Their representatives should not only be kept in close touch with all the plans as they develop, but should also be given opportunities of learning the general principles of motion study so that they can appreciate its potentialities, particularly in the matter of reducing fatigue and contributing to the comfort of the workers. If they are given a good general understanding of the techniques, they will be in a position to explain the schemes to the workers from their own point of view and without misunderstanding.

The motion study courses designed for workers' representatives should be shorter and different in outline from the supervisors' courses, or courses for functional specialists. They should not contain too much theory or work on techniques and for workers' representatives, works committee members and the members of joint production committees the subject matter of the first nine sections of the standard programme should be condensed into one or two sessions with emphasis on the handling of tools and workplace layouts. There should be additional discussion periods on sources of satisfaction and incentives (*see* Chapter 9) and practical work on job examples would be limited and linked with an examination of suggestion schemes. The group should be taught the use of simple process charts in making suggestions for improvements.

Individual operators play a very large part in the success or failure of a motion study investigation, since it is they who have ultimately to use the methods that are developed. A general knowledge of motion study on broad lines will help them to co-operate and will gain their interest. They should also have careful specific training in the use of the methods developed for their own jobs. It has been found that, once operators have had a general instruction in motion study in a training school set up for that purpose, they become much more adaptable and find it easier to learn new work if they have to change from one job to another, or if their work methods are changed as the result of a detailed investigation into their job. They acquire, in addition, a greater interest in their work and are often stimulated to make suggestions for improvements if they find themselves on work that has not been studied or when their job is under investigation. The general training in motion study would normally be included in the initiation training. In most cases, it will not be practical to run special courses for operators already established in the factory.

3. FOLLOWING-UP TRAINING COURSES AND MAINTAINING INTEREST

If the results of a programme of motion study training such as that outlined above are to be permanent, some arrangements must be made for following-up the courses. There must be a definite plan for this follow-up which will be divided into two parts. First, there is the immediate follow-up. This should be a personal matter between the instructor and those taking a course. Some jobs will give more direct scope than others for introducing simple improvements, and since people themselves vary—some liking to be helped to put their ideas into practice and others preferring to be left alone —the approach of the instructor must not be standardised. This immediate follow-up is very important and the instructor should give considerable thought to his approach to each individual.

The second part of a follow-up scheme must be a long term plan. It may take the form of regular quarterly meetings of all supervisors and specialists who have attended courses. If the courses have been successful and have been enjoyed by those taking part, this will not be difficult to arrange. At such meetings reports of progress will be given by each member. These reports can be collected and put together as a quarterly report on the results of motion study to be sent to the board of directors and to everyone who has attended a course. The meeting can either be attended by everyone who has been trained, or it may consist of representatives from each course who are responsible for collecting reports from other members of their own course. The nature of the meeting will depend on the size of the firm and the amount of motion study training that has been given. If the organisation is very large, or is not on one site but scattered over a wide area, the meeting will obviously have to be confined to representatives. The reports presented at the meetings and to the board should give the names and departments of those responsible for the improvements as well as the results of their work.

In order to stimulate others, still pictures should be taken of particularly good set-ups or especially neat ideas. These should be sent out in the form of a regular bulletin for general circulation. In this way, the ideas will be given publicity and as wide an application as possible. Particular care should be taken to see that the name of the originator of an improvement is always mentioned and he should be given personal copies of any photographs so that he can take them home with him.

New methods that are worth filming should be made into old and new method films, projected at the quarterly meetings and added to the motion study film library.

The results shown in reports of progress should always be carefully examined to make sure that they are economic. It is very easy, particularly where many short courses are organized, for those who have attended the courses to achieve small improvements which, added together make an impressive total. When, however, the cost of making these small savings is computed it may be found that some are not worth while. It is more obviously necessary to check the costs of a big investigation, but costs must not be overlooked when assessing the benefits of the more general programme.

Conclusion

Few of the individual items in the full motion study programme outlined in this chapter are new in themselves, but until recently (*see* Appendix *B*) they have seldom been planned as a complete programme in one organisation. In the United States many detailed investigations have been carried out and there has also been a great development in the teaching of elementary techniques to supervisors and others. Unfortunately, very few organisations have used both the elementary and the more detailed forms at the same time. Alan Mogensen was very successful in organising his "Work Simplification" programmes in a number of factories before the war, and some of his pupils were largely responsible for drawing up the "Training Within Industry" programmes which are a much abridged and more standardized version of the same type of teaching. Mogensen himself organised programmes for the U.S. Forces. Although T.W.I. has been abandoned by the U.S. Administration since the war ended, Work Simplification has gone forward steadily and the programmes are being applied in an ever-increasing number of industries.

Work Simplification programmes do not usually include detailed investigations or the organised training of operators. Their primary aim is to get elementary motion study used by as many responsible people in an organisation as is possible. The courses intended for supervisors, therefore, follow a rather different syllabus from that suggested on page 209. They usually include a greater proportion of general management training, covering points on the handling of seniors and subordinates and other matters concerning general industrial relations. A smaller proportion of the course is given to the understanding of the more detailed techniques.

In Great Britain there has been no parallel development equal to work simplification, but T.W.I. is still operating. The T.W.I. programmes are a

SCHEME FOR A SUPERVISORS COURSE

Session	Talk	Illustrations	Practical Work
1.	Introduction. General applications.	Films of old and new methods.	—
2.	Study of the path of movement—chronocyclegraphs.	Chronocyclegraphs of old and new methods.	Developing the new method of one job of which the material can be handled by the group.
3.	Micromotion study.	Putting pegs into the holes in a board. (Film and demonstration of the operation). Wall chart of simo-chart of peg board.	Handling pegboards individually.
4.	Use of process charts.	Simple flow process chart. Simple two-handed chart.	Handling the materials and assisting in making chart.
5.	Characteristics of easy movement.	Suitable selection of films.	Handling material used in the job appearing on the films. Making two-handed chart of the same job.
6.	Workplace layouts.	Photographs of examples of improved layouts. Films of old and new methods of involving changes in layout.	Drawing out the areas of easiest reach.
7.	Factory layouts.	Demonstration of a practical example of the improvement of a familiar layout. Demonstration of string diagrams.	Planning the layout of a domestic kitchen using a scale drawing and templates of the equipment.
8.	Operator training.	Charts of learning curves made in the factory. Examples of training films. Examples of a selection of visual aids to learning.	
9. and following sessions.	The discussion of a sample job brought by each student (one session each).		
Final session.	Problems of installation and summary of course. Report on progress of jobs studied.		

Note: Chronocyclegraphs and micromotion are taught before process charting since they are detailed techniques that supervisors will not be called upon to use in the daily work. A general knowledge of their nature is all that is required as a background for the simpler technique of process charting which the supervisor will learn to use himself. Introduced right at the beginning of a course they also stimulate interest and colour the later outlook of the supervisor.

very good introduction to the application of new ideas, though they are no more than an introduction at present. The "Job Instruction" programme stimulates the interest of supervisors in the training of operators, but it is no substitute for a properly planned training school or training scheme. The "Job Relations" programme emphasises the importance of the careful handling of people as individuals, but it only touches the fringes of personnel management. The "Job Methods" programme, which is the programme most closely related to motion study, is more difficult to use successfully since the ideas that it contains are entirely new to most of those who attend a course. The other two programmes have the effect of throwing new light on existing knowledge or experience, but the "Job Methods" programme is a new subject in itself. It is therefore almost impossible to give any effective instruction in the ten hours allotted to it. In addition to the difficulty of imparting an entirely new idea, the present T.W.I. "Job Methods" programme is made less effective because the example chosen for demonstration, the assembly of the radio shield, is too complex for the purpose. However, in spite of these difficulties, and the shortcomings of the present programme, it is extremely important that foremen and supervisors should realise the value of a study of methods and the need for their improvement. Some instruction on this subject should, therefore, continue to be given within the T.W.I. scheme. It might be possible to replan the syllabus to give more of the theory behind the development of new methods, choosing examples where an improvement is well within the scope of foremen who have received only a limited amount of instruction.

Where schemes of broader motion study instruction, such as the T.W.I. programmes, have succeeded, they have shown the real need in industry for such teaching. Where they have failed, or have had disappointing results, their lack of success only emphasises the importance of applying the full range of motion study in a carefully considered programme, which must be arranged to suit the special needs of each organisation if it is to achieve maximum results. There can be no single ready-made scheme suitable for universal application. Within the programme each section, such as the instruction of supervisors, or the training of operators, should be planned to meet the special needs of each group. It should give each group not only a sufficient knowledge of motion study to allow its members to co-operate when detailed investigations are taking place, but also the experience and practice that will enable them to make as many small improvements in methods as the claims of their other duties will allow. In drawing up a motion study programme, no schemes for the wider application of simplified techniques should be allowed to crowd out the thorough investigations made by the fully trained investigator with the co-operation of all grades in the department concerned. These complete investigations can and should be regarded in the departments as *ours* not *his*. Such co-operative effort is the foundation of any programme and the most direct contribution to increased output obtained with less effort on the part of the operator.

12

OPERATOR TRAINING

HOWEVER good the tools and equipment may be, the results of motion study depend ultimately on the operator's ability to follow precisely the path of movement planned by the motion study investigator. The training of the operator is therefore an extremely important stage in the introduction of motion study and if it is neglected the whole plan will fail.

Before considering detailed schemes of training it is appropriate to examine some of the psychological theories on which these schemes are based. All sound teaching is dependent upon a knowledge of the psychological processes involved in learning. There are various levels of learning, beginning at a purely physiological level, such as the conditioned reflex, and gradually passing through levels where more and more intelligence is needed up to the level at which learning cannot take place satisfactorily unless the learner grasps and applies fundamental principles. Learning in industry is not often concerned with either extreme. It rarely descends to the conditioned reflex and only the most highly skilled work demands a grasp of fundamental principles. However, the early stages of learning a motion study method demand some understanding of simple principles and it is therefore assumed in this chapter that the word "learning" implies a basis of intelligence.

The following are some of the aspects of the learning process which are of particular interest to the motion-study investigator.

Habit Formation

The formation of habits reduces the amount of conscious thought necessary to the performance of a set of movements and with it much of the strain of working. An action which has become a habit is performed automatically when the situation arises that stimulates it. In its simplest form a habit of this sort is like a conditioned reflex but the habitual movements called for by industrial processes are seldom very simple. They are usually very much more difficult to acquire than a conditioned reflex.

To acquire a particular habit that is part or the whole of the movement cycle of a method of work, a conscious effort is necessary over a period of time. This must be based on an understanding of the reason for the movements. An example of a habit formation of this type is the threading of a sewing machine. Beginners should be taught to follow a sequence of numbers on a chart or, better still, on the machine itself and they should be made to understand the reason for each manipulation of the cotton. They should be told, for example, that it goes round point 2 to make a control on its tension and through hole 3 to make a loop to provide the necessary slack for the movement of the needle. To emphasise this they should be shown the result of an uncontrolled tension or an insufficient loop of cotton. When practising threading the machine the movements will tend to follow an excessively long path and to include extra flourishes, but the path will be straightened and the flourishes eliminated with practice and the right movements in their correct sequence will become a habit. The machinist will then go through the movements automatically. She may even be unable after a time to explain, without considerable thought, why or how she makes them, although their purpose and sequence were taught to her in the training period. This ignorance of the details of her movements will be caused by the formation of a habit which will make reasoning unnecessary and make her able to forget the information which helped her to learn the habit.

There are two practical aspects of habitual movements that particularly concern the motion study investigator. The first is the breaking of old habits and the second the establishing of new habits. When a new method is devised and an operator has to be trained to use a new sequence of movements, old habits must be broken if the new method is to be a success. Very often, as in the case of the sewing machinist above, an operator is not conscious of her exact movements, and the first step in breaking down established habits will be to make her see exactly what she has been doing. This is most easily achieved by filming her movements and showing her the results. When she knows what she has been doing she can begin to learn the new movements. In devising a new method care should be taken to make the alterations from the old method as different as possible in those parts of the movement cycle that have become habitual. A movement habit is a physiological pattern of nerve responses and the instant the operator receives the first stimulus to begin a cycle of habitual movements a whole train of responses is set in motion. It is important that this stimulus should not occur if an old habit is to be broken easily. The new movement cycle should therefore be as unlike the old as possible throughout its length. Unless there is a considerable difference between the two there is a danger, particularly in a new method which involves a long cycle of movements, that the new movements may encroach upon the nerve paths of the old habits at various points in the cycle. If this happens the operator will tend to slip back into old habits at each of these points.

Habit formation is, however, more than a mere physiological pattern. An operator must have the will and desire to change habits. Any change requires some individual effort which will not be made unless the reason for the change is made clear. A film of the old method will again be useful here to show the faults of the old method and to convince the operator that a change of habit is necessary.

The age of the operator and the length of time that a habit has been established are further factors affecting the ease with which habits can be changed. Some psychologists consider that any change in established habits becomes almost impossible after a certain fairly early age. James gave this age as 35 but in practice it has been found possible to change the work habits of people very much older than this. Cases could be quoted of operators learning new methods of work at the age of 55 but it undoubtedly takes longer at a later age and requires much more patience both from the instructor and the operator and a strong desire on the part of the operator to succeed.

If the investigator remembers these facts about the formation and breaking of habits during the experimental stages of developing a new method, he

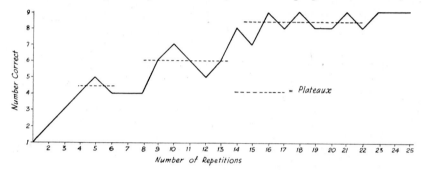

FIG. 54. SIMPLE LEARNING CURVE
showing progress during experiment on learning symbols

can often modify his movement sequence in a way that will not seriously affect his results but which will make the best use of old habits or help in breaking them and establishing new habits.

The teaching of new habits to experienced operators follows the same lines as the training of beginners to use a motion study method but the reasons for each point in the method must be even more carefully explained to avoid mistaken ideas which may arise out of the operator's previous experience.

The Learning Curve

In learning a new method of work, progress is rarely even. Most learners improve in stages and it is important that the motion study investigator should realise this and that he should know when to expect set-backs. Records should be kept of each learner's progress so that these stages can be seen. Psychologists have expressed them in various ways as graphs or curves[1] and have given a number of different reasons[2] for their peculiarities. It is enough for the motion study engineer to know the typical form of a learning or practice curve (*see* Fig. 54). It is usual for an operator to make quick progress

[1] J. M. Blackburn. *The Acquisition of Skill: an analysis of learning curves.* Report No. 73, Industrial Health Research Board. H.M. Stationery Office, 1936.
[2] Collins and Drever.

when he first begins to learn and then to slow down until progress stops altogether or even falls back a little before a further sudden improvement is made. The parts of the curve where progress is arrested are known as plateaux and although they may vary in length and incidence, according to the nature of the job, the individual or the teacher, they occur in all forms of learning. They can sometimes be reduced or smoothed out by correcting a fault in the method of working, by good teaching or by the provision of an additional incentive such as competition between operators, or even by an attempt on the part of the operator to compete with his own record.

Whether a new method is being taught to an experienced operator or a beginner is being trained to use an established method the learning curve should be plotted. A knowledge of the normal shape of the curve will prevent disappointment when a plateau occurs or when the curve drops a little. Experience of a number of learning curves should prevent the setting of final standards of output too early as a result of mistaking a plateau for the final limit of progress. Even when learning curves are understood and plateaux expected it is not however always easy to decide that the final limit has been reached. Some fresh incentive may sometimes cause an operator to beat all previous standards long after he has apparently settled down to a regular rate of output.

Before starting to teach a method of work to an operator three questions must be decided. The first is the amount of the cycle of work to teach at one time, the second is the best distribution of practice periods and the third the amount and kind of information that should be given about the reasons behind the movements.

Part or Whole Method of Presentation

The amount of the workcycle to teach at one time is a question that has raised a considerable amount of controversy. Most psychologists feel that wherever possible the whole of the work cycle should be taught at once rather than that it should be broken into smaller sections. Many experiments have been made in an attempt to decide between this "part" and "whole" method of learning. Some of them are inconclusive, others contradictory and none has dealt with industrial subjects or jobs. They are well summarised by Blackburn[1] who concludes that the "whole" method is generally superior to the "part" method, which, especially in serial learning such as the memorising of poetry, becomes more disadvantageous as the divisions increase in number. He suggests that non-serial type work, such as most industrial jobs, needs further research but he is inclined to think that there is reason to suppose that the "part" method may be better. Practical experience however of teaching industrial work over the last sixteen years has tended to lead to the rejection of this theory and the conclusion that except in certain particular

[1]J. M. Blackburn. *The Acquisition of Skill: an analysis of learning curves.* Report No. 73. Industrial Health Research Board. H.M. Stationery Office, 1936.

circumstances the "whole" method is better. Until further experiments are carried out under real industrial conditions the arguments for each individual case must be analysed and considered, each on its own merits.

When an industrial operation such as assembly work or packing has been properly studied and the method planned according to the best motion study practice, the operation as a whole will form a pattern. This will not necessarily be true of a method that has not been studied. Every motion studied method will have a rhythm of its own. Even in long operations, when the work has to be subdivided between operators the division will be based on the grouping of movements according to their type. Each operator will therefore have a complete rhythm of his own. In teaching rhythmical operations the "whole" method has obvious advantages over the "part" method. These would seem to outweigh the disadvantages. If the work is taught in parts the operator can get no idea of the rhythm and the sequence of movements that form the pattern until he has learnt the last part. For example, if the job is learnt in four parts, working each part up to a certain standard before passing on to the next, the connection between the last movement of part 1 tends to be made to the first movement of part 1, instead of to the first movement of part 2. The same wrong connection is found between the other three parts. As a result, when the parts have to be integrated, movements which have been learnt have to be cut out. This affects the rhythms that have been acquired and complicates the formation of habits.

In addition, as each part is learnt at a different time, the degree of retention will differ for each and the operator will be better at some parts than others when the time comes to put them all together. The higher the standard that is attained on each part the more these difficulties will become apparent.

A further practical difficulty in teaching by the "part" method is that a quantity of material at different stages of completion is needed. This will always tend to make the method unpopular with the teacher and may mean that it is not given full support. It is a difficulty which can be overcome and it should not be given undue weight when the comparative merits of the two methods are discussed, but it is undoubtedly tiresome in the day to day running of a training scheme and if the "part" method is chosen it must be recognised and provided for when the scheme is first planned.

In work consisting of a sequence of movements from one machine to another, such as the operating of presses in a laundry, the "whole" method of teaching is essential. For example, the movements involved in stripping a garment off the press must be combined with the movement of putting it on the next, and since the complete operation uses several presses, any division into parts will result not only in the development of extra movements but also in the whole path of movement being incorrect.

An actual example of the incorrect use of the part method of teaching comes from an engineering works. In teaching a job very common in that industry, the putting of a blank into a press, operating the controls and removing the finished part, an operator was taught the loading of the blank into the press and left to practise this movement without actually operating the controls. She was left to do this until her movements reached a certain standard of proficiency. This meant that she picked up the blank, carried it to the press, placed it in the tool and then, instead of operating the controls, returned immediately for the next part. Her sequence of movements was therefore wrong from the beginning and, in addition, she was inevitably half-hearted in her actions because she lacked the incentive of achieving any production. It would seem more than obvious in this case that on all counts the "part" method of teaching was inappropriate, but in spite of this it was adopted and retained, since although the results were very much poorer than would have been achieved by using the "whole" method of teaching they were better than the trial and error method that they replaced.

In work that involves in one section a particular skill that is difficult to acquire, that section should be taught separately to a standard that it makes it possible to begin learning the job as a whole. For example, in the job of making up in the garment industry it is essential to be able to use a sewing machine properly before beginning to learn a particular method of assembling the parts of the garment. There is little point in teaching operators the detailed movements of handling the part and putting them together if they fumble when they come to the actual machining.

In the majority of cases of this type of work the motion study investigator will be dealing with operators who already possess these fundamental skills and he will be able to teach the whole method from the beginning, but where an operator is new to the work she must be allowed to acquire the fundamental skill before tackling a detailed method. It should be taught to a standard that is sufficiently high not to hinder her when the complete work method is attempted, but no higher.

Distribution of Practice Periods

The next decision that has to be made before training can begin is the amount and distribution of practice periods that will be most effective. Various experiments have been made to discover the ideal arrangement but most have been carried out for academic purposes and are not very useful to industry. In the laboratory it is possible to arrange for any interval between practice periods, whether that interval is to be minutes, hours or even days, but in industry trainees must be at work for the major part of the day. Any considerable variation in the length and distribution of practice periods can therefore be achieved only by moving on to other work between the periods of practice. Except perhaps with new entrants this is not often practicable, for many reasons, but some relief from the close concentration demanded by learning can be given in other ways. New entrants can have their practice periods broken by the necessary initiation talks. All trainees whether new or experienced can be responsible for filling their own material containers, fetching each batch of work and delivering it to the inspector when it is finished. All reasonable interruptions of this type help to give the necessary relief to the trainee.   Blackburn[1] quotes evidence to show that if economy in the total number of hours spent on practice is required the periods should be fairly widely spaced out, but that if the total learning period from beginning work to proficiency is to be as short as possible, practice periods should be close together. In industry this latter consideration is usually the more important.

The weakness of the laboratory experiments from an industrial point of view is that so many have been concerned with the learning of intellectual tasks. Apart from other differences in this type of learning there is a definite goal, the ability to reproduce completely the material learnt. The goal of the learner in industry is much less definite since it is nearly always possible to work just a little better or faster. The acquisition of a manual skill is an indefinite objective compared with the memorising of words or figures.

There have been comparatively few experiments made on sensori-motor tasks but Blackburn[2] suggests that here the method of learning may be more important than the distribution and length of practice periods.   Much more experiment is needed, under industrial conditions but with laboratory control, before any more definite conclusions can be reached.   Until such time as further satisfactory experiments have been made the motion study investigator can judge each case only as he finds it and make such arrangements as are practical in each individual circumstance.

The Transference of Learning

In most of the training examples quoted so far it has been necessary to ask the operators to use their intelligence and to understand the reasons behind the method of work that she is learning to use. The explanation of the reason for using particular movements is extremely important in teaching any method of work. In most industries in this country the majority of operators do not work at exactly the same job for any great length of time. They each do a number of different jobs. The variation between these jobs may arise out of small differences in quality which may call for only slight changes in movements, or they may demand an entirely different set of movements although the same tools are used. In both cases it is important that the operators should have had some instruction in the reason for the original movements so that they can use intelligence when it comes to changing over to a different set of movements.

Some psychologists have attempted to prove that there is no transference of dexterity from one operation to another but to those in industry with experience of training operators this would seem to be a false conclusion.

[1]J. M. Blackburn. *The Acquisition of Skill: an analysis of learning curves.* Report No. 73.   Industrial Health Research Board.   [2] *Ibid.*

An examination of their experimental data explains this difference of opinion. The operators in their experiments learnt their jobs entirely by practice, being shown the movements without explanation and left to perfect them by repetition. The results then only prove that dexterity learnt by mere repetition and practice is not transferred to other work. They throw no light on the problem of dexterity acquired as the result of teaching the reasons behind the movements. Later experiments by Cox[1] produced other evidence that dexterity can be transferred from one job to another if operators are taught the reason behind the methods they are being asked to use. Cox says with reference to his own experiments on the transference of skill, "Skills developed by the mere repetition of one manual operation, confers little advantage in the performance of other operations that may be subsequently undertaken. Where, on the other hand, repetition is replaced by suitable instruction, the skill thus developed at no additional cost in time tends to transfer to other operations over a fairly wide range of manual activity. This transfer is manifested not only in superior ability, but also in superior rate of progress. The advantage thus conferred by training was obtained, in the present experiments, without any loss of efficiency during the training period.

"These results appear of great practical significance, wherever work requiring manual skill is involved, especially when it is remembered that the limits of proficiency to be attained by training may far exceed those attainable by uninstructed repetition. The results indicate the wastage that must be produced by the customary practice of allowing beginners in the assembly room to drop into the work as best they can. And they suggest that a very real advantage would follow from the replacement of this current crude procedure by a short course of systematic training in the general principles underlying manual control illustrated by specific examples from manual operations."

At the same time that Cox was experimenting in the laboratory, similar theories were being tried out in practice, at Metropolitan Vickers in Manchester, on the training of young operators entering the electrical engineering industry for general manual work. A description of this training scheme is given on pp. 229-30. It was very soon found that girls who had been through the training school learnt each job they were asked to do in the factory more easily than those who had not been trained and, in addition, they were much more interested in their work. It was not possible to collect accurate figures proving this point but the general opinion of the motion study staff entirely confirmed Cox's experimental findings. Trained girls showed a marked transference of skill when moved from one job to another.

Learning and Teaching

Having considered, very briefly, some of the psychological processes involved in learning, these theories must be translated into practice. It is

[1] J. W. Cox. *Manual Skill.* Cambridge Univ. Press, 1934.

clear that the quality of learning depends to a large extent on the quality of teaching.

The principles of teaching in industry are the same as the teaching principles in sport, in the schoolroom and in any other sphere of life. While there are many different theories it is generally agreed that the teacher must begin by impressing on the pupil the purpose for which the task is done. He must then make clear the reasons why a particular theory or method has been adopted and must demonstrate and explain the way in which it is carried out, giving the trainee planned and repeated practice and the opportunity of measuring his progress.

It is important to begin by stimulating interest, to get the trainee into the receptive frame of mind essential for learning. In teaching motion study methods this can be done by throwing new light on a familiar scene; by emphasising the significance of method in any activity. Interest once aroused, the new method of working must be impressed upon the learner by a form of teaching which makes full use of all the appropriate senses. To be able to teach a manual operation the instructor must have a detailed knowledge of the movements that are to be made. He must know the reason why they are made in a particular sequence and in a particular way and he must be able to get that knowledge over to the operator. Where a movement cycle has been changed and improved he must be able to explain why the method has been altered and why any other way of working is not as good as the prescribed method. This is only the first part of his work. He must go further and teach the operator not only to understand the method but also to use it.

To make an operator understand what has to be done and the importance of doing it the right way, an appeal must be made to his reason. The verbal appeal of argument and explanation should be simple and direct and should be reinforced by the visual stimulus of demonstration, pictures, and diagrams, and, where appropriate, films. These illustrations not only make learning more interesting but also make the instruction clearer if they are used with verbal explanation. They cannot take the place of verbal teaching but their meaning enters the operator's mind through the eye instead of the ear and in many cases makes a lasting impression, throwing light on the words of the teacher. Except, however, for such general and simple operations as the use of the hammer, screwdriver or file (*see* Figs. 55 and 56) pictures or diagrams alone are no more helpful than words alone. Sight and hearing should be used together to make a double impression on the memory.

Diagrams, pictures and films are now used very widely in the training of operators and the term "visual aids" is commonly used to describe them in all their forms. Their value to the teacher as tools is undoubtedly immense but it must always be remembered that they are not his only tools. Rational explanation must always come first and without it the full value of operator training cannot be achieved.

FIG. 55. THE CORRECT USE OF A HAMMER
Teaching diagram used in training school (*see* pp. 229-30)

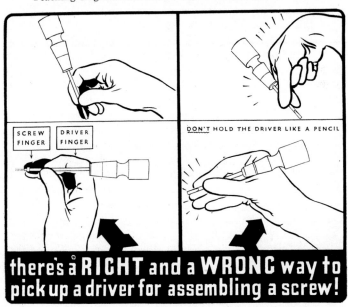

FIG. 56. THE CORRECT HANDLING OF A SCREWDRIVER IN SMALL
ASSEMBLY WORK
Teaching diagram used in training school

The most complete of all the visual aids is the training film. Where the size and scope of a training problem justifies its cost, a simple 16mm. cine film, made especially for the purpose, is of great value. Preceded by a demonstration by the teacher or by an experienced operator it amplifies the impression made by that demonstration. It isolates the movements from the distraction of their setting and background and allows greater concentration. It can be seen by a number of trainees at the same time and each will view it from the same angle and unobstructed. In addition, it provides a demonstration which contains no variations and no mistakes. It shows the standard method in its most perfect form, exactly as the motion study investigator wants it to be used. If it is correctly made it will show the movements from a number of useful angles but always in such a way that the trainee can feel himself in the position shown on the screen, the right hand of the demonstrator appearing to the right of the screen as it is viewed.

It is possible to show greater detail on a film than in a demonstration, and since exactly the same cycle can be shown again and again and stopped whenever the teacher wishes, it can be made to give correct emphasis to points of detail which might otherwise be missed. Slow motion photography can be used to slow down movements accurately and to show detail that is normally too fast for the eye to follow. If an ordinary demonstrator is asked to slow down his movements, accuracy is nearly always lost, since very few operators use the same movements when working slowly as when working normally. In slowing down they lose rhythm and tend to become jerky.

A training film has the further advantage that it puts the motion study method on record in a permanent form. Training supervisors may leave and be replaced, but the correct method continues to be taught. Finally, the film has the tremendous advantage of being a very popular medium of instruction. There is never any difficulty in obtaining the closest attention when a film is being shown.

In recent years there has been much enthusiasm for filmstrip as a visual aid to teaching. To the motion study investigator it appears to be inferior to the cine film and since he has his cine camera and projector he usually prefers to make a slow motion picture rather than the series of still photographs that make up a filmstrip. In essence, film strip is very little different from a series of lantern slides and although the strip itself is a little cheaper and the apparatus for showing it is comparatively inexpensive and lighter to handle it is less adaptable than the slides because it is not easy to vary the order in which the pictures are shown.

Subjects that are suitable for filmstrip are usually equally suitable for showing as a series of line drawings or diagrams, or even as still photographs (*see* Fig. 57). Such a series has the advantage that all the pictures are on view together and the eye can follow them backwards and forward at will. In teaching a motion study method a series of hand positions can often be shown in this way. They should be drawn or photographed so that

PREPARING TO STITCH.

1 THREADING THE BOBBIN CASE.

BOBBIN CASE IN LEFT HAND
OPEN SIDE TO RIGHT: BOBBIN IN
RIGHT HAND, THREAD RUNNING
FROM FRONT TO BACK.

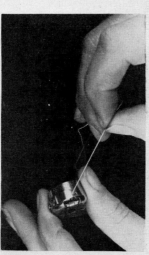

DRAW THREAD
INTO SLOT IN EDGE
OF BOBBIN CASE.

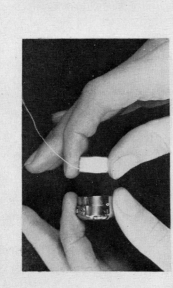

PULL THREAD DOWN
SLOT, UNDER TENSION
SPRING, AND INTO
DELIVERY EYE.

2. REPLACING BOBBIN CASE.

Fig. 57. Part of a Wall Chart

It comprises a series of photographs used in the elementary training of sewing machinists the operator sees the pictured hands from the same angle as she sees her own hands and can even place her own over the picture or in front of it to check their position. Such a series of pictures has an advantage over the cine film or filmstrip in that the operator can have it in front of her while she is actually practising the operation. The cine film or film strip must be viewed at least in partial darkness and usually away from the work bench and its lesson must be remembered long enough to be carried back to the workplace.

A series of hand positions is usually clearer in the form of drawings or diagrams than as actual photographs, because emphasis can be laid on the details that are the most important and there need be no background. Still photographs on the other hand are easier and cheaper to make.

It should always be remembered that movement is essentially physical and can never be wholly understood until it is felt. The operator must be allowed to experience the kinæsthetic sensation of trying the movements herself. For example, it is well known that in teaching swimming it is useless to depend entirely on diagrams and demonstrations of the strokes and the practice of the movements on dry land. The pupil only begins to learn properly in the water, when he can try what he has seen and get the feel of the movements against the resistance of the water. Applied to the teaching of an industrial job this means that visual demonstration and rational explanation are not enough, that the mere following of the correct path of movement without the right rhythm in the right setting is inadequate.

Kinæsthetic sensation is an important means of teaching a manual operation. It is usually enough to allow the trainee to handle the normal materials and tools of the job that she is learning and wherever possible she should work from the beginning on the correct materials and on productive work. There are, however, circumstances in which this is not possible. If a process is intricate and difficult to learn and its material is expensive and easily damaged, or if the normal material is very fine and the trainee finds it almost impossible to see its composition or to criticise the mistakes she makes, coarser materials or models may be called for in the preliminary stages of training so that the correct movements can be learnt to a lower degree of accuracy. For example, in teaching girls to mend fine worsted, where faults in the weaving are made good and breaks in the yarn or loose ends are replaced by running in with a needle, beginners often find it very difficult to see the details of the various weaves and patterns, or to see and understand the mistakes they make. To get over the difficulty some practice on specially woven pieces of a loose coarse weave will give the trainee a better understanding of the different standard weaves and some idea of the feeling of handling a needle in running in an end. The much more commonly used diagram of the weave is far less effective than the actual handling of the special pieces and the running of the needle through the warp and weft threads to feel the pattern as well as to see it.

It is, however, a mistake to leave trainees for too long on models or special materials made on a larger scale. Not only do they lack the incentive of production work but the movements required feel different from the movements used on the normal work. They must not be allowed to form too strong a habit. As soon as possible, learners should graduate to practise on the simplest form of normal material.

Practice on special material or models should always be confined to beginners. Experienced operators learning a new method of work should always use productive materials.

Types of Operator Training

If a method of working is not properly taught the operator will learn by trial and error and as the result of practice. It will take much longer to learn this way than if definite instruction is given and the final result will seldom be the best obtainable. No two operators will do the same job the same way and there will be a much bigger variation between the output of the best and worst operator. Although some variation in output between best and worst will always exist it can be greatly reduced by good teaching. Where operators are not trained to use a standard method the difference between the output of the best and the worst may be as much as 100 per cent. This difference will be due only partly to differences in innate ability. Much of it will be caused by variations in the methods used, although these variations may escape notice till the problem is studied. When a method has been improved by motion study and operators have been taught the standard method, the difference in output between best and worst will be much less, since it will be caused only by differences in speed and ability and will not be increased by the fact that some operators are using slower methods of work than others.

Motion study demands the teaching of standard methods of work to all operators. Individual differences are not regarded in the first instance unless they are exceptionally definite such as those displayed by left-handed or disabled workers. Some psychologists have in the past criticised this aspect of motion study teaching but in more recent times the experience of most industrial psychologists has been that individual differences in sensori motor work of any kind are less important than was previously thought. Individual differences on the mental and emotional planes are, however, even more significant but these have always been considered very seriously by all good motion study investigators (*see* Chapter 9).

In planning the training of operators the motion study investigator is concerned with two distinct kinds of training. The first is the training of experienced operators to use improved methods, and the second the training of all new entrants.

Training Experienced Operators to use an Improved Method. The general principles of teaching set out above apply to all types of training for manual work but they must be used with different emphasis in different circumstances. In teaching experienced operators to use an improved method it may be easier to arouse interest than where beginners are to be taught. The interest already exists to some extent since the job in its old form is their job and they have inevitably taken considerable interest in the investigation. There will probably be a film of the old method of working and this can be used to point out the reasons for the changes that have been made and to convince the operators that the changes really are improvements. Until this film is shown, many of them will have no clear idea of the movements and methods that they have been using. During an early motion study investigation in this country an operator was studied who was assembling four counters as part of a meter. She assembled the first with her right hand, the second and third with her left hand, and the fourth with her right hand again. The two hands were used in sequence and not simultaneously. The motion study method required her to assemble the first and second counters with her left and right hands simultaneously followed by the third and fourth in the same way. She objected that she would never be able to do this because she could not possibly use her left hand. She could not believe that she was already using it just as much as her right hand and was only convinced when she saw a film of herself using the old method.

Although there may be little difficulty in arousing the interest of operators in a new method of doing their own job their co-operation is often less easy to obtain. The investigator may meet with considerable opposition from operators who are inclined to resist any change and to view the new method with suspicion as being something to their possible disadvantage. This suspicion and resistance can usually be overcome if the management will put out a statement to the effect that it is their intention that operators shall lose nothing by co-operating and that the average earnings of pieceworkers will be maintained during the training period until rates are fixed which normally give them increases on their previous earnings (*see* Chapter 8). It must however, be understood from the beginning that after a motion study investigation, piece work prices are always revised. Wherever possible, where the machinery of joint consultation exists, each motion study investigation should be discussed at a suitable meeting between representatives of workers and management before it is begun. At every stage the representative of the operators concerned should be kept fully aware of developments. If this policy is adopted all suspicion should have been dispelled before the training stage is reached.

It is less easy to combat the natural resistance to a change of habits. This is particularly strong where those habits are long established. As we have seen earlier in this chapter, it depends both on the attitude of the worker and on the nature of the change required, whether a long standing habit can be broken at all easily. The investigator must decide whether the results that can be expected from the suggested change are important enough to justify the time that must be spent in breaking old habits. He may occasionally decide that it is better to disregard older and more established operators and to concentrate on the younger and less-experienced workers. The decision will be made only in the last resort, since the experienced workers have a detailed knowledge of the work which is of the greatest value.

In all cases it must be remembered that habits are both psychological and physiological and that in teaching operators to break them an appeal must be made to reason. At the same time some physical assistance may also be given such as a guard or a change in the position of a control which will discourage the old habit. The breaking of habits is essentially an individual matter. Some operators find it more difficult than others. The motion study investigator must always exercise patience and remember that in most cases the operator is not being deliberately obstructive but is merely finding that, although the new movements will ultimately be easier to perform than the old, they are difficult to acquire until old habits are broken. He must also remember that this tendency to cling to old habits is an advantage in the maintenance of the new method. If a method is properly taught it will continue unchanged for an indefinite period once the old habits have been overcome and the new established.

A distinction must be made between the training of the first operator to use a new method and the training of subsequent operators. The training of the first operator should be regarded as experimental and as coming into the third stage of a motion study investigation before the new method has been fully installed. Some minor modifications in the method will always be made during the training of the first operator. However carefully the method has been planned, and however much thought has been given to the workplace layout and the testing of the fixtures, some modifications will be needed if the job is to be made to suit the operator. All details should already have been discussed with supervisor, operator and operator's representative. Their criticisms should have been examined before training begins but practice will always show something that must be altered a little.

The actual process of teaching the movements to the first operator will be slower and more difficult than to subsequent operators. There can be no really convincing demonstration of the method used at speed, either by means of a film or a practical demonstration. The old method film can be used to convince the operator of the need for improvement, but the only demonstration of the new method is that given by the investigator who cannot spare the time to practise it and bring it up to real production speed. The operator can be persuaded that the new method is better than the old but only by trying it herself will she find out how much better it is. Diagrams and drawings may help to teach her movements (*see* pp. 219 and 221) but she will lack the incentive of seeing with her own eyes that the method can give the results the motion study investigator claims for it. Subsequent operators will see her at work and will know from the beginning the rate of output possible. They may even have a film of her at work from which they can learn the details of the method.

In training experienced operators to use a new method it is important to insist from the beginning that the movements are made exactly in the standard way laid down by the motion study investigator for the new method. No modifications should be allowed until old habits are thoroughly broken, except in such obvious cases as those of left-handed or disabled workers. Only when the standard method has been practised and a reasonable degree of proficiency attained should any personal preferences suggested by individual operators be considered. Until old habits are broken the importance of these suggested modifications cannot be fairly assessed. They may seem easier at first only because they are nearer to established habits. In the same way, a cricket or a tennis coach insists on a certain standard style for movements when he is coaching beginners and allows variations only when the standard movements are satisfactory and the pupil is beginning to show signs of mastery.

An example of the voluntary general use of a standard method can be seen in the way most people use a knife and fork in an identical way to conform to the manners and customs of their social group or nation.

Training New Entrants. If training is important for operators who have to learn new motion study methods it is even more important for new starters for whom it ensures the best possible methods from the outset. Incidentally it does much to break down the sense of strangeness felt by newcomers and helps to settle them in their work. In addition, the satisfaction of the operator can be considerably enhanced by a training scheme which explains the principles upon which methods are based, and which encourages rhythmical working and reduces fatigue.

A training scheme for new entrants has two main parts, an introduction to the general life of the factory, and the teaching of methods of work and the theoretical background of those methods. The introductory information should cover a description of the amenities of the factory and the employee services that are available; clubs, canteens, library, educational facilities and any other special feature. It should also make clear the rules about such things as timekeeping, smoking, washing, accident prevention and any special arrangements about hours and tea breaks. It should include a careful explanation of the wages system, and where a payment by results scheme is in operation, instruction in the working out of piecework earnings. In addition there is an opportunity here to give new entrants some information about the firm's products and the markets they reach, with an account of the management of the factory from the directors down to the chargehands. Trainees should visit the different departments in the factory to see how the products are made. This will encourage them to take a personal interest in the firm's activities and to feel at home and to take pride in belonging to the organisation. Where most of the entrants are school-leavers there should be some explanation of the national insurance schemes.

It is obvious that all this information will not be absorbed unless it is divided into small sections and spread over some time. It can be given in the form of half-hour talks used to break up longer periods of practising work methods and both will benefit from the mixture of mental and physical work.

The second and more important part of a training scheme is the teaching of correct methods of work. There are two types of training in work methods. The first and best known is the training given to entrants engaged to do a specific job which it is hoped they will continue to do during the whole of their working life. A high final standard of skill and output is usually required and maximum efficiency is not expected for many months. The second type of training is given to entrants who are intended for general work where jobs, although they may be of a common type with many similar features, change constantly and call for adaptability in the worker and only a limited amount of specific skill.

Training for Specific Work. The training of new entrants to do specific jobs, such as weaving, or operating a sewing machine, follows the same lines as the training of experienced operators to use a new method of work, but in addition to the training in the use of exact methods and movements there must be instruction about the technical background of the work. It is not necessary to elaborate this point since most training schemes concentrate on it to the detriment of any training in methods and movements. It is enough to say that the maximum use should be made of large scale models and drawings to make the instruction clear, since trainees, particularly juveniles, always have difficulty in appreciating the smaller differences in detail in the quality of their work. Where the work, such as weaving, is very fine, they may entirely fail to understand both instructions and criticisms if the normal quality of material is used for demonstration and early practice.

In planning the training of operators to do a single specific job a careful scheme should be worked out to include initiation, theoretical and technical instruction and the teaching of exact methods and movements and any special skills that may need separate instruction. Into this scheme a general plan for the teaching of simple motion study should be introduced. If operators are to take their place beside supervisors and managers in the full motion study plan for the factory (*see* Chapter 11) they must know what it means from the beginning so that later on they can co-operate in the development of improved methods and so that throughout their working life they can appreciate the importance of keeping to the detailed method they have been taught. An explanation should be given of the theory behind the more obvious features of a well arranged workplace; the importance of correct tool and material holders and of chairs and foot rests arranged at the right height; the significance of the areas of easiest reach. This explanation should be illustrated by examples taken from the trainees' own jobs as well as by more general examples. Chronocyclegraphs of the type shown on pp. 72-3 should be used to demonstrate how changes in the placing of tools and materials affect the path of movement. Reasons should be given for the particular arrangement chosen in new method examples. Films of good and bad methods can be shown, and emphasis should be given to the advantages to the operator in the reduced fatigue caused by well-balanced movements and the simultaneous use of both hands.

The length of the training period will depend on the type of work that is being taught but unless the technical details of the job are intricate it will usually take a much shorter time to teach a job by the rational motion study method than by the more usual scheme of demonstration and practice. Individual operators should be tested at intervals, records being kept of daily progress and of the test results. When a minimum standard of efficiency is reached trainees should be transferred to normal production. In times of labour shortage there will always be a demand for training time to be cut down and for trainees to be transferred before they have reached that standard. These demands should be resisted since they are based on a very short-term view and the inefficient work of the partially-trained operator will do much to damage the reputation of the training scheme, since it will soon be forgotten that the training was not completed.

The Training for General Work. It is more difficult to train operators for general work than to train them to do one job well. Instead of performing one intricate set of movements perfectly they will be required to undertake any one of a number of jobs which are only similar in that they belong to the same broad type of work, such as assembly work, packing or machine work. The movement sequences will change as job succeeds job and there is nothing that can be learnt by mere demonstration and repetition. What is required is a transference of skill from one job to another. A different and more difficult type of teaching is therefore needed and any failure in the quality of the teaching will be more serious. Trainees may take longer to learn a specific job if the training is poor but they ultimately learn it, if only by methods of trial and error. They may never learn to transfer their skill from one job to another if they are not taught to do so.

Since it is obviously impossible to teach each operator in detail all the jobs that may fall to her lot during her working life as a general worker, she must be taught how to tackle any work that is put in front of her; how to apply her experience of one job to something only very slightly like it. She must learn to be adaptable. The more adaptable she is the more successful she will be.

In organising a training scheme for general workers a job analysis must first be made of all the work in the factory that they will ever be required to undertake. Work must be graded and the common movement features of each grade must be taught to the trainees. Actual production jobs which contain these common features should be selected and used as work for the trainees.

In training general workers the teaching of simple motion study is of the greatest importance. In many cases these workers will be required to arrange their own workplaces and even sometimes to do work for which no specific method has been laid down. A knowledge of elementary workplace layout and of the simpler characteristics of easy movement is therefore very valuable and useful.

The same initiation instruction should be given as is given to other starters, though information about the technical background of the work will generally need to be wider.

The following extract from a paper read in Washington in 1938 to the 7th International Management Congress describes a successful scheme for the general training of new entrants into an engineering works[1].

"To begin this school, a job analysis was made, of all women's jobs in the factory. It was found that, though the jobs varied considerably, they could be grouped according to typical movements used in performing them and that all jobs had a few common features. The scheme was then set up for a preliminary training to include these common features which were (a) the handling of a screwdriver; (b) the use of a hammer; (c) the simultaneous use of both hands; (d) the arrangement of material. This was followed by specialised training in one of the following groups: fine assembly, simple assembly, drilling and capstan lathe work, coil winding, insulating, testing, inspecting. After the first week of the preliminary training the operators are given a test, the pass standard of which is set so that only the quick learners pass and the remainder repeat their training for a second week. If on the second test girls do not reach the set standard, they may succeed in passing at a lower standard. If they fail completely they are discharged as unsuitable. According to their pass marks, the reports of the teachers, the girls' own inclinations and the factory demand, they enter one of the specialised groups and receive training in that type of work, and once they have reached the requisite standard of proficiency they are transferred to the appropriate department. If this department does not need them when they are ready, they remain for further training in the school but, conversely, if there is a demand for them before they have reached the required standard, they are not allowed to leave the school. Temporary arrangements such as employing old operators who have left on marriage are made by the Employment Department. This rule must be kept or there is the risk of half-trained operators entering the factory.

"Work has to be selected from the various departments which can be used to give such training and the production taken over by the training school. The importance of the trainees performing regular manufacturing work cannot be over-emphasised. In the general running of the school it would often be simpler to have a stock of material which could be assembled and taken down again; this would not create the feeling in the girl's mind that her work was useful and that she had to meet the regular inspection standards which are expected of her later in the factory. The Training School should resemble a manufacturing department in every way and the girls should be paid regular wages while they are training and, in the last week, should be expected, where possible to work on piecework and be eligible for bonus.

"The school is supervised by a foremistress and two assistants, all of whom have been specially trained for the work, the two assistants receiving further

[1] Metropolitan-Vickers Elec. Co., Ltd., Trafford Park, Manchester.

training in general supervision while they are attached to the school so that they can ultimately be foremistresses in the factory. The method they use in teaching the operator is first to explain in great detail the object of the school and the aim of Motion Study. They show the operators films of simple jobs done in the usual way and then done according to Motion Study procedure, thus giving them a general impression of what is expected. The instructor then sets out and performs a simple job, arranging the materials within the areas of easiest reach which are marked out on all the benches, showing each movement in great detail. The instructor remains with the girl, correcting each mistake as she makes it and, with every correction, explaining the reasons for making the right movements. This procedure is followed in every job, with the instructor emphasing the similarities and dissimilarities between each job. The girl will, for instance, be given three or four jobs in succession to teach her to use a screwdriver and, though each will be different, she has to realise that the principles underlying the use of the driver are the same for each. In addition to this individual teaching, the instructors lecture to the girls in each group about the methods used. Every day general lectures on factory procedure are given to the whole school, and every hour the operators perform finger and arm exercises for two or three minutes to ensure suppleness of movement.

"When they have completed their training the girls have a general knowledge of the principles of motion economy and have more particular knowledge of one of the classes of women's work in the factory as well as being familiar with the factory routine."

This training scheme ran for more than six years in its original form, largely but not entirely, training school-leavers, until the normal juvenile entrant became very scarce in the second year of the war. At that time transferred workers were brought in from other areas and groups of girls were recruited in large numbers from less-essential industries. The school premises were enlarged and the scheme stood the strain of the flood of new entrants, answering all the demands that were made upon it. The course for adults was condensed to a minimum of one week and although this was not an ideal arrangement, since trainees did not have time to try a great variety of jobs, not much of the original plan was sacrificed and the results were satisfactory. The same principles were applied at a dispersal unit in the training of part-time workers for small assembly work of a general nature and they contributed very largely to an unusually successful part-time scheme, keeping the labour turnover particularly low.

The same firm set up another general training school in their war-time aircraft factory. It worked on the same lines, training girls to do jobs usually undertaken by men. It was instrumental in keeping a percentage of women workers over men as high or higher in that factory than any in the country.

Training schemes are being more generally adopted now than at the time of the 1938 Washington Congress. Many began during the war but although they were generally successful they were not always as good as it would have been possible to make them. Any training scheme needs special planning to suit the circumstances of each factory. The broad principles outlined above must be adapted in different ways in each case. Success will depend on the quality of the planning behind the scheme, the original job analysis and the care of the personnel department in selecting and placing applicants (*see* Chapter 10). The arrangements that must be made for putting such a scheme into practice will depend on the size of the factory and the number of new entrants in any given period. If the factory is too small or if there are too few new entrants to justify a separate training school the scheme may be divided into two parts, the personnel officer being responsible for background training and the foremen giving instruction in methods of work. The instruction given by the foremen should follow the lines suggested by the T.W.I. Job Instruction programme; the motion study investigator making the job breakdown.

It is much less important that the training should be given in one place or by one person than that it should be given fully in one form or another and that each item should be presented to the operator in the way that is easiest to absorb. In spite of this, however, and although it is perfectly possible to make the training of new entrants an individual matter in a small factory, in many organisations it can and should be group training which should normally be given in a separate training section or school. Such an arrangement has definite advantages where it is possible. Its administration is much simpler and it adds greatly to the adjustment of the individual to the factory. It also helps in the selection of individual operators to fill particular vacancies. Even where careful interviews and tests are given, the experience of each operator's reaction to the work of the training department gives valuable additional information and an opportunity of reviewing the original decision.

Such a training scheme may well be combined with the experimental section of the motion study department but it should always be kept separate from the main workshops though near enough for its connection with them to be obvious to the operators. Since beginners should be trained on productive work and should contribute to the production of the factory right from the outset it must not be too far away from the factory department from which it draws its raw materials. It is not always possible, however, for new operators to be trained in a separate section. If, for example, the work they are learning involves the use of heavy machines it may be necessary for them to work among the experienced operators but even in this case all instruction that does not require the use of the machine should be given in another room.

A training department should be arranged and run as much as possible like a normal factory department. It should have more of the appearance of a workshop than a school and emphasis should always be laid upon the fact that it is a production department.

So far in this chapter little reference has been made to the training of boys and men. While the training of girls and women is more obviously essential because of the type of work that is usually required of them and because they often start work entirely without experience, it is equally important to introduce training in motion study methods for male operators. Separate schemes should be worked out to suit the different grades of workers and the special circumstances of each particular factory, but each scheme should be based on the same general principles as the training given to women operators. To take an example from the engineering industry, apprentices who will ultimately be skilled workmen should spend a period in their trade school which should be entirely devoted to motion study instruction. As practical work during that period the senior apprentices may make fixtures for those motion study investigations that are in progress in the factory at the time. This will serve a double purpose. The reason for the fixtures and the motion study principles embodied in their design will be explained and will serve as examples to the apprentices of the practical application of motion study. At the same time the motion study investigator will get his fixtures made more quickly. Like the training of new women operators this type of apprentice training is an investment for the future.

Training the Instructor

In selecting an instructor, while it is necessary to choose a worker or supervisor who has acquired the skill that is to be taught it is equally important that he or she should have enthusiasm and the ability to impart information. An interest in people, combined with patience and fair judgment, is just as valuable as an outstanding production record. Where the job to be taught involves a particular skill it is necessary for the instructor to have acquired that skill but it is equally important that he should be able to teach it.

Once chosen, the instructor should be given a sound theoretical training so that he realises the reasons behind the training programme that he will be administering and the importance of following it accurately. The T.W.I. Job Instruction course can be used here to stimulate interest but although it does not offend against any of the principles of good teaching it is not, in itself, a sufficient training for an instructor. It does not explain any of the theoretical background of teaching and should therefore, if it is used, be regarded only as an introduction to the subject. The main part of the training should begin with a comprehensive course of motion study so that its aims and practices and the ideas behind an investigation are thoroughly understood. It is not necessary that a training school instructor should be able to make a motion study investigation or develop a new method but it is necessary that the significance of all the points in a motion study method should be appreciated and therefore taught to trainees correctly and with the right emphasis. As much time as possible should be spent on a critical examination of films and demonstrations showing the comparison between old methods and motion study methods of the same jobs. This will impress the need for motion study and the importance of teaching correct movements.

An instructor must be familiar with some of the theories relating to the various processes of learning and in particular with the effect of the learning curve on an operator's progress and the need for patience when the operator reaches a plateau. He must also appreciate the importance of the kinæsthetic sensation as an aid to correct working and know the appropriate uses of the various visual aids.

Finally, he must understand how the training scheme has been planned and why each step in it takes place in a particular way and at a particular time.

The practical part of his training must help him to perform correctly the movements of the job that he will be teaching. It is not essential that he himself should be thoroughly skilled in the work he is to teach. It is much more important that he should be able to explain the reasons for the movements. The operators will acquire speed in time as the result of practice but they will not be able to transfer the dexterity that they acquire to other similar work unless they are taught the reasons behind the series of movements that they have learnt.

Conclusion

Although operator training may not be the most interesting part of a motion study investigator's work it is by no means the least important. The first success of direct motion study improvements must depend very largely upon how well the operator has been trained to use the correct method. Their satisfactory maintenance in the future depends upon the arrangements made for the training of future operators. The motion study investigator must therefore give considerable attention to training schemes, although, to save time, he may delegate most of their day to day application to an instructor.

The initiation training of new starters is less closely connected with the success of motion study investigations but, although its effect is indirect and less obvious, it is equally important ultimately. As methods are investigated one by one throughout the factory, much time will be saved where the operator concerned has received a preliminary theoretical motion study training as part of an initiation course. Instructions will be more easily understood and co-operation will be more readily obtained. Since these last stages in an investigation always occupy such a large part of the total time spent upon it, time saved here is extremely valuable.

13

THE PLACE AND FUNCTION OF A
MOTION STUDY DEPARTMENT

TWO hundred years ago goods were largely produced by men working in their own homes using their own hand tools. The coming of the machine age drew these individual workers and their descendants into small groups to share power units and to use the new machinery, which was too expensive for individual ownership. They became wage earners, under orders from the owners of the machines.

As machines became more elaborate factories grew larger, and science still further enlarged the working groups by developing products and materials that demanded such complex machines and processes that they could only be produced economically in very large quantities by very large groups of workers. The nineteenth century increase in the population of the country provided a wider market which developed further with the consequent rise in the standard of living. Large quantity production became more and more profitable and the large production unit is now a common feature of industrial life.

The steady growth in size of production units meant that increasing demands were made upon those who found themselves in charge. Fortunately, changes were gradual and human beings are very adaptable. Some sort of management system therefore arose within the factories and, as might be expected, intelligent, keen and able men managed well while the less able failed. On the whole, however, technical progress far outstripped the progress of management practice.

F. W. Taylor, at the end of the nineteenth century, saw the need for a more scientific approach to the problems of management and his great contribution to industrial progress is this emphasis on the scientific approach. Since Taylor's day the need for planned management has increased greatly and there is some conscious organisation in every factory. In addition, twentieth century production methods demand the employment of specialists. Few of those responsible for production at any level can have a sufficiently specialised or technical knowledge of every aspect of the work to deal with all the problems that arise. The number and type of specialists to be employed will depend on the size of a factory and the nature of its product and it is the responsibility of those in charge of a factory to decide how these specialists are to be used.

It is usual for the responsibility for production to be in the hands of a chain of people at different levels, beginning with the general manager and ending with the chargehand on the shop floor. This is known as line management and follows a more or less military structure. The general manager has the responsibility for the whole functioning of the company and delegates particular duties to managers who are responsible directly to him; a works manager for example for the works. This works manager in turn delegates to his departmental managers, who pass on responsibilities to their foremen and the foremen to the chargehands. Each is answerable to the man above him for the work of those below him; not only receiving instructions down the line but reporting back up the line.

Outside the line organisation specialists are in charge of their specialist functions but as they have no direct responsibility for production they must always act through the line executive who controls the section in which they are working. There may be a number of these functional specialists in an organisation of any size and the motion study investigator will be one of them. He will have no executive responsibility for production but will act in an advisory and service capacity to the manufacturing departments. If during the installation of a method of work he takes over the temporary responsibility for production he does so not in his own right but as the agent of the line executive whose normal responsibility it is.

The Structure of the Motion Study Department

Since so much depends on the size and type of the factory and the stage of development reached by motion study within the factory, it is impossible to give anything but very general rules about the size and organisation of a motion study department. It is obviously a mistake to begin with too large or complex a structure. It is always better to start small and allow room for expansion as the need arises. So that the department can develop constructively, however, its final state must be visualised right from the beginning. It is therefore worthwhile to spend some time considering the organisation of an ideal full-scale department, although very few firms in this country have yet reached such a stage of development in their application of motion study.

Functions of a Motion Study Department

Before the organisation of the department can be considered, its functions must be examined. Experience has shown that most departments of five years standing or more are required to fulfil four main functions; the making of detailed investigations, advisory work, motion study training and the follow-up of all past motion study work.

1. *Detailed Investigation.* It has been demonstrated throughout this book that the full investigation into individual problems is usually the most important part of the work of the motion study investigator and the part that yields the most easily measured and profitable results. Most of these investigations are

made in the manufacturing departments, particularly in the later stages of manufacture where labour charges are usually heaviest. The higher the proportion of hand labour employed on a job the greater is the scope for motion study. In jobs involving much machine work actual savings are not usually as high, though they may sometimes be equally important if they allow greater machine utilisation.

Although manufacturing departments are usually considered first when motion study is introduced into a factory there are other sections that should not be forgotten. For example, most forms of gauge inspection offer great scope for improvement. This is, perhaps, because quality, not speed, is always the criterion of good inspection work and less attention is therefore paid to the methods used than to their results. A motion study investigation into an inspection job of this kind will usually greatly increase hourly output without spoiling quality. Indeed in many cases the quality will be improved. During the last war the inspection of bomb exploders was motion studied and output per operator was increased by 700 per cent although the quality of the inspection was improved.

Other forms of indirect labour are worth attention. The cleaning of machines that are in continuous use is well worth studying, since anything that will reduce the time that the machine is idle not only decreases the labour charge but also increases output. Improvements here, although they apply directly to only a comparatively small number of men may make a significant difference to the total output of the factory.

There is an indirect labour force of a less specialised kind common to all types of factory and organisation: the maintenance staff of joiners, electricians, plumbers and others. Their work is rarely standardised in the ordinary way but by careful study much can be done to reduce it. The classic example of an investigation into maintenance work is the study made of the work of an electrician and his mate in a large hotel. It was found that when a lamp burnt out in the public rooms or passages it took an average of one hour to replace it. This hour was made up of getting a new lamp from the stores, finding suitable ladders and bringing them to the site and finally replacing the lamp and putting away the ladders. Thirty lamps replaced in this way meant thirty hours of maintenance time. If instead of waiting for lamps to burn out at irregular intervals, all lamps were changed at one time, just before the end of their natural life and before any could be expected to burn out, the thirty could be changed in two hours and at a convenient time to suit other electrical work instead of as an emergency job interrupting other work. The waste of lamps proved to be negligible.

Various clerical and administrative departments lend themselves to full-scale motion study investigation. In a large organisation there is usually considerable and obvious scope in wages, stenographic and accounts departments but there are organisation jobs in other departments which are worth considering. A successful investigation of this kind was carried out in the employment department of a large works which was finding that its existing system of dealing with requests for labour was not adequate under war-time conditions. Here a system was developed on much the same lines as a production control system that had previously been developed for a machine shop. Both these schemes made it possible for the war-time rush of production and its attendant demand for labour to be met without throwing either department out of gear. In the same way drawing offices will often well repay a study of organisation.

As a subject for study all forms of indirect labour, whether on the shop floor or in offices, have often been disregarded in the past, and in this post-war period they are a fruitful field for investigation and improvement. This field must not be ignored as it becomes more and more important to keep down the cost of production.

When a motion study department is well established it may more often be required to develop methods for new jobs than to improve existing methods. This is, of course, much the best way to apply motion study since incorrect methods are never then instituted or bad habits developed, neither is there any resistance to change to be overcome nor difficulty about alterations to piecework prices or output standards. It also means that new work is produced with the minimum amount of labour and at as low a labour cost as possible. The main difficulty about the application of motion study in this way is that until an investigator has considerable experience he will often find it difficult to arrive at the best way of working when there is no existing method to criticise. A further difficulty in the early days of a factory motion study programme is to convince those concerned of the value of a motion study method where there can be no contrast with an existing method. Neither of these difficulties, however, will present any problem to a well-established motion study department.

2. *Advisory Work*. Another function of the motion study department is to act in an advisory capacity to other departments. For example, in one factory where motion study is well developed, no layout is finally approved until it has been passed by the motion study department who examine the plans to make certain that they allow for the best motion study practice in the movement of material and operators and that, if later, a detailed investigation is made into any of the work covered by the layout, no major changes are likely to be necessary. In some instances the motion study department will be asked to draw up the layout from the beginning and it will then rank as a full investigation in itself. But more often the original scheme will be drawn up by the department that is normally responsible for the work and given to the motion study department for criticism and approval only. Whichever is the case, it is essential that the motion study department should see and approve all layout schemes if further changes are to be avoided at a later date. Only in this way can the full benefit of a new layout be obtained. Layouts that are made in the normal way usually provide for the flow of material to some extent,

but often the detailed placing of machines is planned more to make the installation easy and economical than with sufficient consideration of the day to day working of the department.

The motion study department may also act in an advisory capacity in the buying of new machines. Many machines, excellent in other respects, are badly designed from the point of view of use by the operator. Controls and other features should be examined before a machine is bought and any necessary alterations made before it is installed. An example of a machine modification is given on pp. 94-5. The creel of a ribbon lap machine in a cotton spinning mill was modified to reduce the excessive lifting and stretching caused by the manufacturer's design of the creel.

A motion study department can act very usefully in an advisory capacity to the designers of a product. While the design is still on the drawing board it is often possible to make alterations that, without interfering with the appearance or efficiency of the product, will save many hours of labour in manufacture and so reduce the cost of production. This particularly applies to engineering products but it is true of many others. It is more difficult where goods have a fashion bias, such as shoes or clothing where a modification in design is not always possible, but even here many possibilities for making savings will arise.

A field for motion study advice which has not yet been fully explored is the assistance that it might be to sales and publicity departments responsible for such goods as household appliances. These are designed both to do an efficient job and for ease in handling. As the general public becomes increasingly conscious of the importance of ease of movement salesmen might find it very helpful to be able to display illustrations such as chronocyclegraphs to demonstrate the value of the product in terms of ease of use. This sales technique has been applied to business machinery but it might well be extended to many other products.

3. *Motion Study Training.* Any fully developed motion study scheme must include the training of all personnel in motion study principles. Schemes for giving this training are outlined in Chapter 12, and it is enough here to say that the motion study department should be prepared to spend a considerable proportion of its time in giving this training to all groups and sections in the factory. It should include not only formal training in organised groups, but also general propaganda and should be designed to give each employee the amount of motion study knowledge that will help him to do his individual job as well as possible and to co-operate in the whole programme.

4. *Following up Completed Work.* The follow-up of completed work is given a separate heading here, although it is really part of the three other functions of a motion study department. Each branch of motion study work must have its own follow-up arrangements. It is only too easy to feel that once a job is installed, or a course of lectures finished, responsibility

ceases. This is unwise; the investigator should continue to maintain an interest even if it is indirect and merely undertaken to keep his records up-to-date. This kind of follow-up is, however, the minimum. Although direct responsibility for a detailed investigation ceases when the improved method is handed over to the foremen who will be answerable for its maintenance, the motion study department must make a periodic check of conditions and results. It should be made a routine procedure or it will be neglected in the rush of new work. It is important not only to prevent a method deteriorating, but also so that information may be recorded for future reference and use.

The general training schemes need a particularly careful follow-up procedure to keep interest alive and to encourage and assist the further motion study work of those who have been trained. Without it, interest will tend to flag and only a minority will attempt to use what they have learned. The motion study department will add to its experience by following up its training work and will be in a better position to give appropriate training to future groups. The follow-up of advisory work will be undertaken mainly for the sake of gathering information and adding to experience. It will be of interest and of real value to check whether advice given has been taken and if so how effective it has been.

The Relationship Between the Motion Study Department and Other Departments

The motion study department should be included under the general management heading of "Planning" and it should be under the direct control of the person responsible for the planning function in the organisation. In a large firm the planning function may be in the hands of a senior executive with considerable responsibility and a large staff divided into sections covering overall planning, equipment and tools, and standards of output. In such an organisation the motion study department would form a further section of this main planning division, working independently like the others but in close co-operation with them and reporting to the same head. In a small organisation the whole planning function may be divided between one or two people, each responsible for more than one sub-division. In small firms one individual may hold the complete planning function as only one part of a broader management responsibility. In theory the subdivisions are clear and definite and only the size and requirements of the organisation control their grouping. In fact, in small firms, it is rarely possible to separate individual personalities and abilities from the work they perform and the lines of demarcation become blurred. Even in large organisations powerful personalities tend to absorb functions that are strictly outside their own work.

Often in smaller organisations the planning function and its subdivisions has not been thought out in principle and is not being performed as a separate function. In such a situation the motion study investigator will set up his

section independently, reporting directly to a manager or director.   In time
it should become the nucleus of a broader planning department.

The work of the motion study section or department, whatever its size, is
functional and it serves the line organisation in the same way as other functional
departments, but in addition to its contacts as a functional department with
manufacturing or line departments, it works closely with some other functional
departments.   Chief among these is the personnel department (*see* Chapter
10) since the success of motion study methods depends on the training and
performance of the operators assigned to the work.   There will be a tendency
for the motion study department and the personnel department to overlap
over operator training (*see* p. 184) but in some organisations the personnel
department is not responsible for training and in others no training scheme
exists.   Where no scheme exists the motion study department must take on
the responsibility for training.

Of the other departments which are most closely linked with the motion
study department, the department or section responsible for tool design will
probably be the first that the investigator will have to approach during his
first job.   Nearly every motion study improvement means the modification
of machines, tools, jigs, fixtures or other equipment and the advice of the tool
department will usually be required whether or not the alterations are to be
made there.   It is a mistake to ask the tool department to be responsible
for every change in equipment.   Many smaller alterations and such equipment
as simple fixtures, hand tools, tool rests and material containers are better
made elsewhere.   They can easily be made too well and therefore at too great
a cost, and in most factories tool-making is limited in capacity and there is
the danger that motion study improvements may be delayed waiting for a
small fixture or tool that could be more quickly made in the experimental
section of the motion study department.   But before the motion study
department arranges to make even the simplest modifications or new equipment
some arrangement should be reached with the tool engineers so that there is no
feeling that their function is being usurped.   As far as possible, lines of
demarcation should be drawn between the type of work best done in the tool
department and the simpler jobs suitable for the motion study department's
own staff.   A broad distinction can usually be made between the jigs and
tools upon which the accuracy of the product depends and which must therefore
be made with precision, and those others that are largely features of workplace
layout or that need not be made to exact specification.   Again there should
be a distinction between the permanent tool or jig and the rougher version
needed for experimental purposes.

In a large organisation the works engineer's or maintenance department
will be distinct from the tool engineer's department.   It will include joiners,
electricians, millwrights, pipefitters, plumbers and others responsible for the
maintenance of plant.   When a motion study method is introduced this is the
department responsible for the installation of equipment and its relationship

to the motion study department is that of a service department to a production department. Unlike the relationship with the tool design department which may need delicate handling, this is a straightforward arrangement which is unlikely to cause any organisational difficulties.

Staffing the Motion Study Department

The number of staff required in a motion study department depends on the stage of development of the department, the numbers employed in the factory and the type of product. In factories which make a limited number of products in large quantities a smaller staff will be needed than in factories where the product is more varied and runs of work shorter. If the product is constantly changing, a relatively large motion study staff will be needed to ensure that work goes into production in the best way from the beginning. A very rough estimate of a suitable staff for a factory with some variation of product might be one investigator for 500 workers.

In a motion study department staffed by a number of investigators it is important to take full advantage of the possibility of team work. It is a mistake to allow each investigator to specialise too much on any particular type of work. It is better to give a variety of work to each and to encourage the use of the experience gained in this way in group discussions of the work of each member of the staff. Each problem will then have the advantage of informed group opinion from a group of investigators with common experience and interests but independent responsibilities. Experience has shown that group discussions of this type lead to very satisfactory solutions.

In most motion study departments of any size it will be found useful to have a fitter or joiner attached, who can make fixtures and experimental equipment. This is usually more satisfactory for the simpler jobs than to depend upon other departments for this type of service. In addition, clerical, drawing or tracing staff may be needed, according to the nature of the work that is done by the department, but they must be allocated to the department only if it can be proved that they will justify their expense by a comparable saving in investigators' time. The appointment of any additional staff is justified only if it will help the investigating staff to obtain appreciably greater results in any given period. For example, since as much as 75 per cent of any normal investigation may be spent on the installation of the new method, and since the largest part of this installation is the training of the operators an instructor attached to the motion study department can often relieve the investigating staff very considerably. Such an instructor can be made responsible for the detailed hour-to-hour training of operators and since he or she, unlike an investigator, will not be called away at intervals to other duties the training will probably be more effective, while leaving the ultimate control and responsibility in the hands of the investigating staff. The size of a motion study department, however, can never be a measure of its importance. Success can be judged only from the results of the work that is done.

Conclusion

This outline of the functions and place in an organisation of a motion study department can give only general guidance in setting up or developing a department.   In many organisations the department may vary considerably from this model but such variations are important only if they affect the working of the department.   While it is usually easier to work as a member of a well-planned and well-served department only the ability and determination of the individual members of the department can ultimately achieve the best results.   No amount of equipment or ancillary staff can take the place of this, and nothing can be judged as essential to a department that does not contribute economically to the department's main objective: to obtain more production with the same or less effort on the part of the operator and with increased operator satisfaction.

APPENDIX A

ROUTINE FOR AN INVESTIGATION

The preceding pages describe the necessary background of motion study practice and the techniques used in motion study. There is nothing included in this appendix which is not covered in theory in the main text, but it puts down, in a summarised form, which has been found useful in practice, the main points to cover in the investigation of any problem of reasonable size and importance. It is always dangerous to attempt to make a summary of this kind but the following is offered as a general guide. It must not be regarded as in any way comprehensive since the actual procedure will inevitably vary from job to job and from industry to industry.

Preliminary Survey

Information needed in Assessing the Scope and Nature of the Investigation. (The gathering of this information should not occupy more than a few hours.)

1. Source from which the request for the investigation came.
2. Reason for the request.
3. Suggested limits of the investigation.
4. Particulars of job to be investigated.

   (a) Quantity of production.

      (i) Normal weekly figure.
      (ii) Possible fluctuations.
      (iii) Future trend.

   (b) Operators employed on the job.

      (i) Grade and rate of pay of direct labour and total number in each grade.
      (ii) Type and rate of pay of indirect labour (i.e. service operators, cleaners, etc.) and total number of each type.
      (iii) Availability of labour.

   (c) Type of payment (i.e. hourly rate, by results or merit).
   (d) Output.

      (i) Output per operator per day.
      (ii) Comparison between daily output and short period output.
      (iii) Comparison between output of best and poorest operator.

  (iv) If on payment by results actual time allowed per unit of production and date when standard was set.

(e) Equipment.

  (i) Machine efficiency.
  (ii) Approximate cost of machines and availability.
  (iii) Flexibility of machines and other equipment.

(f) Layout of the work.

  (i) Adequacy of existing space.
  (ii) Possibility of additional space or need for reduction in space already occupied.

(g) Design of product.

  (i) Frequency of major and minor changes in design of product affecting manufacture.
  (ii) Possibility of making modifications to facilitate manufacture.

(h) Quality standards.

  (i) Type of inspection.
  (ii) Percentage inspected.

(j) Popularity or otherwise of the job.

  (i) From the operator's point of view.
  (ii) From the supervisor's point of view.

5. Estimate of the scope of savings.

  (a) Through the possibility of a reduction in unproductive movements.
  (b) Through an increase in machine efficiency.
  (c) Through better utilisation of labour.

6. Estimate of the time necessary for the investigation.

  (a) Recording and developing new method.
  (b) Training and installation.

The Investigation Proper

Once approval has been given to go ahead with the investigation it is necessary to collect a considerable amount of information about present practice and in some sections to record movements with considerable accuracy. This stage may cover a number of days, weeks or even months. It is impossible to collect or record all the information in the first instance but before the new method is developed in any final form it is usually necessary to analyse the more general information about the background of the job, going back to record facts in more detail as required. This procedure may be repeated a number of times before any finality is reached. For simplicity in presentation the type of information which may be ultimately required is listed below under the heading "Recording present practice" and the points of analysis and development of motion study method in the following section, though in actual practice there is no hard and fast line between the two sections.

I. RECORDING PRESENT PRACTICE

According to the nature and type of the job and the scope defined during the preliminary survey (*see* pp. 243-4), the techniques described in Chapters 2-4 are used as seems appropriate. It is always well to remember that although the use of micromotion films and chronocyclographs may not be absolutely justified in the extra savings they are likely to make in the new method they may often be justified because of the time which they can save at the installation stage by helping to convince those concerned of the need for change.

Observations should be recorded of the following points:

1. General background information concerning:

(a) The broader movements of the operators on the job and the number and grade of operators at each operation.

(b) The movements of the product and the sequence and nature of the operations and of those operations immediately preceding and following the section under investigation.

(c) The machines and equipment used at each process.

(d) The layout of machines and equipment.

(e) The movement of material to and from operations.

(f) The temporary storage of material and product.

2. Detailed information about:

(a) Operator's body, arm and leg movements on all operations.

(b) The sequence of movements within each individual operation.

(c) The efficiency and actual running speeds of each machine.

(d) The utilisation of all equipment and tools handled by each operator.

(e) Points of workplace layout, in particular the height and nature of seating and the contents of the workplace.

(f) The effectiveness of any financial or non-financial incentives (*see* Chapter 9) existing in the present method.

3. Information about organisation.

(a) Production methods.

    (i) Manufacturing quantities.

    (ii) If to stock, state of stock levels.

    (iii) If to order, frequency of orders.

    (iv) Relationship between ordered quantities and manufacturing quantities.

    (v) Period between order and delivery dates.

    (vi) Records of failure to meet delivery dates.

(b) Supply of material.

    (i) Where the responsibility rests.

(ii) Methods of ensuring the correct supply at the correct time.

(c) Quality of materials.

(i) Standards of inspection of material coming to each operation.
(ii) Standards of inspection of each operation.
(iii) Record of rejects, number and type.

(d) Supervision.

(i) Number of operators for whom each chargehand is responsible.
(ii) Number of chargehands reporting to each supervisor.

4. Particulars of product.

It is impossible to list points about the product since they will vary completely from trade to trade. For example in engineering, drawings should be studied to see if the design can be altered to simplify manufacturing.

II. Analysing Present Practice and Developing the New Method

1. Analyse all records and charts in the usual way for necessity, sequence, combination and simplification.

2. Find out if each operation is performed in the right place in the factory.

3. Find out if each operation or part of an operation is performed by the most suitable grade of labour.

4. Find out if each operation is done on the most suitable machine available.

5. Consider the job as a whole disregarding previous sub-divisions.

6. Consider future operation units, whether the job ought to be done as one unit or sub-divided, bearing the following points in mind:

(a) That all unproductive movements of picking the work up and putting it down and of turning it round to work on different sides should be eliminated.

(b) That the total unit of operation should not be too long for the operator to establish a rhythm as much as possible, since repeated operations are easier to perform than long disjointed ones.

(c) That all divisions should contain movements as nearly similar as possible so that they can be easily learnt.

(d) That those parts of the operation requiring less skill or dexterity than the rest should, if possible, be grouped by themselves so that they can be performed by less skilled labour.

7. Consider the introduction of tools and machinery in part or whole of the operations, remembering that to justify the cost of the introduction of tools the saving the tool itself allows should be the only saving contrasted with its cost and not the total saving of the job, also that the saving resulting from the introduction of the tool should be compared with the best motion study application without the tool and not with the present method.

8. The design of the product should be considered from the point of view of ease of manufacture and any modifications taken up with the designers.

9. The requirements of inspection should be considered to see: —

(a) If the proportion of the product inspected is sufficient or not enough.

(b) If the nature of the inspection is satisfactory.

(c) If material coming to each operator is sufficiently inspected.

(d) The cause of all points appearing on the rejection list, such as:

(i) Bad workmanship of the previous operator.

(ii) Bad methods of the previous operation.

(iii) Bad workmanship of the present operator.

(iv) Bad methods of the present operation.

(v) Faulty design.

10. Analyse production troubles and consider if the product is being made in the right relative quantities considering orders and convenience of manufacturing.

11. Consider the general layout from the point of view of:

(a) Elimination of unnecessary transport of material.

(b) General ease in supervision.

12. Consider whether the production control system is such that the process flows smoothly or if there might be some form of visual control which would ease the supervision.

13. Consider the safety of the operators and whether additional safety measures should be introduced.

14. When developing the new method do not be handicapped by existing conditions or expense, rather disregard these and then, when a theoretical new method is complete, consider if the cost of the proposed changes is justified by savings and modify the recommendations accordingly.

15. Draw up new method possibility charts and analyse carefully for any faults that may not have appeared when considering the general analysis.

16. Draw up a general layout.

17. Draw up the detailed workplace layout.

18. Have drawings made for all tools and fixtures needed.

III. MAKE A PRELIMINARY REPORT

1. Make a report emphasising the following points:

(a) Faults in the present method.

(b) Cost of the present method.

(c) Output per operator in the present method.

(d) Recommendations.

(e) Approximate output per operator expected in the proposed method.

(f) Possible savings.

(g) Cost of the change and how it can be made with the minimum of hindrance to production.

(h) Safety provisions.

IV. INSTALL APPROVED NEW METHOD

1. Before beginning installation make sure that everyone concerned has been informed of the details of the change. The methods to be installed should have been discussed already by all those concerned (including operators and their representatives) during the different stages of the investigation.

2. If on payment by results, before beginning the training of operators cancel the previous piecework prices and cover each operator's time until it is possible to set weekly temporary prices.

3. Train operators in the proposed method in a separate section if possible.

4. Keep learning curves of operator's progress.

5. Remove the various difficulties which arise when any job goes into production.

6. Arrange the final set-up in the shops so that it is ready for the operators to work on when they return from their training.

7. When training is complete establish the job in the shops.

8. Set standards of output and, if there is some form of payment by results, the rate for each job.

9. Make instruction sheets and give to foremen and any others interested.

10. After the job is running smoothly, hand over production and maintenance to the shop supervision.

V. MAKE A FINAL REPORT

1. Make a final report, listing all results and difficulties and how they have been overcome. It is essential that all points should be written up for future reference.

2. Submit results and a brief report to the management.

APPENDIX B

EXAMPLES OF TYPICAL MOTION STUDY APPLICATIONS

The whole object of this book has been to show that a motion study method is the inevitable result of following a certain line of thought and is not merely an addition of bright ideas. To make sure that this essential point was not obscured, most of the examples and illustrations used in the main part of the book have been very simple and non-industrial. This appendix is added to bring the reader forward from theory to practice in the application of motion study.

It is not possible, in the space available, to publish any really comprehensive collection of reports of investigations covering the whole possible scope of motion study, or to include examples from all the industries in which it has been applied.

From a large number known to the writer, the following eight examples have been selected as having a general application outside the particular subject or industry concerned. The first six are industrial applications of motion study. These have been arranged in alphabetical order according to the name of the company contributing them. The last two examples are non-industrial.

The first report, of a motion study programme in operation at the factory of Carr & Co. Ltd., Carlisle, has been included to show a practical application of the scheme described in Chapter 11. It is an example of the development of the application of motion study in a factory where many of the departments are doing a wide variety of work to meet constantly changing orders, particularly on export work.

The second report describes an early example of the use of the string diagram technique in the cotton textile industry at R. Greg & Co. Ltd.'s mill at Stockport. It demonstrates the increased production that can be obtained from a study of movements alone, without the complications of redeployment and all that is involved in reallocating the duties of operatives. More recent textile investigations, which at the time of publication it has not been possible to include are showing very successfully the additional increases in output per operator to be gained from studying not only the individual operations but also their relationship to one another in a whole scheme of redeployment based on motion study.[1]

---

[1] See *Motion Study in Worsted Spinning* and *Motion Study in Woollen Spinning*, published by the Wool (and Allied) Textile Employers' Council, July, 1951.

The third report is abridged and selected from a much larger report of an investigation into the whole work of Lilliput Laundry and Dyeworks Ltd., Dunmurry, Belfast. It has been included as an example of what can nearly always be achieved by studying hand operations in any factory. Although a laundry has the special problems and features of a service industry many of the points raised are common to other industries; for example the importance of correct hand movements and of individual operator training. It is particularly interesting as an example of a factory working without any scheme of payment by results and instituting, after motion study, the financial incentive system described on pages 170-1.

The fourth report is from Metropolitan-Vickers Electrical Co. Ltd., Manchester. It is typical of engineering assembly and a useful example of the effect of motion study on tool and fixture design. Here the analysis has been made by means of detailed process charts. The motion study method illustrates many of the points made about workplace layout in Chapter 6.

The fifth report, from James Neill & Co. (Sheffield) Ltd., Sheffield, shows a typical improvement made in the gauge inspection of small parts. Though the increase in output appears to be very high it is not at all an unusual figure for that type of work. To obtain it the micromotion technique was used as well as the process charts shown here.

The sixth report comes from the "Wescot" Overall Manufacturing Co. Ltd., Egham, Surrey, and it is a further example of the investigation of all the operations in one process. It differs from the laundry example in that the hand movements studied are more complex and the work much less varied. The operations are closely inter-related and none is complete in itself. The original methods had been very carefully planned and the work was being performed very efficiently. To obtain any results it was necessary to study in detail every operation in the making up of the garment.

Though the path of movement, particularly of the material at each operation and between operations, was studied very carefully, the micromotion technique was the main technique used in this investigation. Without the analysis of films the improvements could not have been obtained.

The seventh report concerns the layout of a domestic kitchen. This is included not only because of its general interest to most readers but also because it is typical of the results that can be obtained from a study of layout in a jobbing shop of any kind, where no two jobs are exactly alike. An interesting feature in this case is the modification of inefficient old-fashioned premises into an effective unit without any structural alterations or undue expense.

The eighth and last report is of an investigation into the clerical work of a doctor's surgery and in particular into the organisation of the round of visits. This is a useful example of simple process chart analysis. The problem, in essence, is that of finding a production system and is very like similar problems found in many machine shops. The solution was in fact adapted from a factory production board. It demonstrates in a very simple form the application of motion study to an organisational problem. The more complex the problem the greater will be the results obtained.

A great debt is owed to the companies mentioned above, who have allowed these accounts to be published. The writer is extremely grateful to them all.

REPORT No. 1

A Motion Study Training Scheme

Established by Carr & Co. Ltd., Carlisle

Motion study was first introduced into the factory in the form of single investigations made by one trained motion study officer with a little outside help. Many of the supervisors and managers shared in the development and installation of these new methods and the workers' representatives were consulted before any investigation began. As a result there was a certain general interest in motion study at all levels and many had seen it in action.

When a number of motion study improvements were well established and had served to demonstrate the possibilities of motion study applications in the factory, it was decided to organise a general training programme. This was planned in three parts.

1. Short courses of varying lengths for all managers and supervisors.
2. A series of lectures to the works advisory committee.
3. A training scheme for new entrants.

1. MOTION STUDY TRAINING COURSES FOR MANAGERS AND SUPERVISORS

There were between sixty and seventy men and women managers and supervisors to be trained. These ranged from the assistant works manager and the heads of departments to some quite newly-promoted junior chargehands. Since only ten or twelve could be taught at one time it was possible to divide the larger number into groups, according to their interests and responsibilities, and to arrange a course to suit each. Before planning the syllabus of the courses it was necessary to consider what use each group could be expected to make of motion study. For practical reasons it was decided to run courses for half the number at once and for the other half six months later. The three groups to be trained first were departmental managers, head and senior forewomen and foremen; leaving the remaining forewomen and two groups of chargehands until later.

A skeleton syllabus was drawn up for all groups and this was then adapted to the needs of each group. The adaptation was made partly in the subjects taught and the amount of time devoted to each subject and partly in the detail of each session, where emphasis was laid on the particular points of most value to each group. It was thought that the managers ought to know as much about motion study as the supervisors but that individual managers would not themselves be responsible for making motion study improvements in their departments. On the other hand they would be called upon to criticise the work of their supervisors and to call in the motion study officer either to plan or to approve both improvements and methods for new work. They would not themselves train operators. The foremen, on the other hand, already had an immediate responsibility for the methods used in their sections and were also expected to lay down methods for new or temporary jobs. Some of them trained their own operators, others used chargehands to do this for them. In all this work they would be able to use motion study and in addition they would be expected to apply it to making small improvements on existing methods. The Head and Senior forewomen had much the same responsibilities and any future operator-training scheme would affect them very closely. These points were all kept in mind in planning the syllabus for each group. For example, "Operator Training" occupied two sessions for forewomen, one session for foremen but was not included as a separate subject in the managers' course. On the other hand the foremen had a special session on the "Application of Motion Study to Production Schemes." Again each session of the managers' course was taken at a faster pace than the other groups and illustrations were drawn from a wider field. In choosing non-technical examples and illustrations it was easier to find domestic examples for the men's groups than for the women's, to whom domestic subjects very easily become technical and controversial, obscuring their illustrative effect. Where the same practical work was given to different groups it was noticeable that their reactions were always different.

When a syllabus for each group had been planned notices were sent to all those concerned, inviting but not instructing them to attend. In fact no-one refused and nearly all completed the courses; the few exceptions being due to illness.

Before the groups began their individual meetings all three were addressed together by the works director who made it clear that he considered the subject of first-class importance and that he was directly sponsoring the courses. A general outline of the proposed courses was given at this meeting and films were shown of motion study improvements made in other industries.

The next stage consisted of weekly meetings of one hour's duration. Each group of ten or twelve met in a committee room, seated round a large table. The room had dark curtains and a screen and projector were used. This stage consisted of six or eight sessions on motion study techniques and their application. The sessions took the form of lecture discussions during which practical work was done on non-technical examples. At least one third of every hour was spent on practical work which allowed material to be handled, and nearly every session was illustrated by short films, by wall charts and drawings and by photographs laid on the table. Time was always allowed for questions and discussion. In this way not much more than 20 minutes was given to lecturing and it was found that all groups, except perhaps the most senior, were much

FIG. 58. BAKING OATCAKES.

An improvement initiated by a forewoman during a short course of
motion study training

(TOP) *Original method*: Prepared oatcakes were held by the left
hand and placed individually by the right hand on to the hot plate.
Baked oatcakes were dried on flat racks above.

(BOTTOM) *Motion study method*: Prepared oatcakes are placed on
trays moving on slides in front of the hot plate. Both hands are
used to place the oatcakes on the hot plate with easy rhythmical
movements. Movable hollow racks are provided for the baked cakes.

more at ease during the practical work and therefore learnt more easily through that medium. The practical work usually consisted of charting a job as a group or examining a wall chart already made (in the case of micromotion and chronocylegraph work) while manipulating the material on the table to understand the meaning of each symbol or movement path. An analysis was then made of the chart, and the new method was worked out by the group. Finally the new method was agreed upon and charted again on sheets of paper pinned on to the blackboard. Duplicated notes and any relevant charts or illustrations were distributed at the end of the session.

After six or eight sessions, according to the needs of each group, this stage ended and for the next stage each group was sub-divided into two parts, meeting at different times to examine problems from the factory. Each member brought a problem of his own, though it was found necessary to help with the selection of problems. The motion study officer gave any necessary help in preparing the problem and making a preliminary process chart but no analysis or ideas for solution were demanded before the discussion. In the majority of cases it was found helpful for the group to visit the job a day or two before the meeting, though these visits were restricted to a maximum of five or ten minutes. Wherever possible parts of the material or apparatus were brought to the meeting and demonstrated.

Each of these job discussions used the process chart as a means of fact-finding and of recording the operation in the correct sequence. The analysis was made from this chart by the group visualising the path of movement of the operator to discover obstacles. Suggestions for improvement were then collected and weighed. In nearly every case some tentative new method was outlined before the end of the hour though much was inevitably left to be finished in the factory. The motion study officer then followed the job back into the factory and helped the supervisor to finish it during the ensuing weeks.

When all five or six problems had been discussed each sub-divided group joined up again with its other half and examined some of the results which were already sufficiently far advanced. Problems of installation were also discussed and the course and its objectives were summed up.

The motion study officer continued to follow up the jobs discussed until they reached some conclusion. Some were quickly installed but others developed into large scale investigations. In such cases the supervisors concerned handed over to the motion study officer, since they had neither the time nor the experience for such work, though they remained interested and gave considerable help in the investigation. Other problems were abandoned for a variety of reasons.

Some months after the end of the course a meeting was held to demonstrate results and to talk about any further jobs done by members of the groups. By this time a selection of the most successful jobs had been filmed or photographed and the films and photographs were shown at the meeting. Unofficially most members followed up the jobs done by their own group

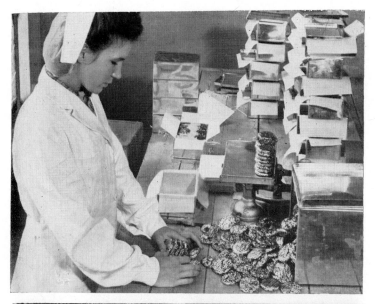

FIG. 59. PACKING FOILED CHOCOLATE BISCUITS INTO SMALL TINS
Another improvement made during a supervisor's course

(TOP) *Original method*: Foiled biscuits were dropped from the foiling machine into large tins, carried to the packing bench and tipped out on to it. The packer sorted and gathered them into piles facing in one direction, lifted them on to the weighing machine and packed them into tins, previously lined as a sub-operation.

(BOTTOM) *Motion study method*: An extension has been provided to the band on the foiling machine and biscuits come to the packer stacked ready for weighing. The weighing machine is below the level of the band and the biscuits move along the shortest path from the band to the tin by way of the scales. A tin of "run off" biscuits is stored on the opposite side of the band, to be packed on the occasions when the foiling machine stops.

and this was not discouraged. The forewomen's and chargehands' courses were run on the same lines six months later.

The results of the problems studied by the first three groups can be summarised as follows:

17 simple improvements successfully introduced as the direct result of the discussions and with little further study.

2 major improvements installed on jobs discussed during the course and referred back to the motion study department for detailed investigation.

7 jobs awaiting further investigation for a variety of reasons.

7 jobs abandoned as showing no results after a short study and where detailed investigations were not justified under existing circumstances.

Apart from these savings other results of the courses were immediately apparent. Some further small improvements were made by supervisors on their own initiative, but more use was made of motion study in planning new work. In the months following the courses it was not unusual to see a departmental manager, foreman, forewoman and chargehand studying a girl at work on a new job just introduced into the department and together working out the best way to do it. Temporary jobs were also planned economically and the more detailed investigations made by the motion study officer received every kind of co-operation and active help. This was particularly valuable in shortening the installation and training stages of each new method.

2. Lectures to the Work's Advisory Committee

This committee consisted of about forty members of all grades below senior management. Most of the members were shop stewards and workers' representatives and it was chiefly to these that the lectures were addressed. The detailed improvements already installed by the motion study officer in several departments had already served as an introduction to the workers, and the whole question of the application of motion study had been discussd with their representatives before any new methods were introduced, but many representatives worked in departments where no jobs had yet been studied and it was important that there should be a general understanding among the workers of the meaning of motion study and an opportunity to decide how it would affect them personally.

Each lecture was planned to last 45 minutes. Because of the large numbers no practical work could be attempted but it was again felt that no more than 20 minutes should be occupied by the lecture. Films or demonstrations of improved methods were arranged to last another 15—20 minutes and all possible wall charts, diagrams and lantern slides were used to illustrate the talks and to hold attention. One film or demonstration at each lecture showed an improved method already installed in the factory. Three of the four lectures covered the techniques of motion study, explaining the apparatus used and demonstrating the analysis of simple methods. Throughout the series emphasis was laid on eliminating unnecessary effort and making

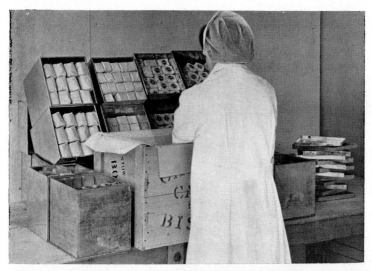

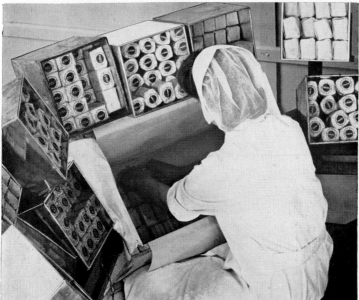

Fig. 60. Packing an Assortment of Small Packets Into
Large Cases for Export

An example of quick and simple improvement made on a temporary
job

(top) *Original method*: The case, placed on the normal packing
table, is too high for comfort and the tins are outside the areas
of easiest reach.

(bottom) *Motion study method*: By tilting the case and placing the
tins round it the packer is enabled to sit at her work and all undue
stretching is eliminated.

movements easier. The fourth lecture on workplace layout emphasised the importance of a correctly designed workplace in facilitating the use of easy movements and included a simplified account of the characteristics of easy movement. At the request of the committee notes were distributed after each lecture. Time was allowed on each occasion for questions.

3. THE TRAINING OF NEW ENTRANTS

To complete the motion study training programme a scheme was planned for the training of all women entrants. At first this would apply only to the younger entrants since older women were not usually placed on work involving any training or skill. At present the scheme is at the experimental stage only but it is hoped that a training of the type described on pp. 226-7 will teach all entrants to tackle a variety of work intelligently and to apply very simple motion study ideas to everything they do. In time it is hoped that a large proportion of the women workers will in this way become "motion minded."

Conclusion

The effect of this programme so far has been that while the larger investigations have continued at a fairly even pace throughout the three years since motion study was first introduced into the factory, the courses have accelerated the improvement of the smaller jobs to such an extent that it is now beginning to be obvious that most of the easier improvements have been made. This has effected a very large total of savings for a comparatively small expenditure and the emphasis in the future will be on planning new work on motion study lines and on making the larger and more detailed investigations that involve mechanical changes and long term planning. In both these the training given to managers and supervisors will be invaluable.

REPORT NO. 2

Investigation into the Operation of Draw-frames in a Cotton Mill

R. Greg and Co. Ltd., Stockport

For a number of reasons the investigation was confined to a study of the actual operating of the draw-frames. The transport of cans to and from the frames was outside its scope and there was no question at that time of one operator looking after more frames. Any savings must therefore come from increased output per frame.

As in most textile investigations it was found that there were two aspects of movement to be considered; the total movements of the operator over the working day following an irregular sequence of operations and the detailed movements involved in each separate operation, for example in the changing of cans.

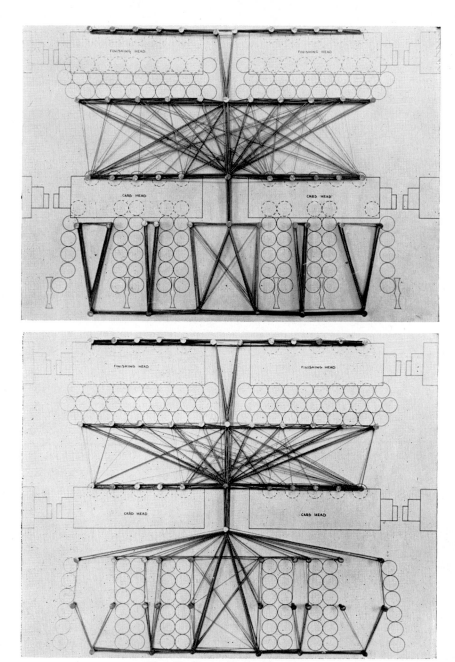

FIG. 61. DRAW FRAME TENTING
String diagrams showing the path of an operative's movements
over a whole day.
(TOP) *Original method.*
(BOTTOM) *Motion study method.*

1 Take sliver from G and hand over guide
2 Walk to draw frame head
3 Break off old sliver (can A)
4 Piece sliver ends & place in guide
5 Re-start machine
6 Remove Can A
7 Move can B to A
8 Carry empty can to C
9 Move can C to B
10 Carry empty can on to D
11 Move can D to C
12 Carry empty can on to E
13 Move can E to D
14 Carry empty can on to F
15 Move can F to E
16 Carry empty can to empty can stack
17 Place in stock
18 Walk to full can stock
19 Select full can
20 Carry to stand
21 Place at position F

Do other work

22 Take sliver G from guide
23 Move can G to F
24 Inspect cans – walking up line
25 Walk back

Do other work

26 Take sliver from G & hand over guide
27 Walk to draw frame head
28 Break off old sliver (can A)
29 Piece sliver ends & place in guide
30 Re-start machine
31 Remove can A
32 Move can B to A
33 Carry empty can to C

34 Move can C to B
35 Carry empty can on to D
36 Move can D to C
37 Carry empty can on to E
38 Move can E to D
39 Carry empty can on F
40 Move Can F to E
41 Carry empty can to empty can stock
42 Place in stock
43 Walk to full can stock
44 Select full can
45 Carry to stand
46 Place at position F

Do other work

47 Take sliver G from guide
48 Move C and G to F
49 Inspect cans – walking up line
50 walk back

Do other work

51 Take sliver from G & hand over guide
52 Walk to draw frame head
53 Break off old sliver (can A)
54 Piece sliver ends & place in guide
55 Re-start machine
56 Remove can A
57 Move can B to A
58 Carry empty can to C
59 Move can C to B
60 Carry empty can on to D
61 Move can D to C
62 Carry empty can on to E
63 Move can E to D
64 Carry empty can on to F
65 Move can F to E
66 Carry empty can to empty can stock
67 Place in stock

68 Walk to full can stock
69 Select full can
70 Carry to stand
71 Place at position F

Do other work

72 Take sliver G from guide
73 Move can G to F
74 Inspect cans – walking up line
75 Walk back

Do other work

76 Take sliver from G & hand over guide
77 Walk to draw frame head
78 Break off old sliver (can A)
79 Piece sliver ends & place in guide
80 Re-start machine
81 Remove can A
82 Move can B to A
83 Carry empty can to C
84 Move can C to B
85 Carry empty can on to D
86 Move can D to C
87 Carry empty can on to E
88 Move can E to D
89 Carry empty can on to F
90 Move can F to E
91 Carry empty can to can stock
92 Place in stock
93 Walk to full can stock
94 Select full can
95 Carry to stand
96 Place at position F

Do other work

97 Take sliver G from guide
98 Move can G to F
99 Inspect cans – walking up line
100 Walk back

Do other work

101 Take sliver from G & hand over guide
102 Walk to draw frame head
103 Break off old sliver (can A)
104 Piece sliver ends & place in guide
105 Re-start machine
106 Remove can A
107 Move can B to A
108 Carry empty can to C
109 Move can C to B
110 Carry empty can on to D
111 Move can D to C
112 Carry empty can on to E
113 Move can E to D
114 Carry empty can on to F
115 Move can F to E
116 Carry empty can to can stock
117 Place in stock
118 Walk to full can stock
119 Select full can
120 Carry to stand
121 Place at position F

Do other work

122 Take sliver G from guide
123 Move C and G to F
124 Inspect cans – walking up line
125 Walk back

Do other work

126 Take sliver from G & hand over guide
127 Walk to draw frame head
128 Break off old sliver (can A)
129 Piece sliver ends & place in guide
130 Re-start machine
131 Remove can A
132 Move can B to A
133 Carry empty can to C

Do other work

134 Move can C to B
135 Carry empty can on to D
136 Move can D to C
137 Carry empty can on to E
138 Move can E to D
139 Carry empty can on to F
140 Move can F to E
141 Carry empty can to empty can stock
142 Place in stock
143 Walk to full can stock
144 Select full can
145 Carry to stand
146 Place at position F

Do other work

147 Take sliver G from guide
148 Move can G to F
149 Inspect cans – walking up line
150 walk back

FIG. 62. DRAW FRAME TENTING
Process chart of can changing. *Original method.*

Observations were taken of the path of movement of the operator over an $8\frac{1}{2}$ hour day. Fig. 61 shows the resulting string diagram. It will be seen that the greatest number of movements takes place at the back of the frames. This indicated that the handling of cans there should be examined to find out whether there were any waste movements. Process charts were made of this operation and it was found that each can was moved unproductively six times (*see* Fig. 62). For example, Can 1 ran out first and the sliver from Can 6, standing ready at the end of the row of cans was joined in its place. The machine was then re-started and Can 1 was removed Can 2 being moved up into its place. Cans 3, 4, 5, 6 and 7 were then moved up one place and another full can placed behind ready for the next change. To eliminate as much as possible of the can handling, in the final motion study method cans were so arranged that a whole row became ready for replacement approximately at one time, cans being changed directly into their final position in one movement (*see* Fig. 63). When it was time to change cans a fresh can was joined to the remaining sliver in each emptying can and the machine did not stop unless there was a break in the sliver or unless one can was more than usually underfilled. As all the cans in this arrangement were full when they were first changed in, instead of the front cans being nearly empty (*see* Fig. 64), it was necessary to place them further from the frames and to run the slivers over guides (*see* Fig. 64). This arrangement had the advantage that it made it easier to see from the other side of the machine which sliver needed

FIG. 63. DRAW FRAME TENTING
Process chart of can changing
Motion study method

18—(H.103)

FIG. 64. DRAW FRAME TENTING
(TOP) Side view of creel. *Original method.*
(MIDDLE) Side view of creel. *Motion study method.*
(BOTTOM) Front view of creel and card finishing head.
Motion study method.

attention (*see* Fig. 64). Fig. 61 (bottom) shows the string diagram of the new method. The same type of re-arrangement was made at the finishing head.

Results

The result of the investigation was:

(1) a 10 per cent reduction in the distance walked by the tenter;

(2) a reduction in the number of operations performed in a day from 888 to 706;

(3) an increase from 15 to 48 in the periods when the tenter was merely watching the machines;

(4) a 15 per cent increase in output at the finishing head under the same machine conditions.

REPORT NO. 3

The Application of Motion Study to a Laundry

Investigation carried out at Lilliput Laundry, Dunmurry, Belfast.

There was a considerable labour shortage in the laundry and heavy over-time was being worked to keep up with schedule. This in turn tended to increase the labour turnover which aggravated the shortage. The investigation was therefore directed at increasing output per operator without calling for increased individual effort. Such an improvement would mean that overtime could be cut down and that some form of financial incentive could be used to increase individual wages while reducing the total labour costs of the laundry.

EXTENT OF THE INVESTIGATION

It was decided that all the laundry processes should be studied so that the maximum improvement could be made. This decision was slightly modified as a result of a preliminary survey of the problem which showed that a study of the work of the washing machines was unlikely to produce any significant savings under existing conditions. New machines were on order, though delivery dates were uncertain, and it was agreed to leave that section out of the investigation.

The whole problem, for the purpose of the investigation, fell into four sections:

1. The checking of dirty work and the packing of clean work. This called for a study of numbers, of the grouping of individual customers and of the classification of articles into types.

2. The work of washing machines, hydros and tumblers. This was essentially machine work. It was decided not to investigate it.

3. The preparation for the finishing processes. This was hand work and involved the study of individual operators, often working in pairs.

4. Finishing work, which could be subdivided into:

(a) Calender work.   This was mainly a hand work problem but the hand work was controlled by machines.

(b) Press work.   This would require the detailed analysis of skilled hand work which involved the exercise of judgment in laying garments on the buck of a press.

(c) Hand ironing.   Because of the great variety of garments handled this would be largely a question of general workplace layout.

MOTION STUDY TECHNIQUES USED

Process charts were made of all the work and every job was filmed and simo-charted.   New methods were then developed from the analysis of these charts and from a study of the path of movement.   Every new method in its turn was tried out experimentally with the operators concerned and equipment and method were modified where necessary.   Operators were then trained and given output targets.

DETAILS OF INDIVIDUAL INVESTIGATIONS

A complete report on every job studied would take up far more space than is available here.   Every possible detail was recorded and studied but much of this detail would be of little general interest.   Examples have, however, been selected from among the individual studies and they are described, very briefly, below:

Calender Section

Preparing and Feeding.   There were three calenders, covering all the flat work of both finished and semi-finished services.   Besides detailed changes in method certain general alterations were made to the organisation of the work and to the layout of the section.

It was the practice to use untrained labour on the preparation of work for the calenders.   This resulted either in the employing of more labour than should have been necessary or in frequent delays in feeding.   The motion study method grouped the operators into teams, each operator taking turns at both feeding and preparation.   Since, under this arrangement, preparers were also trained as feeders, they appreciated the feeders' point of view and knew the importance of correct preparation.   The new arrangement was popular with the operators, who enjoyed the increased variety.

Detailed changes were also made in the preparation and feeding.   Certain criticisms of the existing methods were common to all classes of work passing through the process and although the motion study improvements varied a little for different types of work the principles behind the changes were the same.   The first point of criticism was that feeders had to turn completely round to obtain a pile of prepared work from a table behind them which was placed parallel to the calender (*see* Fig. 65).   The second point was that

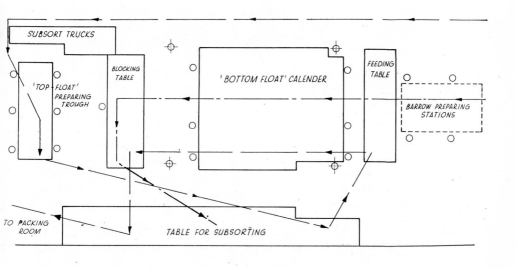

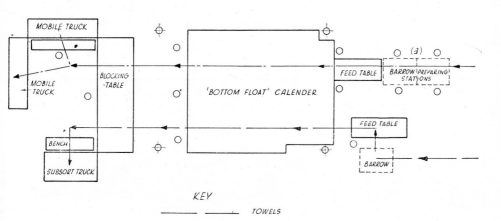

KEY

———— · ———— TOWELS

———— - · ———— SHEETS, COLOURS, ETC.

FIG. 65. LAYOUT OF CALENDER SECTION
(TOP) Original layout
(BOTTOM) Motion study layout

preparers were carrying very heavy piles of prepared work for varying distances from barrows to feeding table. One batch observed totalled 322 sheets and entailed 25 journeys. Both these points were improved by making changes in the design and layout of equipment. In the final motion study method the large feeding table behind the feeders was replaced by two smaller tables (Fig. 65). One, for sheets, was placed at right angles to the calender, and between the two sheet feeders. The other, for towels and smaller work, was placed to the left of the third feeder, again at right angles to the calender. Extension flaps were fitted to the barrows to allow easier preparation and girls on Barrow A merely lifted a pile of prepared sheets from the barrow to their end of the sheet feeding table. This table was narrow and was kept very smooth so that each pile, with the ends of the sheets hanging over the sides of the table could be made to slide along to the feeding end where sheets were fed directly into the calender from the nearest pile. This eliminated both the carrying of the piles by the preparers and the turning round of the feeders to obtain work from the feeding table behind them. The other feeding table served towels and smalls.

Folding. In the motion study scheme the feeding of each article into the calender was arranged so that each left the calender in such a way that the first fold could be put into it as it was being taken off the back. For example, it had been the practice to feed table napkins hem first. They then had to be turned through 90 degrees before the first fold could be put in. By feeding them selvedge first this fold could be put in as they came off the back. This also meant that folding was always correct.

Blocking and subsorting. The blocking and subsorting layout was re-arranged (*see* Fig. 65) to reduce the movements of the operators concerned.

Results on calender work. The motion study method reduced the labour force by 16 per cent—an increase in output per operator per week of 20 per cent. The increase in output per operator hour was considerably greater, since much less overtime was worked.

These figures include supervisors who, in the motion study method, concentrated on training and supervising the operators and were not expected to do any productive work as in the past.

Press Section

The work of the press section could be divided into two distinct groups; the units concerned with single types of work such as shirts or coats and the miscellaneous units. The first group was investigated as a straightforward problem of the grouping of presses for the easiest handling of a particular article. Here the motion study methods were developed from a film analysis of all the detailed movements involved. The most economical lays consistent with first class quality were worked out as a routine and press layouts were then devised to enable the operators to perform the correct sequence of

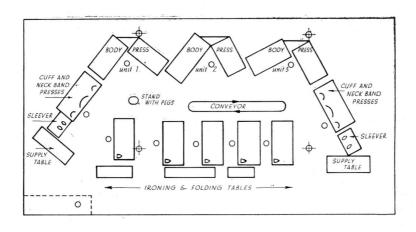

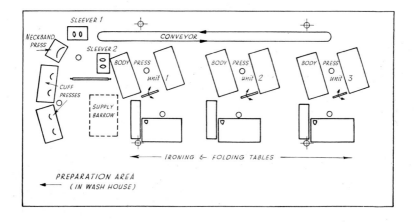

FIG. 66. LAYOUT OF SHIRT UNIT
(TOP) Original layout
(BOTTOM) Motion study layout

movements with the least effort. The change of layout of the shirt unit is shown in Fig. 66. The new layout was also designed to allow a certain reorganisation, placing one folder with each operator on the body presses so that responsibility for poor work could be accurately assessed. This did much to maintain the high standard already in existence when the investigation began.

The results of the study of the shirt press unit showed an increase in output per operator of 44 per cent. The coat unit showed a similar increase; in this case of 43 per cent. These results were very largely achieved by reducing the operators' movements in handling the garment. This involved the planning of the lays in the most economical way. The layout of the presses was then altered to accommodate the planned movements and lays. A change in layout alone would have had little effect.

The investigation into the work on the miscellaneous press units followed rather different lines. Here the work was carefully classified and a general series of movements was developed for each classification. The operators were very carefully instructed and the supervisor was trained to continue the instruction of new operators. The increases in output per operator hour were naturally more difficult to assess on miscellaneous work but over a period the total number of garments produced by each operator on the miscellaneous units showed an increase of 56 per cent.

Sorting

The work of the sorting room was studied in two parts; the organisation of the supply of work to the sorter and the individual methods used by the sorter. Changes in the organisation of the work allowed the sorters to work without interruption.

The workplace layout of the sorting booths was modified to allow the introduction of improved methods of handling (*see* Fig. 67).

(a) The bench was turned round so that work was thrown off with the left hand, leaving the right free to check off, describe and price.

(b) The bins used for the storage of work during sorting were removed. The bench surface was levelled and the work made easier by the elimination of stooping. It was still considered necessary to segregate the sorted from the unsorted work on the bench, so a central partition was provided for this purpose.

(c) A single desk replaced the two originally provided. It was placed to the right of the sorter since all writing was done with the right hand.

(d) The bins removed from the benches were modified to replace the nets formerly used for the storage of collar and handkerchiefs, eliminating the two-handed work of opening nets.

(e) String cutters were provided instead of scissors and placed to the right of the desk so that the string could be cut as each parcel was moved on to the bench.

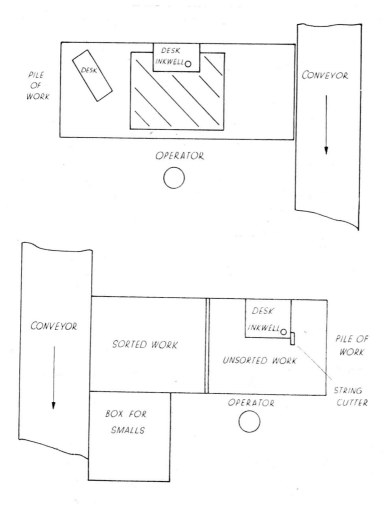

FIG. 67. SORTING BOOTHS
(TOP) Original workplace
(BOTTOM) Motion study workplace

These modifications and the altered system of obtaining a correct mark allowed the following improved method:

ORIGINAL METHOD	MOTION STUDY METHOD
Preparatory	
(a) The parcel was picked up from the floor and cut open with a knife.	(a) The parcel was moved on the bench, the string being cut with a cutter on the way.
(b) The book, with the customer's mark on the cover, was taken out, opened and put to the operator's left. The mark was not then visible on the current page and any further reference to it could only be made by turning back to the cover.	(b) The book was opened at the current page and placed in front of the operator. It was intended in future that books should have a cutout making the mark visible on every page. Meanwhile the sorter marked the current page.
Checking and Marking.	
(a) The operator lifted each article from the bin to her right hand side. She then moved to the left to describe and price the work in the book. She repeated this for the complete pile.	(a) and (b) Checking and marking were combined to save handling. Each article was picked up, examined for mark and if already marked checked off in the book by the right hand during its disposal on to the left hand section of the table by the left hand. If it needed marking this was done after checking in the book and the article was disposed of while the pen was being replaced. When the parcel was completely checked all articles were pushed on to the conveyor in one movement.
(b) The pile was then examined for the mark and if necessary articles were re-marked, the right hand stretching over to the left to take the pen from the central desk. Each article then passed from left hand to right to be thrown on to the conveyor.	

Originally each article was lifted from a 10 in. deep bin which caused the operator to stoop. The new layout kept all articles at bench level. It was observed that the desks provided under the existing scheme were seldom used because to use them meant extra movements; they were therefore re-designed to keep the laundry book in front of the sorter as she worked, and she was then taught to palm her pencil so as to have it ready to check off and price each article. Because each article was checked, priced and marked at once, with the laundry book and its mark in front of the sorter there was no need for her to rely on her memory for the mark, as had too often been the case formerly.

Results on Sorting. The personnel of the sorting room, including supervision and register was reduced by $12\frac{1}{2}$ per cent. The smaller staff was able to deal with the same amount of work and also to dispense with most of the overtime work except in emergencies.

Packing

To give each packer an equal amount of work the method of subsorting was altered from an alphabetical to a numerical system. This also made easier the allocation of space in the different blocks.

The existing arrangement of racks, parallel to one another had many disadvantages. In addition, gangways were narrow and congested and there were often insufficient bins. A new layout was made with the racks arranged in an L-shape, with a standard gangway three feet wide. It was then possible to see all the marks on all the racks from any one point along them and the standard gangway was wide enough to allow stooping to the bottom rack. Space was saved and possibilities of error reduced by parcelling immediately after checking down.

Results on Packing. The staff covering both finished and semi-finished services was reduced by slightly more than 20 per cent.

Total Results of the Laundry Investigation

As a result of the investigation the total personnel of the laundry on all operations showed a decrease of 14 per cent. There was in addition a decrease in overtime working which further reduced the labour cost and was likely in time to reduce the labour turnover. The operators were not paid by results before the investigation began and no system of direct payment by results was subsequently introduced. They were however given a merit award when they had reached and maintained a weekly output target established for each job after the motion study method had been developed. The laundry achieved a considerable overall reduction in labour cost in spite of the increase in the earnings of the individual operators.

REPORT No. 4

Preparation of Leads on Small Electro-Magnets

Metropolitan-Vickers Electrical Co. Ltd., Manchester

Two leads from the electro-magnet coil consisting of insulated flex had to be cut to length and fitted with soldered terminals. It was important that the length should be maintained within fairly close limits. The terminal used was a small metal eyelet around which a bared length of flex could be wrapped and twisted. The eyelet was then pressed over the flex to ensure a tight terminal and was finally dipped in hot solder.

ORIGINAL METHOD

Fig. 68 illustrates the equipment used and its arrangement on the work bench. The two-handed Process Chart, Fig. 69, records the movements made in detail.

The equipment provided, while it enabled the operation to be completed as required, entailed considerably more movement on the part of the operator than was thought necessary.

It will be noted that only one lead could be dealt with at a time and the process chart reveals unbalanced movements.

Fig. 68. Original Workplace for Finishing Electro-magnet
(For letters see Process Chart).

LEFT HAND   RIGHT HAND

Left Hand	Right Hand
1. PICK UP ELECTROMAGNET	
2. TURN OVER IN HANDS	2. TURN OVER IN HANDS
3. PLACE IN FIXTURE	3. PLACE IN FIXTURE
4. PULL WIRES TO RIGHT	4. GRASP WIRES
5. OPERATE GUILLOTINE (A)	5. HOLD ENDS OF WIRES
	6. DROP ENDS INTO TRAY
7. HOLD WIRES	7. PICK UP END CUTTERS (SPECIALLY GROUND)
	8. TEAR OFF INSULATION FROM BOTH WIRES IN TURN
	9. PUT DOWN CUTTERS
	10. TWIST STRANDS OF BOTH WIRES IN TURN
11. RETURN HOOK ROTATING LEVER (B) TO START	11. PICK UP EYELET
	12. PLACE ON HOOK (C)
13. HELP RIGHT HAND	13. GRASP ONE LEAD, LOOP OVER HOOK
14. OPERATE LEVER (B)	14. HOLD WIRE BELOW EYELET
	15. UNHOOK EYELET
16. TWIST LEAD	16. TWIST EYELET ON LEAD
17. RETURN LEVER (B)	17. PICK UP OTHER EYELET
	18. PLACE ON HOOK (C)
19. HELP RIGHT HAND	19. GRASP OTHER LEAD, LOOP OVER HOOK
20. OPERATE LEVER (B)	20. HOLD WIRE BELOW EYELET
	21. UNHOOK EYELET
22. TWIST LEAD	22. TWIST EYELET ON LEAD
23. PLACE EYELET UNDER PRESS (D)	
24. HOLD	24. PULL HANDLE OF PRESS AND RETURN
25. REMOVE EYELET AND PUT OTHER EYELET UNDER PRESS	
	26. PULL HANDLE OF PRESS AND RETURN
27. REMOVE ASSEMBLY FROM FIXTURE	27. REMOVE ASSEMBLY FROM FIXTURE
	28. DIP TWO EYELETS IN FLUX (E)
	29. DIP TWO EYELETS IN SOLDER POT (F)
	30. TAP AGAINST SCREEN TO REMOVE SURPLUS SOLDER
	31. PLACE ON ROTARY TRAY

FIG. 69. PREPARATION OF LEADS ON SMALL ELECTRO-MAGNETS
Process chart. *Original method.*

IMPROVED METHOD

A new tool capable of carrying out all the necessary operations was designed and made. This is illustrated in Fig. 71. The movements required to operate this tool are shown in detail in the Process Chart Fig. 70. It will

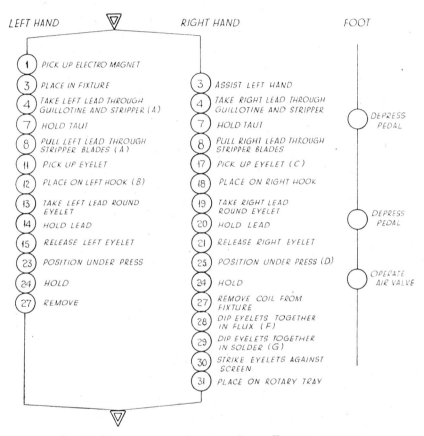

FIG. 70. PREPARATION OF LEADS ON SMALL ELECTRO-MAGNETS
Process chart, *Motion study method*

be noted that foot operation of the tool has relieved the hands of a considerable amount of movement and the simultaneous working on the two leads has resulted in a perfectly balanced sequence.

Results:

The use of the equipment and method described resulted in an increase per operator of 110 per cent.

Fig. 71. Improved Fixture and Workplace
(For letters see Process Chart)

Report No. 5

Inspection of Magnets

Jas. Neill and Co. (Sheffield) Ltd.

The magnets were inspected before final packing. The job consisted of the gauging of six dimensions and a visual inspection for finish. From the process chart, Fig. 72, it can be seen that the magnets were inspected by four operators, each gauging either one or two dimensions (*see* Fig. 73). Detailed process charts were made of the movements of each operator to supplement the information on the main chart.

An analysis of these charts produced the following ideas:

Old Method	New Method
1. The gauging of the six dimensions was treated as six separate operations; in addition a small hole was cleaned out. Each magnet was therefore picked up and put down a number of times; each of these movements being unproductive.	Each magnet was picked up, visually examined and passed in one continuous operation through the cleaning of the hole and the gauging of the six dimensions before being finally put down.
2. In addition the more detailed charts showed that the examiners used the right hand almost exclusively for holding the gauges.	Gauges were duplicated and fitted to a fixture on the bench in such a way that the examiner could gauge with a magnet held in each hand.

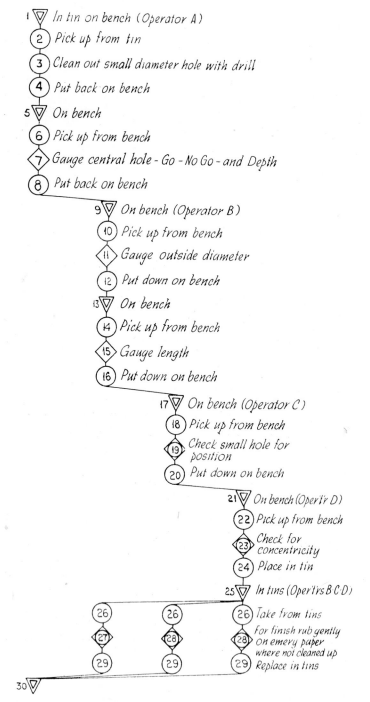

1 ▽ In tin on bench (Operator A)
2 Pick up from tin
3 Clean out small diameter hole with drill
4 Put back on bench
5 ▽ On bench
6 Pick up from bench
7 Gauge central hole - Go - No Go - and Depth
8 Put back on bench
9 ▽ On bench (Operator B)
10 Pick up from bench
11 Gauge outside diameter
12 Put down on bench
13 ▽ On bench
14 Pick up from bench
15 Gauge length
16 Put down on bench
17 ▽ On bench (Operator C)
18 Pick up from bench
19 Check small hole for position
20 Put down on bench
21 ▽ On bench (Oper'r D)
22 Pick up from bench
23 Check for concentricity
24 Place in tin
25 ▽ In tins (Oper'rs B C D)
26 / 26 / 26 Take from tins
27 / 28 / 28 For finish rub gently on emery paper where not cleaned up
29 / 29 / 29 Replace in tins
30 ▽

FIG. 72. INSPECTION OF MAGNETS
Process Chart, Original method.

FIG. 73. INSPECTION OF MAGNETS
(TOP) Original method of inspection
(BOTTOM) Original method of packing

OLD METHOD

3. Most examiners held a number of magnets at a time which increased the difficulty of positioning each magnet in the gauges.

4. As a subsidiary and additional operation the magnets were again handled by examiners B, C and D who visually inspected them for finish before passing them to examiner A for packing.

5. Examiner A counted and packed all magnets after inspection for finishing, which necessitated further handling. Large sheets of paper were placed between each layer of magnets.

NEW METHOD

Each hand picked up, gauged and put down one magnet at a time.

Magnets were inspected for finish when first picked up and, if rejected, were put on one side for polishing in a batch before further inspection.

The examiner disposed of inspected magnets on to strips of paper building up into layers in a 3-sided box. This box, when full, contained a definite number of magnets—eliminating counting, and was so designed that the magnets could be slid into the packing case on their paper strips without disturbing their arrangement.

OPERATOR'S HANDS   *FEET*

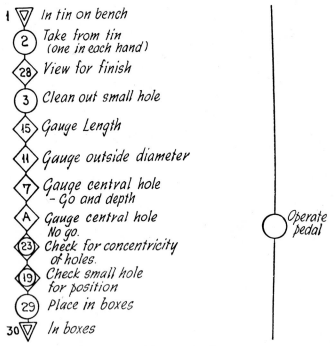

FIG. 74. INSPECTION AND PACKING
Process chart, Motion study method

The duplicate gauges were so arranged on a fixture on the bench that the operator could gauge one magnet with each hand in the easiest position, at the same time operating the concentricity gauge pins with the foot pedal (*see* Fig. 75). Rejects were placed in small containers at each gauge. If a reject occurred in one hand the other hand continued its gauging alone; both hands

FIG. 75. INSPECTION AND PACKING
Motion study method

beginning the next cycle together so that the rhythm of subsequent cycles was not broken.

For the sequence of the new method *see* Fig. 74.

Results

The output per operator was increased by 500 per cent, enabling the inspection to be carried out by one operator who easily kept up with production, thus reducing the danger of damage to finish, since there was no accumulation of magnets waiting for inspection.

19—(H.103)

Report No. 6

Making an Overall

"Wescot" Overall Manufacturing Co. Ltd.

The investigation covered every operation from the time the material left the cutting room until it reached the warehouse as a finished garment. Where the work of the cutting room affected later operations that also was studied.

Limiting Features of Material and Design

There were certain unalterable features of material and design that to some extent ruled the existing method and round which the motion study method had to be built. The most important of these was the fact that because the shade of different pieces of material and even of different parts of the same piece varied it was necessary to make each overall from parts cut from the same portion of the same piece. The practice in the cutting room was to lay the material out on long tables with as much as 120 edges to be cut at one time, made up from a number of different pieces. This resulted in bundles of similar parts which must be maintained in strict order throughout all operations so that, for example, part number nine in one bundle of similar parts was joined eventually to all the other number nines in the remaining bundles of other parts.

A second limiting feature of this type appeared in the arrangement of double-stitched seams. These were designed so that double-stitched seams joining similar parts faced the same way. For example, both shoulder seams were required to face forward. This controlled the side from which the parts must be fed into the machine guide for seaming.

General Analysis of the Whole Process

As the first step in recording and analysing present practice, process charts were made to obtain a general picture of the operations and of their place in the whole plan of making the garment. The individual operations were then recorded in greater detail by means of further process charts and every operation was filmed and simo-charted. Finally the path of movement of the various parts of the overall and of the operators' hands performing each operation was carefully analysed, though without taking actual chronocyclegraphs.

A general analysis of the operations as seen on the first process charts produced one or two suggestions. For example, it was questioned whether it was necessary to cut some of the facings in two parts and join them together again later. It was found, on consultation with the cutting room, that without wasting material they could be cut in one piece and the suggestion was accepted.

The sequence of operations appeared at this stage to be logical, though it was appreciated that the final operations of hemming bottoms, putting in sleeves and putting on collars could take place in any order and that this order should not be decided upon until the other operations had been studied. It was later found that it was easier to hem the bottoms as the last operation and this change was made.

The sequence of operations in making the sleeve was studied as a sub-assembly, independent of the main assembly of the garment. Here it was found that it was better to make both button hole and eyelet before joining the hind arm seam, while the parts could be handled flat. This made it possible to use guides to eliminate marking, and handling was much reduced.

Suggestions about combining two or more operations led to the developing of certain machine modifications where the work was absolutely standard for all sizes of garment. On the other hand in some cases, where two rather different types of handling were called for within one operation, it was thought better to make a further division rather than to combine one operation with another.

Except for suggestions about the use of guides and about means of avoiding crushing the material, ideas for simplification did not arise very much at this stage, though at a later stage, during the study of the detail of individual operations, simplification played a very large part in attaining the final increase in output.

THE DETAILED STUDY OF INDIVIDUAL OPERATIONS

Following the examination of the sequence of operations as a whole, each individual operation was analysed. It was immediately found that many operations had common features which if studied and improved in one operation might be adapted to another. For example, in several operations a machinist had to pick up her scissors to make a nick in the material. It was found that these nicks could be made in bulk in the cutting room and this was done in every case. Again, considerable wasted movement was found in the frequent breaking down of parts into bundles of lefts and rights in order to perform an operation on one side only, followed by the rebuilding of a composite bundle of lefts and rights. This was eliminated throughout the final motion study method unless other more important considerations made its retention essential in a particular operation.

A further common feature which was open to criticism was the tying and untying of bundles between processes. It was not possible to replace this by one common procedure but it was ultimately eliminated in every case.

When all the obvious common points had been dealt with each operation was studied in turn. In each case five aspects of the operation had to be examined:

1. The order of parts coming to the operator.

2. The method of presentation of each type of quantity material and its effect upon the path of movement followed in the assembly of individual pieces.

3. The position of pieces during stitching and its effect on continuity of stitching.

4. The position of pieces leaving the machine and the handling involved in putting away finished parts.

5. The arrangement of finished parts for passing to the next operator with particular reference to:

    (a) The sequence of parts in the bundle.
    (b) The effect on handling at the next operation.
    (c) The transport to the next operation.

Of these points number three was the most important since the actual stitching was the only productive part of the work cycle, the rest being ancillary to it. It was therefore necessary in every case to deal with the machining first to ensure that it was as perfect as possible. The other points were then dealt with in their relation to it and a careful watch was kept that they allowed it to be done in the easiest way and that they did not occupy an undue proportion of the cycle but allowed the maximum efficiency. For example, because most of the pieces were both large and heavy there was a tendency for the material to drag on the table and be pulled out of line. Where necessary therefore the tables were modified to reduce this effect and a further modification allowed the material to be stretched out directly in front of the needle before stitching began. This second modification ensured continuous machining down long seams.

Having examined the actual stitching, the order of parts coming to the operator was next studied. Where two parts were to be joined together was especially important since if one of the sets of pieces arrived differently arranged from the others unnecessary movements were used in handling every garment.

Even where all the pieces were arranged in the same way there was still the possibility of finding wasted movements if they were not presented in such a way that the machinist could follow the shortest and easiest path of movement between picking up and stitching each piece. For instance, in stitching the hind arm seam the seams of both sleeves were required to lie the same way which meant beginning stitching at the top on one sleeve of each pair and at the bottom on the other. It was found that it was the practice at the previous operation to lay all cuffs together tidily. As a result every other sleeve had to be turned round before the hind arm seam could be stitched. It was finally arranged that the previous operator should lay the sleeves alternately cuff to top since this gave her no extra work but merely required some training.

Having, as far as possible, simplified the presentation of pieces and their position during stitching it was always necessary to consider how one operation was linked with the next and to arrange for the disposal of machined parts in the simplest way that would place them in the best order and position for the next machining operation. For example, in the new method long parts, which, after machining, inevitably finished up hanging down the back of the table, were disposed of on to a movable bar placed in a frame which was operated by a foot pedal. The only hand movements required here were those of breaking the thread and throwing the end a little forward.

In considering the movement of bundles of work from one operation to the next it was necessary to make sure that parts were in the correct sequence for the next operator and that the whole bundle was in a state to be moved without any additional operations of tying or untying. At the same time the material had to be maintained as free from creases as possible.

Three main systems were eventually established for the transport of work between operations. All flat work was moved on numbered bars which hung on racks between operations. When she was ready for another bundle each operator moved the next bar on to a stand beside her machine. This stand was designed to be at the height and in the position that was best for that individual operation and each piece was worked directly from the bar through the machining process and on to another bar which, when filled in its turn was moved on to a numbered rack between that operation and the next. The now empty bar was then replaced by another full bar from the previous operation and moved into place behind the machine to receive pieces as they were machined. Sleeves, on the other hand, which would not lie flat because of their curved seams, were run off after most operations into containers in a continuous chain without separating them from one another.

After the assembly of fronts and backs revolving circular carriers with pegs on their circumferences replaced the bars and as the side and shoulder seams of each garment were completed it was hung in its correct order on the next peg, the full carriers moving to the next operation on overhead rails. All these arrangements and others kept the work in the correct order and in good condition and made it easy for each operator to find her next bundle and to handle it when found.

In considering these transport arrangements and in most other points in the investigations, although maximum machine efficiency was the first aim during the individual study of each machining operation it was never possible entirely to isolate any one operation from the rest. The investigations of individual operations, which began as separate studies, gradually and necessarily merged into one composite study, planning, replanning and compromising so that each operation fitted in with the rest. A further important point in the transport and temporary storage arrangements of the new method was the maintaining of a bank of work (approximately two hours output) between each group of operators. No machinist was then tied down to the pace of the previous operator and there was no danger of the whole line working to the pace of the slowest operator.

An example of an individual operation studied in detail (Attach Front Facings)

The operation consisted of machining the facings to the fronts from the nick provided for positioning the collar edge to the point of the lapel and from there to the bottom hem.

ORIGINAL METHOD

The work was carried out at a standard sewing machine table with a work-box to the right of the machinist and a trestle on her left. The material consisted of right and left fronts in bundles of thirty pieces and facings in one bundle with lefts and rights arranged alternately. The right fronts were laid over the workbox and the left fronts over the trestle. The facings were placed on the machinist's lap.

To attach a front facing the front was placed on the machine table so that the first short run of machining, from the collar nick to the point of the lapel, was in direct line in front of the needle. *See* simo-chart Fig. 76 (680-756). The facing was then positioned on top of the front and the neck edges laid carefully together (756—820). (In the case of the left front facing the position of the pieces was reversed). The machinist then used her scissors (798—848 R.H.) to make a nick in the facing, cutting through a nick already made in the front in the cutting room. Then she machined the short run from the nick to the point of the lapel, holding the rest of the neck edge out of the way. At this point she stopped (850—882).

She then used both hands to turn the pieces through a right angle to bring the front edge into direct line behind the needle (882—1000). Because of the length of the coat much of the material was then resting in her lap. She next machined down the front edge as far as possible (1000—1050) until the pieces began to get out of position, when she stopped to adjust them (1050—1068). This slipping out of position was caused by the weight of the material dragging on the table and by the disorder of the material in her lap. The need for re-arrangement meant that several short runs of machining were required to complete the stitching of the edge (1000—1246).

On the right fronts there was a further hindrance to machining in the eyelet stays which had been attached in a previous operation. These were made of the same material as the overall and often became caught up as they passed over the machine table. In releasing them there was a tendency to jerk the material and to slow the machine run.

The two machinists responsible for this operation disposed of their finished work in different ways. One was provided with a chute to carry the work to the next operator who turned out the facings for both machinists. When the chute was almost empty it was a very quick means of disposal but when it was fuller or when it became blocked owing to the work not being taken out it was necessary to push the work down by hand or with a rod. The material then became badly crushed (*see* Fig. 78a).

The second machinist had no chute. When she had stitched one front she began the next but after stitching a few inches stopped and broke off the first front, lifting it back to her side of the table and laying it over a second trestle. This took longer than running the work into the chute but it kept it in better condition and the machinist was independent of the next operator.

MOTION STUDY METHOD

As in all the operations studied in detail during the investigation into the making of the whole overall, the first aim in developing the motion study method was to make the stitching as continuous as possible. To do this all

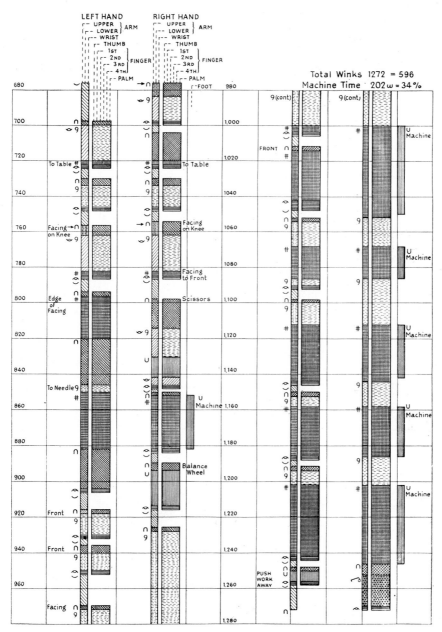

FIG. 76. MAKING AN OVERALL — ATTACH FRONT FACINGS
Simo-chart of original method

hindrances to machining had to be examined and as far as possible eliminated, whether they appeared during stitching or in connection with the preparation or disposal of the material. The first of these to be considered in this case was the dragging and slipping of the material during the stitching down the length of the front which was largely caused by the position of the material in the machinist's lap. To allow the whole length of the front to be stretched out in front of the needle the table top was redesigned to include an extension to the left of the machine on which the long pieces of material could be positioned at full length before stitching began. The width of this extension and the depth of the machine table behind the machine was planned to ensure that as the pieces were stitched they would slide evenly forward without slipping or dragging (*see* Fig. 78). To eliminate difficulties caused by the eyelet stays catching and jerking the material the original type were replaced by stiffer smaller stays which did not hinder the stitching. These changes made it possible for the machinist to stitch the whole length of the front in one run (Fig. 77, 1188—1348).

The position of the treadle was altered to allow the machinist to sit at a slight angle to the machine, using both hands freely to control the material.

The use of the scissors (Fig. 76, 798—848) was eliminated in the motion study method by having the nicks in the facings cut in bulk in the cutting room.

The simo-chart of the original method, Fig. 76, showed two main therblig sequences in preparation before machining (678—798 and 882—1000). It was clear that this duplication was caused by the machinist concentrating in the first place on arranging the material in line in front of the needle for the machining of the short edge of the lapel and being obliged to rearrange it afterwards for the machining of the long edge. To combine the two periods of preparation for stitching this policy was reversed in the motion study method and the work was first placed in position for the long run. By laying the left hand flat on the material and turning the hand it was found that the short edge could be brought temporarily into line in front of the needle while the short run of stitching was made. The right hand assisted in this (Fig. 77, 1050—1140). As soon as this run of stitching was finished the hands were lifted and the material slipped back into position for stitching the long edge with no further preparation.

To reduce to a minimum the positioning of pieces on the new extension before any stitching began, the fronts waiting to be stitched were supported on a rail immediately behind the new table extension. The machinist reached back, grasped the top edge of the front and swung it over on to the extension; the distances being so arranged that the neck edge just reached the needle. The facings were prepositioned on a narrow platform parallel to the extension so that each could be lifted on to its corresponding front without further positioning. To make sure that facings and fronts arrived in the same sequence and with the material the correct side up to avoid turning individual pieces, it was necessary to go back to examine the preceding operation. The final arrangement had the effect seen in the simo-chart Fig. 77 (966—1084) where 118 winks covered the whole preparation period, slightly less than half the preparation period of the old method.

To take advantage of the best features of the chute method of disposal, while eliminating its disadvantages, the path of movement of the finished pieces was studied. It was seen that to bring pieces back to the front of the machine lengthened their path of movement since their position after machining was hanging down the back of the table. A moveable flap was therefore designed to be fixed behind the machine. It was operated by a pedal and during

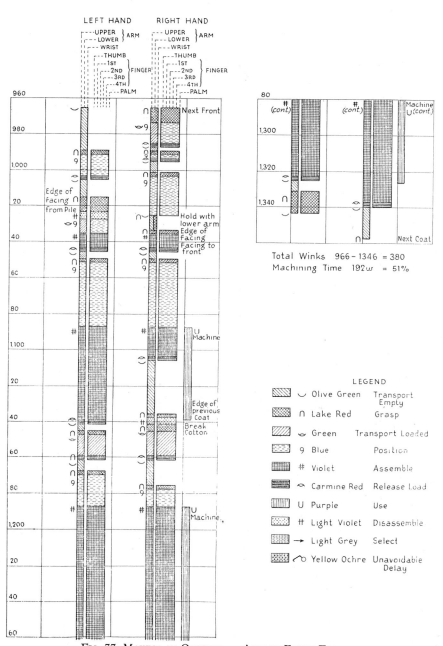

Total Winks 966 – 1346 = 380
Machining Time 192ʊ = 51%

LEGEND

⌣ Olive Green	Transport Empty
∩ Lake Red	Grasp
⌢ Green	Transport Loaded
9 Blue	Position
♯ Violet	Assemble
⌒ Carmine Red	Release Load
U Purple	Use
♯ Light Violet	Disassemble
→ Light Grey	Select
⌢ Yellow Ochre	Unavoidable Delay

Fig. 77. Making an Overall — Attach Front Facings
Simo-chart of new method

stitching was open and away from the table, allowing the work to slide down between it and the table in the usual way. When the stitching was complete and a few inches of the next front had been machined the first front was broken off and the ends thrown a little forwards over the flap which was brought towards it by operating the pedal. When the pedal was released the flap carried it away, leaving space for the next piece to hang down. This device was quick and easy to operate and kept the finished work in good condition and without creases. (Fig. 77. 1140—1188). The disposal took a little longer than the best cycle of the chute method but on an average was better and presented the pieces in a more suitable condition for subsequent operations.

Savings

In the motion study method the work cycle was reduced by 38 per cent. The machining time, because the longer runs maintained a higher speed, was reduced by 5 per cent and the stitching occupied 51 per cent of the whole cycle instead of 34 per cent.

INSTALLATION

It had been decided, when the investigation began, that the new method should be developed and installed in stages to allow the minimum of disorganisation and to give the investigators time to train every operator. This plan was followed and the sleeves were finished and installed first, followed by backs, fronts and final assembly. Full results from any section were not of course obtained until the whole investigation was completed. Until this point was reached certain operations inevitably became unbalanced and there were bottlenecks. Various makeshift arrangements had to be made to keep the parts moving smoothly.

As the operators had been drawn into the development of the new method from the beginning, little difficulty was experienced in changing from old methods to new but it was necessary to maintain a very close watch over the detailed arrangements of material for some time afterwards, since any mistake at a previous operation tended to make the next operator slip back into old habits.

Since the maintenance of the new methods and the training of future operators was the responsibility of the supervisors, they were given a short course of lectures on motion study, followed by a detailed explanation of the new methods and an explanation of any special problems or difficulties involved in them. Detailed instruction sheets were made out for every operation.

METHODS OF PAYMENT

As the study of each section began the existing piece-work price was suspended. The operators were paid their average earnings calculated over the best four of the previous six weeks. When all the jobs had been studied and installed new rates were set and introduced; first for all operations up to final assembly and then for the final assembly jobs. The opportunity was

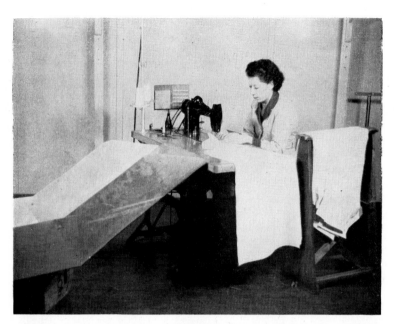

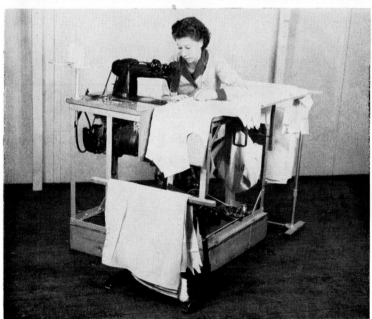

FIG. 78. MAKING AN OVERALL—ATTACH FRONT FACINGS
(TOP) Original workplace
(BOTTOM) Motion study workplace

taken to change from a points system to a direct money rate, in the belief that the incentive value of the direct money rate would be greater since it was easier to calculate.

Conclusion

Within six months of the completion of the investigation 30 per cent more overalls were being produced in the factory each day with almost exactly the same labour force, and individual earnings had risen on an average by $12\frac{1}{2}$ per cent.

REPORT No. 7

Replanning the Kitchen of an Old House

The problem presented to the investigator was to adapt the kitchen premises of a house some seventy years old to suit the needs of a modern family. For a variety of reasons it was necessary to plan the best possible kitchen within the limitations of the existing building and without making major structural alterations.

The household moving in consisted of four adults and three children and meals were required to be served both in the dining room and the nursery. It was intended that they should be carried from the kitchen on a trolley. Arrangements had to be made to provide a sitting room for a cook-housekeeper which could also be used for such work as ironing, laundry sorting and sewing.

CHANGING THE LAYOUT

The kitchen premises consisted of a large front kitchen divided from a smaller scullery by a lobby containing a door into the backyard. At the entrance to the scullery there were store cupboards and a cold slab used as a larder. The front kitchen had been used both for cooking and for meals.

The existing plan obviously revolved round the winter use of an old-fashioned solid-fuel range with a gas stove for occasional use in winter and more regular use in summer. Since the front kitchen had been used for meals the sink had been relegated to the scullery. The range also heated the water but was obsolete and extravagant of fuel. The new family intended to cook on a gas stove and to exchange the range for a modern slow combustion boiler which would also heat the room.

With these ideas in mind observations were made of typical meals cooked for the new family on their own equipment. These observations were then plotted as a string diagram on an outline of the kitchen and scullery used by the family who were leaving, but disregarding the range and adding a refrigerator in the larder (*see* Fig. 79). An analysis of the string diagram showed a constant heavy traffic between stove and sink and considerable movement between stove, sink, table and kitchen cabinet. Movements between these

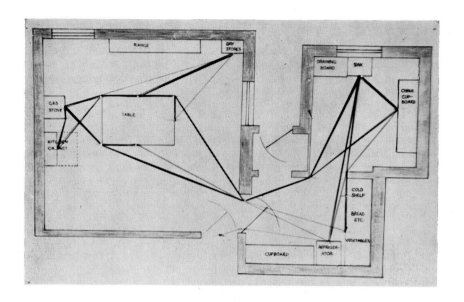

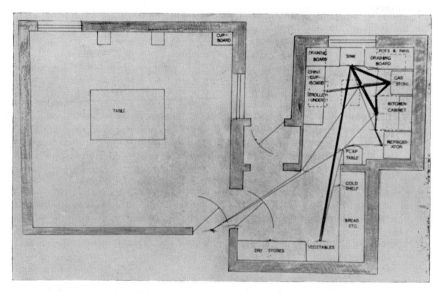

FIG. 79. REPLANNING A KITCHEN

(TOP) String diagram of typical meal cooked in the existing kitchen
(BOTTOM) String diagram of the same meal cooked in the motion study kitchen

points and the stores and larder were less heavy.   Much unproductive movement was clearly due to the fact that the cooker was in the front kitchen and
the sink in the scullery and it was obvious that the new plan should attempt
to bring the two closer together.   Since it was now unnecessary to cook in
the front kitchen it was decided to attempt to make the scullery serve for
vegetable preparation, cooking and washing up, leaving the front kitchen available as a sitting room for the cook-housekeeper.   The existing area used for
larder and stores would not then need to be disturbed since it would be con-
veniently close to the new kitchen.

A further examination of the string diagram also showed that the kitchen
table had a close connection with the sink and the cooker.   It was decided
that the table of the kitchen cabinet would be adequate for most of the preparation work if there were another small table to give additional working
space.

In making the final decisions about the layout of equipment within the
new kitchen the detailed path of movement of the cook was considered.   Fig.
80 shows an enlarged drawing of the new layout as it was finally made.   The
china cupboard has been moved to the opposite wall and converted into a wall
cupboard with space beneath for a trolley.   There are now two draining boards
and cooker, kitchen cabinet and refrigerator standing along the wall where
the china cupboard used to be, with a small folding table on the wall between
the refrigerator and the doorway.   Shelves above the right hand draining board
and over the cooker hold saucepans.   The kitchen cabinet holds a supply of
all seasonings and dry stores in regular use during cooking.   Dishes and cooking basins are kept in its lower cupboard and kitchen cutlery in its drawers.
Cooking implements such as scissors and wooden spoons are hung on the inside
of the cabinet doors against coloured silhouettes (*see* Fig. 33, Chapter 6).
Bulk stores and food used in the dining room without further preparation
are kept in the cupboards in the larder area, to be picked up or put away
as the trolley passes through.   In the same area the cold slab is used to
hold a meat safe containing foods not suitable for the refrigerator and bread
and cake tins.   Vegetables are kept in a rack between the cold slab and the
store cupboards.

This arrangement allows the shortest and easiest path of movement in
all normal circumstances both for cooking and for washing up.

Preparing, Cooking and Serving Meals

Most of the materials used are found in the kitchen cabinet and the refrigerator with water from the sink only a step away and pans within easy
reach.   All preparation and cooking can therefore take place without wasted
movements.   When the meal is ready it can be served up either directly from
the cooker on to the trolley or by way of the cabinet table.   Dirty cooking
utensils can then be placed directly into the sink.   Vegetables are drained
into the sink and served up on the left hand draining board or directly into

the vegetable dishes previously placed on the trolley after being warmed at the cooker. China for the meal is loaded cold on to the trolley from the china cupboard or warm out of the oven or the rack above the boiling rings.

Washing up

Dirty cooking utensils are placed directly into the sink as soon as they have been emptied. When they have been washed they are immediately

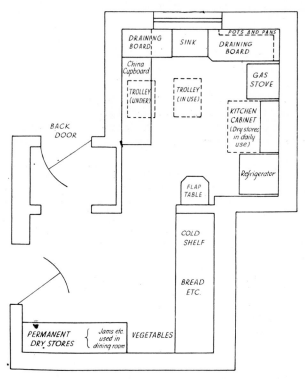

FIG. 80. REPLANNING A KITCHEN
Enlarged drawing of motion study layout

replaced on the correct shelf. Dining room dishes and cutlery are returned to the kitchen on the trolley and stacked on the right hand draining board, the trolley being replaced under the china cupboard to receive clean silver and cutlery when it has been washed and dried. China is washed and drained on the left hand draining board, being picked up by the right hand, dried and placed piece by piece by the left hand in its final position in the china cupboard while the right hand picks up the next piece.

Conclusion

As in any factory layout investigation the movements required by the different processes, in this case cooking and washing up, were observed and analysed and the new layout was developed to allow an improved sequence of movements. But the problem differs from a factory layout problem in that only one operator is concerned, working under a different type of supervision at a job which is never exactly the same from one hour to the next. It was unprofitable to study each operation in detail but the final layout was designed to allow the most economical and easiest general movements though as in most other kinds of domestic work much even then depends on the use made of the layout by the operator. There is still a great difference between the movements of a good operator who plans ahead and a poorer operator who does one job after another as the need arises without special thought. This is typical of domestic work but it is also true of such work as factory maintenance work. In either case it is necessary to train the operator to use the equipment economically and to plan the work in advance..

Fig. 79 shows a string diagram of cooking the same meal in the new kitchen as was plotted on the original layout.

REPORT No. 8[1]

An Investigation into the Clerical Work of a Doctor's Surgery

This investigation was confined in the first place to a study of the clerical work involved in the daily round of visits and to a consideration of the layout of the surgery.

RECORDING PRESENT PRACTICE

The investigator began by observing and charting the activities of the doctor and her secretary in planning a day's round and keeping the normal records of visits. (*See* Process Chart, Fig. 81).

The situation as seen by the investigator was as follows:

Personnel

There were two doctors who shared an office and a secretary. Since one acted as the other's assistant, both to some extent dealt with the same group of patients.

Records

(1) A Log Book. This was kept beside the telephone and in it was entered against the time received, all messages, whether they were received by telephone or delivered verbally or in the form of a written note.

---

[1] Most of this material appeared as an article in the Supplement to the *British Medical Journal*, September 16, 1950 (Vol. ii, p. 132).

(2) Patients' Record "Cards." The majority of these were National Health Service envelopes but the private patients were card indexed on individual white cards of about the same size.

(3) A Visits Book. This was ruled off into columns for the patients' name and address and for each day of the month. Names and addresses were

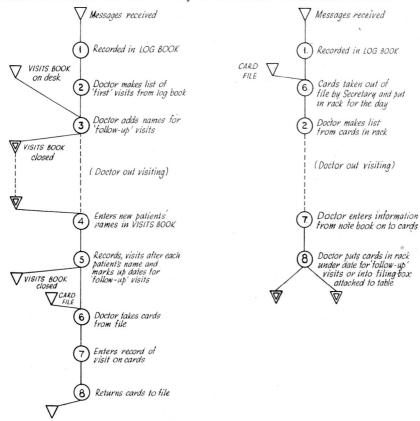

FIG. 81. DOCTOR'S SURGERY
Process charts of visiting round routine
(LEFT) Original method
(RIGHT) Motion study method

entered as the first visit was made and were therefore not in alphabetical order. A mark in the appropriate column indicated the date on which the next visit was due and this mark was crossed when the visit had been made. At the end of each month those not signed off were transferred to a fresh page to start the next month's list. This meant about two hours work for the doctor which could not be delegated and it was essential that it was done on the last day of the month.

Procedure

When either of the doctors was preparing to go out visiting she needed to know (1) what new messages had come in asking for visits ("new visits"), and (2) which of the patients known to be ill required further visits and which chronic patients were due for a visit ("follow up visits").

She therefore consulted the Log Book for "new visits" and the Visits Book for "follow up visits." If she needed further information about the patients she also referred to their cards in the file and then made out her list.

On returning from the round new names were recorded in the Visits Book and the day's visits were marked off against them and against the names already in the book, with a further mark under the day on which the next visit was due. Information was then entered on the patients' cards with case notes added.

DEVELOPING AN IMPROVED METHOD

The only record that could possibly be eliminated was the Visits Book. The Log Book was inevitable in some form and the keeping of the cards was a statutory obligation on the doctor. The Visits Book was traditional but an examination of its use showed that much of its function had departed with the introduction of the new Health Act. It had been the chief source of information for monthly accounts. Few of these were now necessary and its remaining function was as a reminder for follow-up visits. If this could be managed in some other way the Visits Book would be virtually obsolete.

An examination of the sequence of events suggested that more use would be made of the record cards if they were taken out of the file at an earlier stage and by the secretary at her convenience rather than by the doctor who was nearly always in a hurry after completing her round. They would be useful to the doctor when making up her list. This led on to the idea that by keeping the cards of current patients in a separate place they might be used to remind the doctor about future visits in place of the Visits Book.

It was obvious that the cards could be used in this way only if some arrangement could be made to keep them safely in a special file of some sort. An adaptation of a production rack originally used in a general machine shop was designed and made (Fig. 82). The columns were laid out on the lines of the Visits Book but instead of using 31 columns, one for each day of the month, the seven days of the week headed the first seven columns followed by "week 2," "week 3" and "week 4." The eleventh column was headed with the name of the next month and the twelfth with the name of the following month. In this rack was kept the cards of all current patients and cards were moved from column to column as they were visited and as further visits were necessary. The rack was designed to screw on to the wall and a bar was fitted across it to carry a sliding table. Below this table were boxes for the cards that were ready to be returned to the permanent file as no longer requiring visits. At the side was another small box for prescription pads, certificate

FIG. 82. DOCTOR'S SURGERY. *Motion Study Layout.*
(TOP) Wall rack for patients' record cards
(BOTTOM) Secretary's corner

books and the National Formulary, since the desk was used for writing the prescriptions and certificates arising from the visits. The doctor moved the table along each day until it was under the cards for that day and entered information on to the cards on the spot so that there was no danger of any being mislaid. The rack was used for private patients' cards as well as for National Health Service cards and accounts were made out directly from the information on the private cards on which the doctor recorded the fee as the visit was entered.

The assistant doctor had a similar board containing her own patients' cards and any others temporarily put there for her attention by the senior doctor. By this interchange of cards both doctors benefited from each other's case notes.

To find space to put the racks, shelves and a large cupboard were removed. These had previously been necessary, in a dispensing practice, for the storage of drugs but the regulations of the new National Health Service made it necessary to keep only an emergency store of drugs which could be concentrated on the remaining shelves at the opposite side of the room. The glass-topped table under the drug shelves, used for testing, was also moved to the other side where it was placed next to the sink. In this way all the dispensing and testing were concentrated at one end of the room instead of being divided between the two sides. Fig. 83 shows the original layout. In the new layout (Fig. 83) the centre desk was abolished and the other desk was moved further along the wall, leaving space for filing cabinets holding the National Health Service record cards. This not only allowed more space in the surgery but also brought the secretary's desk, filing cabinets, telephone and card racks within one convenient area (*see* Fig. 82).

A chart, Fig. 81, shows the new method.

Conclusion

The Visits Book had served its purpose in the past but had lost much of its usefulness under new conditions when few bills had to be made out. Under the new conditions the surgery was now mainly an office and only served as a dispensary in a very minor way. Record keeping and form filling had largely replaced the dispensing of drugs and the sending out of accounts. It was therefore time to reorganise the system of work and to modify the records and the layout of the room. By eliminating the obsolete operations and by rearranging the remainder, and by designing equipment to simplify them, much redundant work was cut out. The new arrangements not only made it possible to get through the essential clerical work but to do it more efficiently and completely.

During the period in which the system has been in operation it has amply fulfilled the functions for which it was instituted. It has also had certain subsidiary good effects. Records are now always up to date when cards are called in by the Executive Councils and a further advantage has been that the cards in the rack show where the doctor is likely to be found when she is out on her rounds. Telephone numbers have been added to the cards where they exist, to make this easier, and on occasion even a casual helper has been able to trace the doctor for an emergency call.

A further use has been made of the rack to hold temporarily any specialists' reports or other letters received in the morning's mail and referring to the

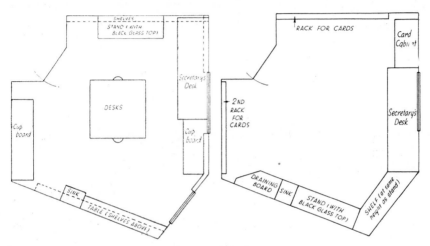

FIG. 83. DOCTOR'S SURGERY

(LEFT) Original layout

(RIGHT) Motion study layout

day's visits, before there is time to examine them or transfer them to the permanent records.

The bottom quarter of the rack was altered to accommodate the year's midwifery engagements under monthly headings. These cards are left in the rack and act as a permanent reminder until the final examination has been made.

Cases seen on behalf of another doctor during holiday periods or other absences are recorded on insert cards and left in the board until the date of the doctor's return. They are then sent to him for filing in the patients' National Health Service envelope. No further report is necessary.

THE USE OF PHOTOGRAPHY IN MICROMOTION STUDY

Equipment[1]

In making a film for micromotion analysis the main object is to obtain a record of the operation which is a clear picture of every part taken from a convenient angle for analysis and including a counter appearing in sharp focus allowing the length of the elements of movement of each part of the body analysed to be compared with one another.

1. *Camera*

Any kind of cine camera that will produce this result is satisfactory, but there are certain features that should be considered when buying a camera especially for micromotion photography.

(a) *Drive.* Most cine cameras have a clockwork drive which runs for just over a minute at normal speed. This may sometimes be inadequate when filming long operations and a camera which can be run for the full length of a 100 foot spool is useful. A hand cranking device on a clockwork camera will meet the need and there are a few clockwork cameras that can be rewound during the running time of the motor.

(b) *Capacity.* A camera taking 16 mm. film is the most satisfactory, though other substandard size cameras can be used. 16 mm. cameras should take 100 feet of film. A capacity of 50 feet is not adequate.

(c) *Speeds.* 16 frames per second is the usual speed for micromotion analysis but 64 frames per second, the normal slow motion speed, is sometimes useful for demonstration work or to record very fast movements. A speed of 24 frames per second is necessary if there is any likelihood of films being used with a sound commentary.

(d) *Footage indicator.* It is essential that the amount of film remaining in the camera at the end of a shot should be indicated. Most cameras, but not all, are fitted with some sort of indicator, which may measure either feet or metres.

(e) *Lens.* While it is quite possible to get fairly satisfactory results with a camera with a standard lens, it is an advantage to have a choice of lenses. To simplify the changeover where a choice is available the camera may be

---

[1] Equipment recommended in this section is obtainable in Great Britain in 1952.

equipped with turret head holding 3 lenses, but as long as the lenses can be changed by any means the camera will be suitable.

There are four types of lens useful for micromotion work.

A 1-in. focusing lens, maximum aperture $f/1.9$ or the equivalent is useful for most subjects but if it is used at maximum aperture it has a short depth of focus and the distance between the camera and its object must be measured very accurately. It is the lens normally used for slow motion work because of the short exposure time inevitable.

A 1-in. fixed lens, maximum aperture of the order of $f/3.5$ will not be so useful for slow motion photography owing to the extra illumination necessary but has the great advantage otherwise that accurate measuring and the setting of the focusing scale are not necessary.

A wide angle lens of 15 to 20 mm. focal length will be useful where space is cramped and the camera must be positioned uncomfortably near the subject.

A long focus lens of about 3-in. focal length is useful where only a narrow area is to be filmed and the camera cannot be placed very close to the subject. This lens has the great merit of enabling close-up pictures to be taken from quite a distance away from the subject, but it must be used with a tripod.

(f) *Viewfinder.* A camera with interchangeable lenses should have an adaptable viewfinder mask which can be adjusted to correspond with the focal lengths of the lenses used. It is as well to check this when buying a camera.

2. *Tripod*

A tripod is essential for some types of filming and its use will usually give better results than can be obtained when the camera is held in the hand. It should screw into the base of the cine camera and it must be reasonably rigid although it should be as light and as easily erected as possible. It should have a spreader to fix the angle of the legs and to prevent their slipping apart. The head must be made so that the camera when fitted to it will tilt or swivel as required and be capable of being fixed firmly in any desired position. For use where space is very restricted a "universal tripod" or clamp may be used.

3. *The Exposure Meter*

Among all the available types, calculator, chemical, visual and photo-electric, only the last-named is really to be recommended. Any standard type made by a reputable firm will be sufficient for the purpose. It is not necessary to buy anything elaborate.

4. *Types of Film*

16 mm. reversal film is the usual choice for micromotion work. Kodak Super X is normally fast enough but in some cases Super XX will be needed. Other "substandard" film either 9.5 mm. or 8 mm. can be used but the larger picture given by 16 mm. is an advantage for analysis and it is easier

to obtain suitable 16 mm. projectors both for viewing and for analysis. If many copies of a film are required a negative film can be used which will make copying cheaper.

5. *Lighting Equipment*

For use in a factory of any size it is convenient to have lighting equipment that is reasonably portable. Portable lighting sets can be purchased quite easily but perfectly satisfactory results can be obtained with improvised equipment. The set must contain:

(a) Lighting stands and light holders which are adjustable in every direction so that lights can be arranged in various ways. At least four independent stands are usually needed.

(b) Reflectors fitting on to the light holders. There are two types of reflectors, floodlight and spotlight. The latter are occasionally useful but floodlights are essential for general lighting. The backs of the reflectors should be covered with dark non-reflecting paint or material.

(c) Lamps. Studio lighting usually consists of permanent lampholders containing large 500-1000 watt lamps. These are too cumbersome for portable lighting sets and instead photoflood lamps are used which, although no bigger than a 60 or 100 watt lamp, give a light approximately equal to the studio lamps. They are obtainable in two sizes and function on the principle of over-running the filament to give the same actinic value as a 1,000 watt lamp. They actually consume about 275 watts and have a useful life of either two hours or twelve hours according to size.

(d) A switchboard should be used into which the lights can be plugged so that all run from one cable and plug (which should be fused). The switch controlling the board should be so arranged that all lights switch off simultaneously but are switched on in stages to prevent blown fuses.

6. *The Counter*

The counter commonly used for micromotion study is electrically driven and has a pointer which makes twenty revolutions per minute round a dial marked off into a hundred divisions. Each of these hundred divisions therefore represents one two-thousandth of a minute. Gilbreth devised this scale and called each two-thousandth of a minute a "wink." A second pointer can be introduced to record the revolutions of the main pointer and if necessary a third pointer recording the revolutions of the second.

7. *Miscellaneous Equipment to be kept with the Filming Outfit*

(a) Measuring tape—marked in feet and inches and, if necessary, metres; (b) record sheets—on which to record descriptions of shots taken, including exposures and lens setting; (c) smoked glass—to evaluate lighting effects; (d) screwdriver; and (e) insulating tape.

8. *The Projector*

A projector suitable for film analysis is an essential part of micromotion equipment. It should embody three essential features:

(a) Provision for projecting single frames in succession, as well as the normal projection, with a grid or thermal condenser to prevent the heat of the projector lamp from burning the film when showing single frames as still pictures.

(b) A reversing switch so that the film can be run backwards.

(c) Rewinding gear.

16 mm. projectors are designed for amateur use and require a minimum of attention, but if they are to give good and reliable service that minimum must be given conscientiously. When a projector is new, the instruction book should be studied carefully before making any attempt to show a film. The main points requiring attention are:

(i) Lubrication. Detailed instructions for lubrication will be given in the makers' instruction book. Oil must be applied sparingly. Over-oiling may do as much damage as insufficient oiling.

(ii) Cleaning. Dust and particles of film emulsion form a hard deposit (mainly in the film gate) which may seriously damage a film running through the projector. All exposed parts of the mechanism should be cleaned at frequent intervals and particular attention should be paid to the film aperture and the gate. A special type of brush can be obtained for this purpose. Any excessive lubricating oil must be wiped off carefully.

(iii) Care of lamp. The lamp and the mirror will be in the correct position when the projector is bought but if means of adjusting them are provided they may become loose. The instruction book will supply all the information necessary for the operation of changing a lamp and of centreing the mirror if it is adjustable. It is always advisable to keep a spare lamp in the projector box for emergencies.

Taking a Film

1. *Preparation of Equipment and Material*

The contents of the box or case containing the filming equipment should be checked and any other equipment should be collected in the motion study department. Checking from memory is unreliable and may lead the photographer into finding himself without an important piece of equipment when everything else is set up and ready for filming. Reserve supplies of expendable items such as photoflood lamps and film should be included in the equipment.

Tables containing information which will be needed during filming (e.g. film speed numbers, ranges of fixed focus lenses) should be fixed in suitable places about the filming box and the camera. During filming and when setting up the camera the habit should be formed of keeping small articles required during the filming always in the same place.

The investigator should make a detailed survey of the layout before the filming date and with the information obtained he should work out a detailed plan of action. This plan may go into small details such as sequence of shots, or it may simply be a general plan according to circumstances but a definite plan of some kind will do much to reduce filming troubles.

2. *Loading the Camera*

Information about loading and unloading procdeure will be found in the camera instruction book. If this is not available the same information can be discovered from a close inspection of the camera. To re-load a camera rapidly and safely under the actual conditions of film-taking is a matter of practice. To load a daylight spool into a camera another empty daylight spool must be available as a take-up spool. The photographer is likely to use both 50ft. or 100ft. spools and should therefore have a spare spool of each size at hand. For convenience, one of these spools, preferably the 100ft. spool since it is likely to be used most, is always kept in the camera and the other inside the camera case. To avoid chargers or daylight spools being exposed to strong light, loading or unloading should be done in a place screened from direct light (the shadow of the photographer's body will be enough). Every time the camera is opened it should be cleaned out with a soft brush or blown out to get rid of the pieces of grit or film particles which will have accumulated. The film can then be put in according to the makers' instructions for the particular camera in use. Before the camera is closed again, the button should be pressed for a second or two to allow the cameraman to check that the film is running correctly.

When it is known that the film is running correctly, the camera is closed and the footage indicator set, if this is necessary, to the mark preceding the centre mark. The button is then pressed and the camera left running until the footage indicator reads zero, when all the leader strip will be wound on to the take-up spool. The camera is now ready to begin work. After "shooting," when the footage indicator shows that all live film has been used up, the trailer strip must be run off before the camera is opened for unloading. It is usually quite easy to tell from the sound of the clockwork when the trailer has gone through. The spool should be wrapped up immediately after it has been unloaded from the camera and the wrapper should be marked "exposed."

3. *Camera Position*

In deciding on this certain points must be considered:

(a) Everything that is to be analysed must be included in the picture and, so that these points should fill the frame and appear as large as possible, nothing that is irrelevant should be included.

(b) The masking of one movement by another must be avoided.

(c) The counter must be readable at all times.

(d) The shooting angle must be designed to produce a picture that is easily understood.

(e) Movements in the background, unconnected with the job, should not appear in the picture. If necessary a screen should be used.

4. *Position of the Counter*

In a film made for micromotion analysis the counter must be visible on every frame. When a tripod is used this should not be difficult to achieve but when the camera is held in the hand the cameraman will have to bear the counter in mind all the time if he is to keep it in the picture. He will also have to remember the effect of parallax. It is a good practice to plug in the counter as soon as it is unpacked from the filming box or there will be a danger of forgetting later that it is not running. To make analysis as easy as possible the counter must not appear distorted. To avoid this it must be placed parellel with the camera lens and it should be well illuminated and sharply in focus.

5. *Setting up the Lighting*

A photographic image is formed by reproducing light contrast. It follows that the lighting must be so arranged that there is enough contrast to form a photographic picture. Too much contrast, on the other hand, will tend to make parts of the picture appear all white or all black without any detail.

Since an image in the normal human eye is formed not only by light contrast, but also by colour contrast, it is not easy to judge the illumination of a scene in terms of light contrast only. It is easier to do this, however, if the scene is viewed through a piece of smoked glass which will make it appear almost like a black and white picture.

The recommended procedure for setting up the lights is first to spread the available photofloods evenly over the scene and then to introduce some measure of contrast by increasing the distance of the lights on one side of the object. Since the light intensity at any particular point is inversely proportional to the square of the distance from the source to that point, slight movement of the lamps will produce a pronounced contrast. After that the deepest essential shadows should be inspected and should be given special illumination if necessary. If the counter has a black dial, it must be treated in the same way. Finally any light patches which are too bright and any undue reflections must be subdued. Unless special effects are intended a lamp should never be placed very close to a bright surface such as a face, a hand, or a white garment. In micromotion photography the background can be left to take care of itself, unless it forms an essential part of the job when it should be treated like the main subject.

If the effect of one particular lamp cannot be picked out with certainty from the light given by all the other lamps, moving that lamp to and fro will clearly locate its effect. When the cameraman thinks that the lighting is satisfactory and final he must make sure that no direct light from any lamp is reaching the camera lens and that the lamp shades will not appear in the picture.

6. *Adjusting the Camera*

After the position of the camera and the lens have been selected, the location of the tripod or the cameraman is marked with chalk on the floor. The necessary camera settings are then made.

(a) The selected lens is set up in front of the camera aperture and the lens hood is fixed. (The lens should be screwed home firmly).

(b) The viewfinder mask is adjusted to the correct focal length of the lens in use. The cameraman should make a habit of doing this as he changes his lens.

(c) The clockwork is wound.

(d) The camera speed is set or checked.

(e) A measuring tape is used to set the focusing distance. This measurement should usually be taken from the counter as any blurred effect on the clock may cause an incorrect analysis. On many small lenses the focussing scale may appear difficult to locate and hard to operate. The cameraman will be wise to make himself familiar with the peculiarities of his lenses before embarking upon a filming job but since there are only two scales on a cine-lens (f/numbers and distance) the distance scale can easily be identified by the infinity sign ∞ at one end of it. Fixed focus lenses do not require the setting of any distance scale and normally involve no measuring, but it may be necessary to measure the distance of the nearest object to see that it is within the safe range of lens used.

7. *Setting the Parallax Correction*

If a parallax correction is provided for the viewfinder, it should be set as soon as the distance has been measured.

8. *Setting the f/number (Exposure)*

A cine camera has always the same length of exposure when working at a given speed. If a speed of 16 frames is normal, the exposure length will be halved when working at 32 frames and quartered at a speed of 64 frames. Therefore variations in exposure can be made only by changes in aperture. For each type of film there are two film speed numbers (for daylight and for artificial light). It is safest to have the correct speed numbers of the film used clearly marked on the equipment, i.e. on the carrying case, the camera, or the exposure meter. A general reading of the exposure meter taken at a distance approximately equal to the width of the field of vision will give satisfactory results if there are no violent light contrasts in the picture. If one part of the object is of particular importance and is either very light or very dark a reading close to that part should be taken as the basis for exposure. In general, readings of both kinds will be taken and weighed against one another and a compromise will be reached. When the correct f/number has been determined it must be set on the f/number scale of the lens.

When all these settings have been made they should be checked again. Scales on 16 mm. equipment are so small and so close to each other, that setting one may easily disturb another that is already set. If the camera has been on its tripod during these settings, it is certain to have moved in relation to its object. Therefore, careful re-setting of the camera on the tripod is necessary as a final precaution. When that has been attended to everything is ready for shooting.

INDEX